DEVELOPMENTAL PSYCHOBIOLOGY

ANNALS OF THE NEW YORK ACADEMY OF SCIENCES
Volume 662

DEVELOPMENTAL PSYCHOBIOLOGY

Edited by Gerald Turkewitz

The New York Academy of Sciences
New York, New York
1992

Library of Congress Cataloging-in-Publication Data

Developmental psychobiology / edited by Gerald Turkewitz.
    p. cm. — (Annals of the New York Academy of Sciences. ISSN 0077-8923 ; v. 662)
    Includes bibliographical references and index.
    ISBN 0-89766-737-9 (cloth : alk. paper). — ISBN 0-89766-738-7 (paper : alk. paper)
    1. Developmental psychobiology—Congresses. I. Turkewitz, Gerald. II. Series.
    [DNLM: 1. Behavior, Animal—physiology—congresses. 2. Developmental Biology—congresses. 3. Psychophysiology—congresses. W1 AN626YL v.662]
    Q11.N5 vol. 662
    [QP356.25]
    500 s—dc20
    [156′.5]
    DNLM/DLC
for Library of Congress   92-49415
                                         CIP

CCP
Printed in the United States of America
ISBN 0-89766-737-9 (cloth)
ISBN 0-89766-738-7 (paper)
ISSN 0077-8923

ANNALS OF THE NEW YORK ACADEMY OF SCIENCES

Volume 662
October 20, 1992

DEVELOPMENTAL PSYCHOBIOLOGY[a]

Editor and Symposium Organizer
GERALD TURKEWITZ

CONTENTS

[a] This volume is the result of the City University of New York—Hunter Symposium Series, Spring 1990 (February–May 1990).

Part IV. Behavioral and Structural Development of Sexual Differentiation

Financial assistance was received from:

- BIOLOGY PROGRAM OF THE CITY COLLEGE OF NEW YORK
- BIOLOGY PROGRAM OF THE GRADUATE SCHOOL AND UNIVERSITY OF THE CITY UNIVERSITY OF NEW YORK
- HUNTER COLLEGE DIVISION OF SOCIAL SCIENCES
- NATIONAL INSTITUTE OF MENTAL HEALTH, TRAINING GRANT IN COMPARATIVE BEHAVIORAL NEUROSCIENCE MH 15341

Developmental Psychobiology

Introduction

GERALD TURKEWITZ

Department of Psychology
Hunter College[a] and
Graduate Center of the City University of New York
and
Departments of Pediatrics and Psychiatry
Albert Einstein College of Medicine

This volume stems from a series of symposia organized by the Hunter College doctoral subprogram in biopsychology and the City College doctoral subprogram in biology. It received substantial support from the Division of Social Sciences of Hunter College, the Biology programs of the Graduate Center of the City University of New York and the City College of New York and a National Institute of Mental Health training grant in Comparative Behavioral Neuroscience—MH 15341.

In addition to the authors, whose works are included in this volume, Robin Panneton-Cooper, Gilbert Gottlieb, Myron Hofer, and Sergai Khayutin also took part in the symposia. Professor Khayutin's unfortunate death prevented inclusion of his work in this volume; Professor Gottlieb's schedule and Professor Hofer's schedule and the birth of Professor Cooper's twins precluded their preparation of chapters. However, I would like to acknowledge the important contribution of all of the participants both to the study of developmental psychobiology and to the richness of the symposia series. Although chapters by Gottlieb and Hofer are not included in the book, their presence is strongly felt and reflected in many of those that are included.

The symposia on which this book is based were not meant to cover the breadth of developmental psychobiology, or to reflect the thinking and work of all those who consider themselves or who have been considered developmental psychobiologists. It was meant instead to indicate something of the strength, vitality, insight, and richness that can be the product of searching for an understanding of the biopsychological sources of order in the development of behavior, when such a search is not constrained by dichotomous thinking. Dichotomous thinking with regard to the subject matter of biopsychology involves some variant of segregating behavior into components that are specific either to the nature of the organism or to its nurture. The specific terminology used to label the dichotomies seen as fundamental varies, e.g.,

[a] 695 Park Avenue, New York, New York 10021.

genetic vs. environmental, innate vs. acquired, hard vs. soft wired, etc. However the essence of dichotomous approaches is the same regardless of the terminology; that is, all behavior is attributable to two general classes of input which can be roughly considered biological or experiential. The analytic task is then seen as determining which of the two classes determines a particular behavior or component of a behavior. Earlier dichotomous approaches characterized molar aspects of behavior, e.g., parental behavior or sexual behavior as instinctive or learned; while more recent dichotomies tend to sort less global aspects of behavior, such as nursing in the case of parental behavior or mounting in the case of sexual behavior, into biologically and experientially determined aspects of behavior. It is this analysis of behavior into smaller components that has led to the apparent resolution of the nature-nurture question. According to this resolution, all behavior is an outcome of both nature and nurture. Having stated this, most or at least many of the proponents of an "interactionist" position then go about determining which components of a behavior are genetic and which acquired. They also determine how much of a behavior is attributable to genetic sources and how much to environmental sources. This approach is interactional in the sense that it views molar outcomes as involving both environmental and genetic factors. However, it is interactional only in the limited sense that a fruit salad can be said to be interactional. That is, the components are all required and yet the constituents maintain their integrity, even while contributing to the conglomerate that is the salad. In developmental psychobiology, this approach has frequently contributed elegant and incisive studies that have documented a number of precise mechanisms, particularly at the molecular level. The approach has been less successful at identifying and explicating relationships between levels of organization, and has frequently resulted in reductionism with outcomes at higher levels of organization being attributed to the operation of mechanisms at a lower level of organization. In this usage, psychobiology has been the search for the biological determinants of psychological function rather than an examination of the relationships between biological and psychological factors. This volume brings together investigators who have utilized research strategies and conceptualizations that are interactional in a different sense. Either explicitly or implicitly and to lesser or greater extent, the authors have subscribed to an approach that sees biological and psychological factors as interpenetrating and fused during the course of development. The analytic task for these investigators still involves the identification of components that contribute to organization. However, these components are seen to be transformed by the organization to which they contribute. The interactions between biological and psychological factors are viewed to be such that separating them would do violence to their nonadditive nature.

An understanding of development is of particular relevance to this type of biopsychology because developmental considerations determine the components that enter into adult levels of organization. Thus, the requirement that at each stage of its development, the organism be adapted to its circumstances limits the number of degrees of freedom available for subsequent development. That is, although the young organism can be viewed as being in a transitional state that will eventuate in becoming an adult, it is also necessary to recognize that it is simultaneously a quite complete and effective organism. Furthermore, it must be recognized that at no point in the transition from immaturity to maturity can developmental processes result in an organism that is not adapted to its current circumstance. This places obvious constraints on both developmental pathways and outcomes, and results in the kind of nonlinear and nonobvious factors that are frequently found to affect development. It is precisely this nonlinearity and nonobviousness that make it impossible to specify in a prior manner those factors that are likely to enter into the determination of any particular outcome. This being the case, developmental psychobiological understanding is dependent on the positive identification of the sources of a particular outcome and cannot be achieved solely by eliminating reasonable potential sources. If, for example, it was found that prior exposure to young was not required for normal maternal behavior, that would say nothing about what the source for maternal behavior was nor even what general class, i.e., biological or experiential, was involved. This is because sources for maternal behavior are not necessarily those that would have been selected had the task simply been to design an organism that would exhibit maternal behavior.

The chapters that follow examine diverse areas of functioning and consider a variety of organisms. They share in common a concern with uncovering hidden sources of development, and examining the way in which the development of components—including, among others, neural, muscular, learning, and social—combines to produce important functional outcomes. Taken together, they make a strong case for the generality of nonlinearity of biopsychological development.

Developmental Strategies in the Analysis of Ingestive Behavior

W. G. HALL AND SUSAN E. SWITHERS-MULVEY

Department of Experimental Psychology
Duke University
Durham, North Carolina 27706

The feeding behavior of mammals remains poorly understood. Although we have become increasingly knowledgeable about the number and complexity of physiological signals that may contribute to the modulation of food intake, appreciation of how the behavior is activated and expressed is primitive. Developmental study of ingestive behavior offers the prospect of investigating feeding when it may be simpler and more readily understood. Early in development, controls of the behavior may be more easily identified, and components or features of the behavior more easily isolated for study. Then, in the course of physiological and neural maturation, additional controls that appear during development can be identified and studied successively as the system becomes more complex and its organization changes.

Analysis of the development of ingestion in rodents has taken advantage of this strategy, both in isolating appetitive and consummatory components of ingestion for individual study and in identifying a sequential emergence of control. Recently collected data confirm, in fact, that early controls of feeding are rudimentary. In particular, it now appears that in young pups, dehydration may be the primary stimulatory signal for ingestion and that gastric fill may be the only postingestive inhibitory signal.

COMPONENTS OF THE INGESTIVE SEQUENCE

In this paper, we describe developing behaviors of young rats that will become feeding and drinking in adults. We term these early and precocial behaviors *independent ingestion* because the responses are studied independent of the mother and suckling. Our developmental analysis has emphasized the component and sequential nature of ingestive behavior, and this emphasis on appetitive sequences has led to a recognition and identification of behavioral elements in ingestion and a beginning understanding of their control.

At least three categories of behavioral components in the ingestive sequence can be distinguished: activity and search; orientation and approach; and oral consummatory responses. The oral consummatory component has

1

largely been the focus in investigations to date. Analysis began with the question, what does a newborn rat pup do with food or fluid placed in its mouth? Wirth and Epstein first addressed this question by holding rat neonates to a flowing water spout.[1] In such tests, pups were not required to produce the preceding components of the appetitive response sequence in order to indicate whether they possessed the substrates for adultlike lapping and swallowing. This procedure for studying the final consummatory component of ingestion was extended in our laboratory using controlled deliveries of test fluids through oral cannulas; pups were free to move about while their willingness to ingest could be measured[2] (FIGURE 1).

UNDERSTANDING CONTROL OF THE ORAL COMPONENT

We learned that from birth and earlier, rat pups will actively lap, mouth, and swallow fluids.[3-5] This early independent ingestion is deprivation dependent, with pups as young as 1 day of age showing increased intake with increased deprivation from the mother and milk. Not only do neonates ingest orally infused diets, they will also consume solutions spread on the floor of their warm test containers.[6] The termination of ingestion in both test situations has behavioral parallels to the satiety sequence seen in adult animals.[7]

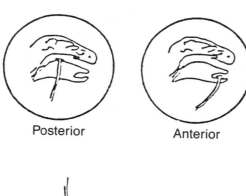

Posterior   Anterior

FIGURE 1. Drawing of 6-day-old pup with a thin polyethylene cannula implanted sublingually in the front of the mouth. An infusion of diet made through the cannula must be actively licked, lapped, and swallowed or will passively drip out of the pup's mouth. In response to the infusions of sweet solutions, pups show active mouthing behaviors consisting of movements of the jaws and tongue which continue after the infusion has ended. In the experiments described here, some infused diets were sucrose (10%). Because young rat pups have little or no sucrase enzyme activity, they do not readily digest or absorb sucrose solutions. For experiments lasting several hours, where sucrose diets might have led to dehydration, we used saccharin solutions (0.05%) which pups also readily ingest and which are nonnutritive. In some experiments Kool-Aid flavoring was added to the diet.

In short, young pups appear to possess neural substrates and effector systems needed for the oral response component of adultlike ingestion, despite the fact that they normally do not eat solid food until the third postnatal week.

Dehydration May Be the Only Physiological Stimulus for Ingestive Responding in Rat Neonates

It had been well established that acute, experimentally induced dehydration could be a stimulus for independent ingestion in neonates.[1,8,9] However, until recently, we had not viewed dehydration in young pups as an essential stimulus for ingestion after milk deprivation because a nutrient deficit or an empty stomach seemed at least as likely a signal. But because deprivation of milk results in both cellular and extracellular dehydration[8,10] as well as caloric deprivation, in previous studies dehydration was confounded with nutritional deficits and empty stomachs. Thus the specific stimulus for enhanced ingestion after deprivation had not been identified.

We removed the confound of dehydration in young, food-deprived pups and found no increase in ingestion after only caloric deprivation.[11] In these experiments, 6-day-old pups' hydration was maintained during a 22-hour "deprivation" period by a continuous infusion of isotonic saline through an indwelling gastric cannula. Comparison groups received infusions of milk or no infusions. Two hours before testing ingestion of oral infusions, the gastric infusions were stopped to allow time for pups' stomachs to empty. We found, as expected, that deprived pups that received no infusions during the deprivation period ingested large volumes of the diet (FIGURE 2A). In contrast, pups that had been maintained in hydrational balance with isotonic saline infusions consumed little of the diet. Their intake was similar to milk-loaded control pups, despite having empty stomachs and being nutritively and maternally deprived. To the degree that we distinguish hunger from thirst on the basis of the responsiveness of behavior to specific physiological stimuli, these findings suggest that *rat pups are born without a hunger system.*

The Stomach Generates a Primary Postingestive Inhibitory Signal in Ingestion

Dehydration stimulates ingestion in young pups, while the primary immediate postingestive inhibitory control of intake appears to be gastric fill. A pyloric noose that prevents movement of ingested solutions from the stomach to the intestines[2,12,13] has provided a particularly useful means of evaluating the signals originating from the stomach. Deprived 6-day-old rats with closed pyloric nooses ingested volumes comparable to those of pups ingesting normally. Therefore, *stomach fill alone was sufficient to stop ingestion.*[14] Stomach volumes measured at the termination of ingestion revealed that pups'

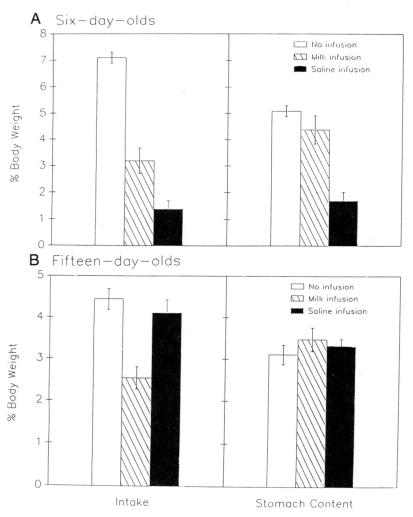

FIGURE 2. Intakes (left) and stomach contents (right) at end of ingestion tests in rat pups that received isotonic saline, milk, or no infusions during a 24-hour deprivation/treatment period. A: Six-day-old pups. B: Fifteen-day-old pups. Note that in 6-day-olds, saline infusions reduce intake to the same degree as nutritive milk infusions despite the fact that stomachs remain empty. (Reproduced from Reference 11 with permission.)

ingestion stopped at the same degree of gastric fill whether they were ingesting normally or with closed nooses. If postgastric nutritive or hydrational signals had been required to inhibit ingestion, then pups with pyloric occlusion should have consumed more and their terminal level of stomach fill should have been higher. In addition, and in contrast to adults,[15] inhibition resulting from gastric fill was a product of the amount rather than the chemical makeup of the solution that fills the stomach. We found that milk, isotonic saline, and glucose preloads all resulted in intake termination at an equivalent point of gastric fill in young pups with occluded pyloruses.

The Onset of "Feeding" in Older Pups

The results just summarized place the emergence of feeding control, other than gastric-fill inhibition, in the postnatal period sometime after 6 days of age. *We found that, by 15 days of age, stimulation of ingestion comes to depend on more than just dehydration.* When hydration was maintained in 15-day-old pups during overnight deprivation using intragastric infusions of isotonic saline, pups ingested just as much as deprived control pups[11] (FIGURE 2B). Thus by this age, there appears to be a stimulus for ingestion after deprivation other than dehydration.

Emerging Nutritive Inhibition of Ingestion

Providing pups with caloric gastric loads also revealed new influences on the ingestive responses of 15-day-olds. Preloads of milk and glucose reduced intake relative to saline loads. More importantly, and similar to adults,[16] these loads resulted in a termination of ingestion at lower volumes of gastric fill.[14] This finding indicates that *by 15 days of age, there is an inhibitory modulatory signal that is postgastric.* More recently we have found that as early as 9 days of age, nutritive gastric loads begin to inhibit intake more than nonnutritive loads[17] (FIGURE 3).

Use-Dependent Modulation of a Response Component

In many ways, the data summarized to this point are a satisfying affirmation of the developmental strategy. They depict an instructive ontogeny for control of ingestion, one with opportunities for identifying mechanisms and correlating them with neural maturation. However, a striking characteristic of the oral component of ingestion, and one that has long been appreciated for adults as well as pups, is that physiological explanations never completely account for the occurrence or patterning of ingestion; ingestive experience is recognized to have a major influence on behavior. During our recent work, we have found that one of the most straightforward, though overlooked, contributions that experience can make is to immediately diminish an ongoing response based on recent stimulation or activation of that response. Stated in another manner, responses can habituate with "use" and the degree to which they habituate influences their subsequent expression. Habituation has

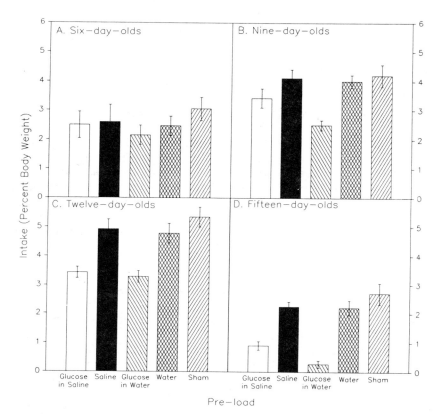

FIGURE 3. Intake [mean ± standard error of the mean (SEM)] from the floor of test containers of a sweetened milk diet during a 30-minute test. Tests were conducted 2 hours following gastric pre-loads. Data are expressed as percentage deprived body weight (before gastric loading). Note inhibition by glucose-water at 9, 12, and 15 days of age and inhibition by glucose-saline at 12 and 15 days of age. (Reproduced from Reference 17 with permission.)

the potential to be a fundamental characteristic of all component responses in appetitive sequences. In particular, we have found that *habituation is a significant feature of the oral component and, as such, a potential integrator of ingestive controls.*

STUDIES USING BRIEF INFUSIONS

Our perspective on oral experience emerges from our developmental analysis and from an experimental approach that provided an unusually explicit control of the oral presentation of ingestive stimuli. In our work, oral experience with a diet was programmed by providing pups of different ages with a series of brief intraoral infusions of sweet, nonnutritive solutions through oral cannula. The duration of each programmed infusion was brief, and the volume delivered quite small. Small infusions minimized the amount of gastric filling, and during the entire experiment, pups received only a fraction of the amount of diet they would have consumed if they were allowed to freely ingest a diet that was continuously infused or lapped from the floor. Postabsorptive signals were effectively eliminated by the use of the nonnutritive solutions.

To assess oral responsivity, we recorded the duration of oral responding, as evidenced in mouthing activity, to each infusion in the series. Thus, in these experiments, each brief infusion served both as a stimulus that provided oral experience with a diet and as a probe of oral responsivity to that diet, indicated by amount of mouthing. When pups were tested with these small, brief, oral infusions, the effects of oral experience were marked. Pups showed dramatic decreases in ingestive behavior; oral responsivity to the repeated stimulus presentations decreased steadily[18] (FIGURE 4). Oral responding declined to a level of virtual nonresponsivity, and this occurred despite the fact that pups had ingested very little volume, that levels of gastric fill were likely

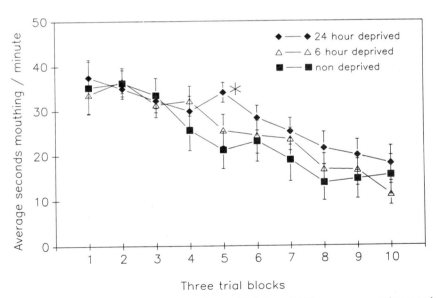

FIGURE 4. Patterns of mouthing response to 3-second infusions of 10% sucrose presented once each minute in 18-day-old pups. Mouthing responses were recorded continuously during testing and are represented here as average seconds mouthing per trial over blocs of three trials. Pups were tested after 24 hours or 6 hours deprivation or tested nondeprived. (Reproduced from Reference 18 with permission.)

to be low, and that the diet was not absorbed. The decrement in oral responding that occurs with repeated oral stimulation was an effect of the *specific* oral sensory or proprioceptive experience with the diet; responding was restored by simply changing the flavor of the infused diet. This restoration of responding argued against general metering or fatigue as a cause of declining responsiveness and indicated that the oral experience effect is relatively specific. Further, the remote possibility of postingestive effects contributing to the decline in oral responding under these conditions was ruled out in experiments in which a group of pups received identical brief infusions delivered not orally, but intragastrically. Then, during a second infusion period, these pups received oral infusions. Oral responding in this subsequent test for pups that had received the first series of infusions intragastrically was identical to that of pups that had received no infusions at all. Thus, the repeated *oropharyngeal experience* with a diet, not the gastric or postgastric effects of the diet, produces a distinctly diminishing responsiveness to the diet.

This oral-experience-based effect not only appears to have a role in punctuating bursts of ingestion, but also has implications for influencing intake on a longer term basis. When a 30-minute or 3-hour interval was interposed between an initial stimulus series and a subsequent infusion test, pups that had received the previous oral experience continued to show a significantly reduced level of responsiveness relative to their own initial responding and relative to the responding of a group that had received no stimulation[19] (FIGURE 5). The effects of experience that accrue from ongoing ingestive experience are thus potent and relatively long lasting, having persisting effects on ingestive responsiveness and thus potentially persisting effects on intake control.

ORAL HABITUATION

The patterns of declining oral responsiveness to repeated oral infusions resemble patterns of decrementing responding that have been described in many other behavior systems and in animals from aplysia to humans, including rat pups. In these systems, decreased responding has been termed habituation. We use "habituation" here descriptively to reflect a specific and relatively long-lasting response decrement resulting from repeated stimulation.[20,21] The results described above indicate that, in developing rats, the mouth habituates to presentations of fluid stimuli.

We do not use "habituation" to suggest a process occurring in the mouth at the receptor level; such a peripheral process might more accurately be termed sensory or receptor *adaptation*. While receptor adaptation and habituation are *logically similar* processes, receptor adaptation refers to a decrement that can be attributed to peripheral rather than central processing and that characteristically is quite short-lived. Although both adaptation and

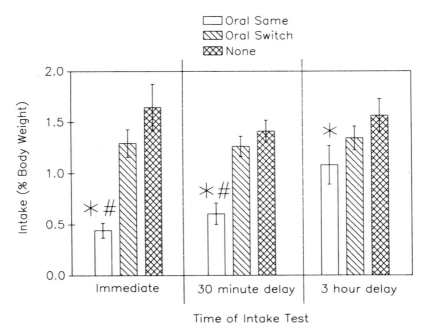

FIGURE 5. Intake of a 4-minute continuous infusion of a flavored saccharin (0.05%) solution in 12-day-old pups immediately following habituation or at a delay of 30 minutes or 3 hours. Pups in group "oral/same" received the same flavored diet during habituation and ingestion testing. Pups in group "oral/switch" received a different flavor during habituation and ingestion testing. Pups in group "none" received no infusions during habituation and a random flavored solution during ingestion testing. (Reproduced from Reference 19 with permission.) * $p < 0.05$ compared to group "none." # $p < 0.05$ compared to group "oral/switch."

habituation are likely to contribute importantly to the patterning of ingestive behavior, the finding that the decrement in ingestive behavior can persist for at least 3 hours rules out adaptation as a possible explanation for the suppressive effects of oral experience in the paradigm described above.

These data from developing rat pups reveal an impressive potential of the mouth in controlling ingestion. The oral habituation process provides an animal with an experience-based control of intake, a straightforward way to influence its present ingestive behavior based on ongoing experience. Habituation allows the intrinsic effects of the oral experience generated by sensory and proprioceptive events of eating to be readily appreciated by the central nervous system. Although the role of the mouth is not usually viewed by psychobiologists from a habituation perspective (though see Thorpe[22] and other ethological perspectives, e.g., Tinbergen,[23] for suggestions that feeding control originates with the behavioral regulation provided by habituation), the concept of habituation provides a way of conceptualizing what has been meant in psychobiologists' reference to the "oral phase" or "oral factor" in feeding control, a control that has also been termed "oral metering."

THE INFLUENCE OF PHYSIOLOGY

Our initial studies were designed to examine the contribution of oral experience to the control of ingestion in relative isolation from other ingestion-related physiological signals. In the absence of such signals, oral experience was demonstrated to have profound suppressive effects on ingestive behavior. Returning some of these physiological signals to the test situation revealed an impressive *integrative* capacity of the oral habituation system. First, the influence of gastric fill was first assessed in pups after a mild, 6-hour, deprivation internal designed to produce empty stomachs by the time of testing. Pups were tested with a series of brief oral infusions as described above. Some pups also received a 5-minute continuous gastric load, constituting an appreciable amount of gastric fill, through indwelling gastric cannulas while a control group received only oral infusions. The mouthing activity of both groups was continuously recorded.

Beginning with the third oral infusion, the mouthing responses of gastrically loaded pups began to decline more rapidly than the responses of control pups and remained lower throughout the duration of testing (FIGURE 6A). Thus, in this situation, oral habituation rate is modulated by gastric filling. The habituation process is sensitive to the postingestive physiological signal and appears to integrate it with accruing information about oral experience.[24]

A further investigation of the gastric modulation of oral habituation revealed that an additional physiological signal, deprivation state, also influences oral responding. We found that the same gastric filling that markedly increased habituation rate after short periods of deprivation had no effect in 24-hour deprived pups. This phenomenon is illustrated for 24-hour deprived, 12-day-olds in FIGURE 6B, where it can be seen that the same gastric load that resulted in more rapid oral habituation (FIGURE 6A) now has *little or no effect* on oral habituation. The rate of oral habituation in 24-hour deprived 12-day-olds is *insensitive* to level of gastric fill.[24] In this case, deprivation changes the manner in which another physiological signal, gastric fill, affects oral habituation. Such suggestive demonstrations illustrate a compelling capacity of the oral habituation system to appreciate multiple state-related signals along with ongoing ingestive experience.

The significance of the habituation property of ingestive systems thus goes beyond just explaining how oral factors contribute to the inhibition of ingestion. Habituation is a process with both an intrinsic experience-encoding property and a number of parameters that may be modified by other signals arising during the course of ingestion. Parameters such as the initial level of responding, the rate of habituation, and the duration and specificity of the habituation effects may be modulated by state-related physiological sig-

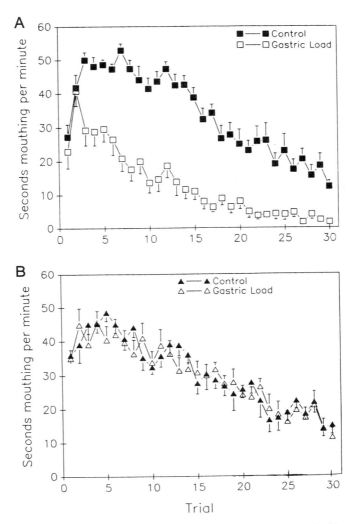

FIGURE 6. A: Patterns of decrementing mouthing activity (means ± SEM) in 6-hour deprived 12-day-old pups in response to a series of oral infusions of 10% sucrose. Each point represents the number of seconds mouthing per minute in each trial. Control pups received oral infusions only while "gastric load" pups received both oral infusions and a 2-ml continuous infusion of 10% sucrose through indwelling gastric cannulas over 5 minutes starting at the same time as the first oral infusion. Beginning with the third infusion, the responses of gastric load pups were significantly lower than control pups. (Reproduced from Reference 24 with permission.) **B:** Patterns of mouthing activity to 10% sucrose infusions in 12-day-old pups after 24 hours deprivation. Control pups received oral infusions alone while "gastric load" pups received oral stimulation and gastric loads as described in A.

nals. The oral habituation process is able to serve as the integrator of such postingestive physiological signals into ongoing behavior. The animal thus has a realtime interface for its physiological state and recent feeding history as well as a way of expressing these in ongoing behavior by controlling oral responsiveness. To put it simply, whenever a bout of ingestion is terminated, the cause may be oral habituation—with postingestive consequences serving to alter the rate of habituation and the duration of the habituation effect. Moreover, because influences on the parameters determining responsiveness may be broadly sensitive to subtle features of physiological state, habituation, more broadly, could be the proximate mechanism for effecting long-term regulation of energy balance and body weight. In short, the mouth and its inherent habituating nature may be the focal integrator for control of ingestive behavior.

IMPORTANCE AND SIGNIFICANCE OF HABITUATION FOR THE ORAL COMPONENT OF INGESTION

Previous attempts to characterize the role of the mouth in the control of feeding have been incomplete for at least three reasons. First, they have neglected the sequential nature of feeding and required animals to perform a complete sequence of locating, identifying, and ingesting the diet. Different processes may control search, orientation, and consumption,[25] and any of these controls could inhibit ingestion. Second, there has usually been little explicit control of ongoing oral experience. Temporal control of stimulus presentation is particularly important in evaluating the significance of habituation in ingestion. We utilize the oral infusion technique as a means to isolate the oral component and gain temporal control of diet presentation. Lastly, a most important problem of much work on oral factors in feeding is that adult rats, the typical subjects of these experiments, have had considerable feeding experience.

Understanding the role of the oral component in ingestion requires a system that minimizes the contribution of previous ingestive experience. Note that in developmental studies, tests of pups 18 days of age and younger are essentially tests of feeding-naive animals because such pups have had limited opportunity to learn about the consequences of ingestion. Specifically, young pups are unlikely to have learned anything about the postingestive or satiating properties of diets other than their dam's milk. For this reason, studying ingestive control, particularly the role of experiential processes, is best accomplished by developmental analysis where these factors can be controlled.

In addition to this absence of satiety-related conditioning in young pups, the appetitive component of independent ingestion—activity, search, orientation, approach—has not yet emerged in pups' behavior.[25] Thus it has been natural/convenient for experimenters to study the ontogeny of ingestion by studying the consummatory response, and to elicit it with oral infusions or other techniques that minimize the requirements for appetitive behavior. Because pups are not experienced with the normal appetitive → consummatory sequence of ingestion, tests making use of oral infusions do not violate expectations of a particular sequence of events leading up to feeding, as making similar infusions can do in adults.[26]

We believe that similar mechanisms for appreciating oral experience are also functional in adults and fundamental to control of their ingestion; however we have not yet studied oral experience effects in adults with the procedures described here. Because of the issues of previous feeding experience and expectation about the feeding sequence just discussed, detecting and demonstrating what may be a primary and integrative role for oral habituation in adults could be difficult and will require thoughtful strategies.

USING DEVELOPMENTAL ANALYSIS TO UNDERSTAND OTHER COMPONENTS OF INGESTION

As we indicated at the outset, developmental analysis helps distinguish components of ingestion and calls attention to the possibility that different appetitive components have *separable substrates* and *differential controls*. Our own work demonstrates this principle with behavioral and physiological data. Other recent studies have made the point pharmacologically. For example, intriguing differences of ingestive components have been described by Smith and colleagues.[27,28] These investigators report that dopaminergic systems appear to be involved in orienting and maintaining ingestion from the floor, but not in the ingestion of oral infusions.

Distinctions such as these regarding the components of ingestive behavior may seem somewhat arbitrary and overly simplified. But, especially for the case where the interest is in relating behavior to brain and physiology, it is important to remind ourselves that we are not looking somewhere in the brain for a single behavior or for a single site controlling all the behaviors making up feeding. Instead appreciation of the sequential nature of feeding leads to a recognition that each response component depends on separate neural output machinery and may thus be separately and independently controlled and represented. Understanding feeding as a whole may require first understanding where and how individual components, such as the oral consummatory component, are modulated and only then trying to figure out how the various components are put together sequentially and controlled.[25] The behavioral components that make up the feeding sequence may be under independent control, and their occurrence in the suite of feeding-related responses is given coherence by the stability of the environment—there need be no neural unification of feeding-related controls.

Our reason for employing the oral infusion technique should thus become obvious. We utilize the oral infusion technique first as a way to gain temporal control so that oral experience can be explored and second as a means to isolate the oral component for study from other responses in the sequence. In order to assess oral responsiveness in isolation from other components of ingestion, we need a specific probe of the oral component, and oral infusions provide this approach. While we would presume that the oral habituation responsible for reducing oral responsiveness would continue to prevent intake even when animals are also required to show the appetitive/search/identification components of ingestion, there could be an interaction between the components that would reduce the effectiveness of oral experience.

Our data support the importance of oral habituation processes in ingestive control. The data do not reveal much, however, about the potential interactions between components in the ingestive sequence. Are, for example, the effects of habituation on oral responsiveness translated to a diminished appetitive responsiveness? Or, in an orally habituated animal, would a vigorous search be undertaken, with intake simply blocked once consumption has begun? Questions about the relationship of one component to another are particularly important because they bear on the degree to which components in the ingestive sequence are coherent or unified. If such coherence exists, it may reflect a hierarchical control of behavior, emergent developmentally and perhaps dependent on conditioned links between components. This perspective dictates a careful dissection of how each ingestive component is modulated followed by an investigation of the development of interactions between components and the contribution of experience to these interactions.

DEVELOPMENT AND FEEDING

It is exactly this power of the developmental strategy in exposing the individual components of ingestion and their changing hierarchical relationships that makes its application to feeding control so valuable. We look forward to developmental revelations about the shifting nature of feeding control to eventually clarify the essential mechanisms determining the expression of ingestive behavior and to provide a general model for the analysis of appetitive behavior in general.

REFERENCES

1. WIRTH, J. B. & A. N. EPSTEIN. 1976. The ontogeny of thirst in the infant rat. Am. J. Physiol. **230:** 188–198.
2. PHIFER, C. B. & W. G. HALL. 1987. Development of feeding behavior. In Techniques in the Behavioral Sciences: Feeding and Drinking. F. M. Toates & N. E. Rowland, Eds. **1:** 189–230. Elsevier. Amsterdam, the Netherlands.
3. HALL, W. G. 1979. The ontogeny of feeding in rats. I. Ingestive and behavioral responses to oral infusions. J. Comp. Physiol. Psychol. **93:** 977–1000.
4. JOHANSON, I. B. & W. G. HALL. 1980. Classical conditioning of an odor preference in 3-day-old rats. Behav. Neural Biol. **29:** 132–136.
5. SMOTHERMAN, W. P. & S. R. ROBINSON. 1987. Prenatal expression of species-typical action patterns in the rat fetus (*Rattus norvegicus*). J. Comp. Psychol. **101:** 190–196.

6. HALL, W. G. & T. E. BRYAN. 1980. The ontogeny of feeding in rats. II. Independent ingestive behavior. J. Comp. Physiol. Psychol. **94**: 746–756.

7. ANTIN, J., J. GIBBS, J. HOLT, R. C. YOUNG & G. P. SMITH. 1975. Cholecystokinin elicits the complete behavioral sequence of satiety in rats. J. Comp. Physiol. Psychol. **89**: 784–790.

8. BRUNO, J. P. 1981. Development of drinking behavior in preweanling rats. J. Comp. Physiol. Psychol. **95**: 1016–1027.

9. BRUNO, J. P., E. M. BLASS & F. AMIN. 1983. Determinants of suckling versus drinking in weanling albino rats: influence of hydrational state and maternal contact. Dev. Psychobiol. **16**: 177–184.

10. FRIEDMAN, M. I. 1979. Effects of milk consumption and deprivation on body fluids of suckling rats. Physiol. Behav. **23**: 1029–1034.

11. PHIFER, C. B., M. LADD & W. G. HALL. 1991. Effects of hydrational state on ingestion in infant rats: is dehydration the only ingestive stimulus? Physiol. Behav. **49**: 695–699.

12. DEUTSCH, J. A. & M.-L. WANG. 1977. The stomach as a site for rapid nutrient reinforcement sensors. Science **195**: 89–90.

13. HALL, W. G. 1973. A remote stomach clamp to evaluate oral and gastric controls of drinking in the rat. Physiol. Behav. **11**: 897–901.

14. PHIFER, C. B. & W. G. HALL. 1988. Ingestive behavior in preweanling rats: emergence of postgastric controls. Am. J. Physiol. **255**: R191–R199.

15. DEUTSCH, J. A. 1985. The role of the stomach in eating. Am. J. Clin. Nutr. **42**: 1040–1043.

16. KRALY, F. S. & G. P. SMITH. 1978. Combined pregastric and gastric stimulation by food is sufficient for normal meal size. Physiol. Behav. **21**: 405–409.

17. SWITHERS, S. E. & W. G. HALL. 1989. A nutritive control of independent ingestion in rat pups emerges by nine days of age. Physiol. Behav. **46**: 873–879.

18. SWITHERS-MULVEY, S. E., G. L. MILLER & W. G. HALL. 1991. Habituation of oromotor responding to oral infusions in rat pups. Appetite **17**: 55–67.

19. SWITHERS-MULVEY, S. E. & W. G. HALL. Control of ingestion by oral habituation in rat pups. Behav. Neurosci. (In press.)

20. HARRIS, J. D. 1943. Habituatory response decrement in the intact organism. Psychol. Bull. **40**: 385–422.

21. THOMPSON, R. F. & W. A. SPENCER. 1966. Habituation: a model phenomenon for the study of neuronal substrates of behavior. Psychol. Rev. **73**: 16–43.

22. THORPE, W. H. 1966. Learning and Instinct in Animals. Harvard University Press. Cambridge, Mass.

23. TINBERGEN, N. 1951. The Study of Instinct. Clarendon Press. Oxford, England.

24. SWITHERS-MULVEY, S. E. & W. G. HALL. The brainstem integrates oral habituation and gastric fill but not deprivation in rat pups. (Submitted.)

25. HALL, W. G. 1990. The ontogeny of ingestive behavior: changing control of components in the feeding sequence. *In* Handbook of Behavioral Neurobiology: Neurobiology of Food and Fluid Intake. E. M. Stricker, Ed. **10**: 77–123. Plenum Press. New York, N.Y.

26. HALL, W. G. & G. P. SMITH. 1990. Unpublished observations.

27. BRODER, L., G. P. SMITH, A. TYRKA & J. GIBBS. 1990. Independent ingestion and intraoral infusions of 10% sucrose produce different patterns of central dopamine metabolism in 14-day-old rats. Soc. Neurosci. Abstr. **16**(Part 2): 912.

28. TYRKA, A., G. P. SMITH & J. GIBBS. 1990. SCH23390 inhibits intake of sucrose more during independent ingestion than during intraoral infusions in rats as early as postnatal day 7. Soc. Neurosci. Abstr. **16**(Part 2): 912.

The Roles of Experience in the Transition from Dependent to Independent Feeding in Ring Doves[a]

PETER D. BALSAM, JAMES D. DEICH,
AND ROBIN HIROSE

Psychology Department
Barnard College of Columbia University
New York, New York 10027

All animals must obtain food throughout their lifetime. For many species, food availability and type vary with long-term climatic changes, with seasonal changes, and with the time of day. These changes require substantial flexibility in feeding behaviors. This adaptability is evident in examples of locale-specific feeding behavior in single species,[1] such as milk bottle opening in birds[2] or potato washing by Japanese macaques.[3] Furthermore, when the locale-specific feeding behavior is a novel response to a previously available food, or when subpopulations differ in the response they make to identical food, the evidence for this flexibility being experientially based is especially strong. Specifically, individual experience can influence *where* to look for food,[4,5] *what type of object* to look for as food,[6,7] and *what behaviors* are used to acquire food.[8]

In altricial species, changes in these three aspects of feeding necessarily accompany the developmental transition from dependence on the parents for food to independent feeding. As this transition occurs, the young need to find food in new locations—away from the parent. The young must respond to sensory characteristics of new foods, and new responses must become active elements of the feeding repertoire.

The Columbidae family (pigeons and doves) provides good examples of altricial species that undergo all of these developmental changes in feeding. The developmental pattern is similar in all members of this family[9] and has been described in detail for the ring dove, *Streptopelia risoria.*[10-12]

After a male and female ring dove have mated, the female typically lays a clutch of two eggs which are incubated by both parents for 14–15 days prior to hatching. Initially, the young are unable to feed themselves. The parents feed the squab "crop-milk",[13] a cheeselike substance produced in the crop. Both parents participate in the regurgitative feeding of the young. These feed-

[a] The research reported here was supported by National Science Foundation grant BNS-8919231.

16

ings are initiated by the parents after hatching, but by the time the young leave the nest on about postnatal day 10 (PD 10), the squab beg vigorously to obtain parental feeding. The begging consists of the squab thrusting its beak at the parent's beak while making very rapid fluttering motions with its wings. The begging is sometimes accompanied by a whistlelike call. During regurgitative feeding, the parent grasps the bill of the squab between its beaks and makes vigorous pumping movements with its upper body, particularly with its neck and head.[10,12] From around the third day post-hatching until the squab begin getting food on their own, the parents feed the squab crop-milk mixed with increasing amounts of seed.[14] The amount of crop-milk fed to the squab increases through about PD 5 and declines thereafter.

FIGURE 1 shows the squab's and parents' behavior surrounding feeding interactions in a representative family during the transition from dependent to independent feeding.[15] Like the squab depicted in FIGURE 1 (left panel), all of the young that we have observed will beg for food at least through the time of weaning. Parental feeding of young (FIGURE 1, center panel) begins to decline near the end of the third week and ceases by the end of the fourth week post-hatch. Males will generally continue to feed the young after the females have stopped.

As illustrated by the behavior of the squab depicted in FIGURE 1 (right panel), pecking begins around PD 14 and increases in frequency.[12,14,15] Squab begin to ingest seed successfully by about PD 16 and continue to improve in efficiency. By PD 28 they are nearly as efficient as adults at ingesting seeds.[14]

These changes in the feeding behaviors of ring dove squab illustrate that the transition from dependent to independent feeding in altricial species involves changes in the locations of food, the behaviors used to obtain food, and the nature of food itself. In the next section, we discuss how individual experience plays a role in producing these changes.

ROLES OF EXPERIENCE IN THE TRANSITION TO INDEPENDENT FEEDING

There may be considerable variation in the environments in which the young of altricial species develop adult feeding behaviors. Young of different parents might have to adapt to different local conditions of adult food types and density. Young animals might also have to adapt to variability in specific juvenile food sources over time, including that provided by the parent. Under these conditions, we would expect to find that individual experience influences the ontogeny of feeding behaviors. For example, in years of famine young animals may remain dependent on their parents longer than they might in years of plenty.[16] Additionally, as the food sources available to specific parents and young may differ by locale or change over time, there may need

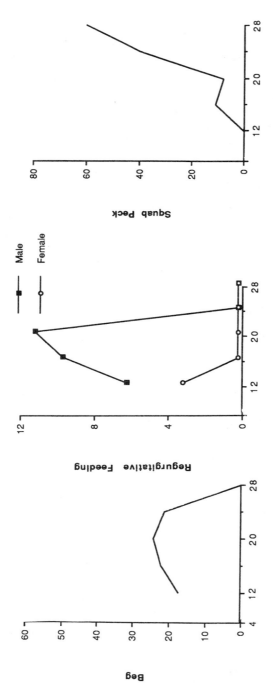

FIGURE 1. Squab 7. Squab and parent behaviors in a single family that surround feeding interactions. Each figure shows the percent of 10-second intervals containing a given behavior during the first 60 minutes after lights came on in the morning. The left panel shows squab begging; the center panel shows intervals in which parents regurgitatively fed squab. The right panel shows intervals in which squab made at least one peck at seed on the floor.

to be considerable flexibility in the specific foraging and consummatory behavior exhibited by the young.

For example, adults of the Columbidae family seem able to adapt to considerable local variation in food sources. Individual members of particular species of this family feed in different locations, feed on different foods from locale to locale, and ingest different foods from one time to another.[4,7,17,18] Consequently, the young of these species must acquire adult feeding behavior under a wide range of circumstances. Therefore, an analysis of the developmental transition from dependent to independent feeding requires consideration of how experience might mold the individual's search for, identification of, and acquisition of food.

One role that experience might play is to modulate the time or rate at which the young change over from infantile to adult feeding behaviors. It is possible that operant contingencies determine the young animal's choice of whether to engage in the juvenile or adult feeding behaviors. In this view, the changeover ought to be modulated by the reliability of the juvenile and adult behaviors at providing food. For the ring dove, this would mean that there should be a change in the success of begging and pecking as means of feeding during the period of transition from dependent to independent feeding. FIGURE 2 shows the changes in the efficiency with which begging and pecking result in ingestion of food. Each of these data points represents the mean of six squab. The data on pecking and begging are from separate experiments. As the figure shows, begging becomes less likely to result in parental feeding while pecking becomes more likely to result in the ingestion of seed. This pattern gives credibility to the hypothesis that the transition to pecking is modulated by the relative success that each individual has at obtaining food in these two ways. Note that we cannot say if it is the absolute level of success for pecking or its success relative to other behaviors that determines the time course of the transition. However, on the basis of a considerable literature on the determinants of choice,[19] we expect that the relative payoff is the controlling variable. In any case, one likely role of individual experience is to modulate the overall rate and timing of the transition from dependent to independent feeding.

Since the transition appears to depend on the efficacy of the consummatory response, we have also examined how the development of pecking, itself, may depend on experience. In the remainder of this chapter, we focus on how experience affects the development of adult feeding in ring doves. First, we describe our experimental analyses of how ring dove squab learn to identify an object as food and how they learn the consummatory behavior itself. Next, we consider how squab might learn where to search for food by drawing on data from a number of different species. Finally, we consider the generality of what we have learned from the study of the ring dove for other altricial species.

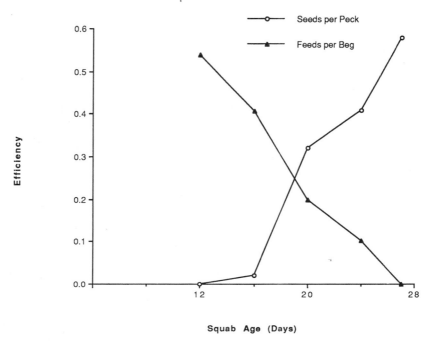

FIGURE 2. Change in efficiency of begging and pecking. The pecking efficiency is the number of seeds eaten divided by the number of pecking movements in a 20-minute test session. The efficiency of begging is measured by the number of 10-second intervals with parental feeding divided by the number of intervals with begging during the first 60 minutes after lights were turned on each morning.

Learning What to Peck At

In our first approach to the question of whether normal development of pecking depends on experience, we reared squab without any exposure to seed.[14] We achieved this by grinding seed into a fine powder and gradually making this the only source of food available to parents prior to hatching. This powdered seed was also the only source of food available to the families after the squab hatched. Beginning on PD 14 and on all subsequent days, squab were put into a chamber with seed on the floor for 20 minutes. We found that powder-reared squab pecked very little during these test sessions as compared to seed-reared subjects indicating that direct experience with seed is important for development of the adult response.

We then began to analyze the nature of the experiences necessary for normal development to occur. Two groups of squab were reared on the powdered diet and given a 20-minute seed test from PD 14 to PD 21. Following the test period, one group of subjects was immediately returned to their parents. A second group of subjects was treated identically to the first group except they were returned to their parents after an hour's delay. As FIGURE 3 shows, all subjects pecked a little during the early test sessions but only those squab that were reunited with their parents immediately after the test came to peck at seed at high rates. Casual observation of these squab after they were reunited with their parents indicated that the parents frequently fed the young. This led us to suspect that interaction with seed followed by parental feeding might be an important experience in the ontogeny of pecking.

Hirose and Balsam examined the interval between squab pecking and feeding by the parent in the naturally occurring interaction of parents and squab.[15] As was the case for the subject shown in FIGURE 4, squab are frequently fed within a few minutes of exposure to seed as indicated by the generally brief period between feedings and prior squab pecking. Since feeding behavior can be affected by ingestional consequences over delays of this magnitude,[20,21] it is possible that associations between seed or pecking and nutritional consequences play an important role in this transition.

Balsam, Graf, and Silver analyzed whether experience with seed followed by feeding was sufficient to increase squab pecking.[22] In these studies, squab were reared on the powdered seed diet but given a daily 20-minute experience with seed and feeding. Across experiments, various groups of squab were given a 20-minute exposure to a treatment context on

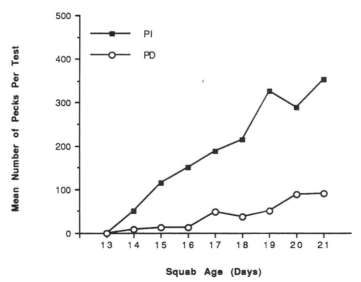

FIGURE 3. Mean number of pecks in a 20-minute test is shown for two groups of squab reared on a powder diet so as to have no experience with seed outside the test situation. Both groups were placed in a chamber whose floor was covered by seed during testing. One group was immediately returned to their parents (group PI) whereas the second group (group PD) was reunited with their parents after an hour's delay.

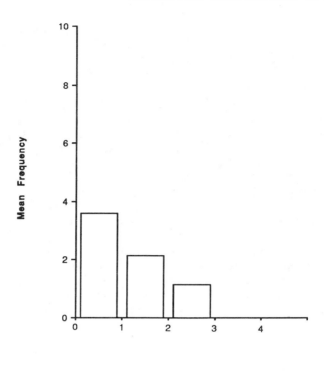

Delay   (Minutes)

FIGURE 4. The distribution of intervals from when one of the parents of squab 7 fed it until the preceding squab's peck. These data were obtained from the first 60 minutes after lights came on in the morning on PD 12, 16, and 20 since this squab was not fed on PD 24 or 28.

PD 14–21. In one group that was allowed to only see seed (S), squab were gently wrapped in a foam blanket and positioned above a grain-covered floor. In a second group, squab were allowed to see grain and peck at it (SP), but not allowed to eat it. These squab were free to move about and peck at a floor to which grain had been glued. In a third group, squab were allowed to see grain, peck at it, and eat it (SPE). This group was free to move about a floor that was sprinkled with fresh seed. A fourth group (C) was given a 20-minute exposure to the test context without any seed present. All of these groups were fed immediately after the daily exposure to the test situation. On PD 21 or 22, these subjects were all tested with seed spread across the floor. The mean number of pecks recorded during this test is shown in FIGURE 5. Three levels of pecking were observed. There was a low level of pecking in group C indicating that there is some tendency for seed to elicit pecking even in subjects that have no prior experience with grain. Significantly more pecking

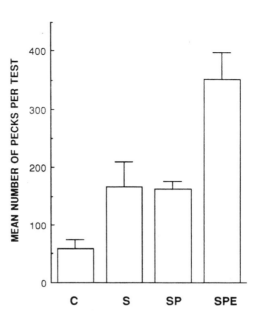

FIGURE 5. Mean number of pecks during a 20-minute test with seed spread across the chamber floor. Prior to the test, different groups were exposed to a week of treatment in which they were either exposed to the test chamber alone (C), exposed to the sight of seed (S), exposed to seed and allowed to peck at it (SP), or exposed to seed and allowed to see it, peck at it, and eat it (SPE). All groups were fed immediately after the treatment exposure.

occurred when visual exposure to seed was followed by immediate feeding (group S). The effects of seeing grain and making pecking movements followed immediately by food (group SP) were not different than the effects of visual exposure alone (group S). However, the squab's pecking was significantly enhanced by the experiences that are concomitants of eating grain (group SPE). Thus two kinds of experience appear necessary for the development of normal pecking levels. A Pavlovian contingency between the sight of grain and food seems sufficient to generate moderate levels of pecking, and contingencies involving the ingestion of seed itself further enhance pecking.

We interpret this pattern of results to mean that the Pavlovian contingency is sufficient for teaching the squab what items to peck. There is a tendency for the squab to peck at grainlike objects, but this is a weak tendency and it rapidly habituates unless seed is paired with positive ingestional consequences.[22] The pairing of the sight of grain with food selectively increases the tendency of the squab to peck at seed. We have not analyzed this aspect of pecking enough to say whether the enhanced pecking is the result of a general motivational effect, enhanced attention to seed, and/or a change in the incentive properties of the seed. Nevertheless, it is clear that the Pavlovian contingency directs the pecking at appropriate targets.

The data also indicate that successfully ingesting seed further increases the level of pecking. We believe this to be an effect of the operant contingency on the frequency of pecking. As the success of pecking increases, the squab become more likely to execute this particular feeding response.

Learning How to Peck

In all of the previously described studies, our measure of pecking was based on the number of head thrusts toward the seed-covered substrate. Successful pecking requires the squab to move its body to the proper location, execute an accurate head thrust, and perform a gaping movement in which the opening and closing of the beak is effective for grasping the target seed. Additionally, the body positioning, thrust, and gape components must all be properly coordinated for a peck to result in the successful ingestion of food. Hence, there was uncertainty about which components of pecking were facilitated by the Pavlovian association and/or by the experience of seed in the mouth. We, therefore, began an analysis of the ontogeny of all of these components of pecking and of their coordination.

We adapted a previously developed[23] system that permits continuous monitoring of avian gape. Briefly, a small magnet is attached to the lower half of the beak and a magnetically sensitive integrated circuit (Hall-effect device) is attached to the upper half of the beak. The output of this circuit is proportional to gape (interbeak distance). This system permits nearly continuous recording of gape by a computer system. We simultaneously videotape the squab so that the behavioral context in which gaping occurs can also be examined.

The signal generated by this system during a successful peck at a piece of grain by an adult ring dove is shown in FIGURE 6. The upper panel shows the distance between the upper and lower beaks. The initial segment shows beak opening as the head moves downward towards the grain target. Maximal gape here is typically 2–4 mm larger than the target seed's diameter. With the two beak halves on either side of the seed, the beak is closed and a plateau appears in the gape signal as the seed is held at the beak's tip. At this point, a backwards movement of the head occurs and the seed is moved deep into the oral cavity. The tongue aids this process by sticking to the seed and pulling it backwards.[24] The next several gape peaks represent this mandibulatory process. The final gape peak is associated with swallowing. The lower panel shows the velocity of the gaping movements. Negative velocities indicate closing of the beak. These displacement and velocity patterns are stereotyped both within and across individual adults.

We have been able to obtain records of squab's gaping movements in a variety of feeding situations.[25] The bottom row of FIGURE 7 shows two of the most commonly occurring food pecks that did involve gape in squab less than three weeks old. For comparison, the top row shows two adult gape records. The gape on the right is one that accompanied a successful peck at seed. The one on the left was an unsuccessful one. Note that both the successful

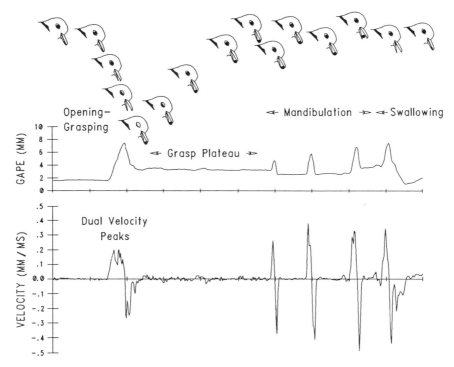

FIGURE 6. Gape record of a successful peck at seed in an adult ring dove. The upper panel shows the changes in the distance between the upper and lower beaks. The lower panel shows the changes in velocity of the opening.

and unsuccessful pecks show the characteristic adult dual-velocity peak opening. Since the early pecks of young birds are frequently unsuccessful, the panel on the upper left is the appropriate comparison for the squab's pecks. The squab's early gape, as shown in the bottom row, are typically simpler than those of the adult, involving either only one clear velocity peak or a square-wave velocity pattern. Furthermore, the coordination of head thrust with gape is fairly variable as the food peck is developing. Gaping sometimes occurs in the squab without accompanying head thrust, some thrusts end short of the substrate, and some contacts with the substrate occur without any gape.

Overall, most early food-directed pecks have an accompanying gape signal that bears limited resemblance to that of the adult. Hence we wondered whether squab needed experience with seed or if maturation alone would be sufficient for the emergence of the adult gape. Tankoos, Deich, Hirose, and Balsam reared squab on either powdered or regular seed diets until they were 21 days of age,[26] as this is an age at which seed-reared ring doves are quite

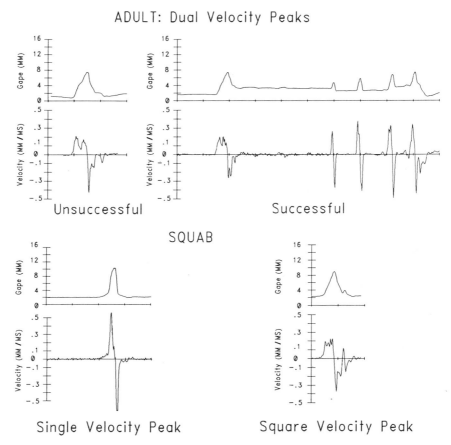

FIGURE 7. The top row shows the gape records from a typical unsuccessful (left side) and successful (right side) adult peck. The lower row shows two of the most common gapes that accompany pecks in squab less than three weeks old.

competent at getting grain. As expected, the seed-reared birds showed gape forms that were predominantly of the adult form. Powder-reared subjects, on the other hand, showed much more variable and immature forms of the gape. Therefore, maturation alone did not result in the production of the adult-like gape. After a week or so of experience with seed, the powder-reared subjects acquired the adultlike grain peck indicating that the form of the gape does show considerable plasticity during ontogeny.

In order to evaluate the role that Pavlovian contingencies might play in the development of the gape, Deich and Balsam restricted the diet of squab and their parents to powdered grain to ensure that the squab had no experience with whole grain.[25] Beginning on PD 16, two squab were restrained by being wrapped in a soft sponge blanket and suspended 10 cm above a floor covered with grain. After 20 minutes of such exposure, each squab was fed a mush composed of equal amounts of powdered seed and baby cereal mixed with just enough water to allow the mixture to flow smoothly through a syringe. Each squab was fed an amount adequate to slightly distend its crop. Squab were tested on PD 22 to PD 25 when they were free to move about on a grain-covered floor. Neither squab pecked during these tests. On subsequent days, each squab was placed in the test chamber and exposed to a procedure that allowed for multiple pairings of seed and food within each session. After an intertrial interval that averaged 60 seconds, grain was sprinkled onto the floor. Ten seconds were allowed to pass, and the squab were then hand fed a small amount of mush as quickly as was possible. Ten such pairings were administered each day. The revised procedure resulted in pecking by both squab. One subject began pecking on PD 29, and the second subject pecked on PD 35. Thus both squab made their first pecks at an age when seed-reared squab would have shown the adult form of gape.

The gape records for the first pecks generated by the Pavlovian procedure were obtained for both subjects. The two squab did not differ in any systematic way. Representative pecks for one of the squab are presented in FIGURE 8. These pecks did involve gape in loose coordination with thrust, but as the figure shows, the gapes generated did not appear very similar to that of the adult. In fact, they appear somewhat similar to the first gapes of much younger squab as depicted above. Single velocity peaks and square-wave velocity profiles predominated. Our examination of the videotapes in combination with these gape data indicated that thrusting and gaping both occurred steadily and in no clear relationship to each other. Additionally, the squab showed head thrusts that involved no gape at all. It appears that neither simple maturation, nor Pavlovian pairings of the sight of grain with feeding, nor their combination is adequate to produce the stereotyped adult gape topography. Our evidence suggests that experience with handling and ingesting seed itself is required for the development of the adult gape topography.

The coordination of the squab's gape and thrust components is also different from the adult behavior. This is consistent with the hypothesis that experience is necessary for the development of this coordination as well as for the development of the gape component.

One potential source of this experience comes from the interaction of parents and squab during begging and regurgitative feeding. Wortis posited that the thrust component and the gape component of pecking were associated during begging, and subsequent early pecking at grain resulted from attempts to peck at the parent's beak as the parent was eating.[12] However, we found that gaping simply did not occur during begging.[25] Alternatively, it is possible that regurgitative feeding provides the opportunity for the squab to associate gaping and thrusting with getting fed. Again our observations make this seem improbable since the rhythmic thrusting movements during regurgitative feeding do not appear very similar to the ballistic thrusting move-

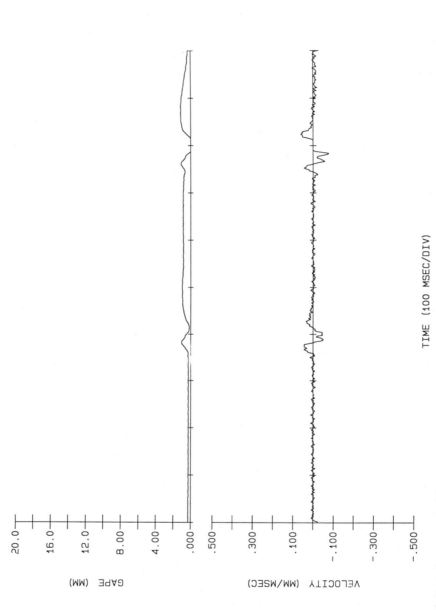

FIGURE 8. Typical gape record of first pecks shown by squab exposed to Pavlovian pairings of the sight of seed with feeding. These squab have no other experience with seed.

ments that are part of pecking at seed. Further, the beak is opened much farther during regurgitative feeding than is typical of independent feeding. Lastly, informal observations of the direction in which initial food-directed pecks were made did not fit with the idea that they were attempts to peck at the parent's beak. Typically such initial pecks were made in the vicinity of the parent, but were clearly directed toward the substrate and the grain that it contained. Hence, it is unlikely that the experiences provided by begging and regurgitative feeding contribute heavily to the form of the pecking gape or to its coordination with the head thrust.

A more tenable explanation of the acquisition of the gape component and its coordination with the thrust component would suggest that Pavlovian pairings of the sight of grain with feeding direct the thrust component of the peck towards grain. Next, either as a result of a tendency to gape at grainlike objects, or as a result of variability in response form combined with tactile feedback from the grain, a variety of initial forms of gape and a variety of gape/thrust coordinations occur, and those that are effective in ingesting grain tend to recur. This hypothesis then posits two steps in the acquisition of the adult consummatory response. First, the occurrence and direction of the thrust component are determined on the basis of Pavlovian pairings of the sight of grain with feeding, and second, the gape component and its coordination with the thrust component are moved toward the more effective adult form by a process of response shaping. Operant conditioning is proposed as the underlying operative process because neither maturation nor extensive Pavlovian training is sufficient to produce the stereotyped adult response. Furthermore, the gape of a different member of the Columbidae, the adult pigeon, has been shown to be susceptible to operant control.[27] Lastly, the movement from the multiple and variable gape forms early in ontogeny to the stereotyped adult form is consonant with the hypothesis of operant learning.

Learning Where to Find Food

We have not yet begun the experimental analysis of how squab learn where to find food, but we think it likely that squab learn about what cues to use to guide their search; what search strategies to use; as well as about specific locations where food may be found.

In adult doves, food seeking is visually guided. The dominance of the visual cues may be a consequence of the experiences dictated by the structure of the feeding environment during ontogeny. In newly hatched squab, gaping can be elicited by tilting the head upwards into the position typical of regurgitative feeding. At about PD 7, the gaping response can be elicited by a touch on the beak. By about PD 12, begging is the predominant feeding behavior and it is elicited by the sight of the parent. Then, over the course of the next week, the feeding behavior switches from being directed toward the parent to being directed at seed.

These transitions in the sensory control of the dominant feeding behavior could easily be the result of changes in the predictive validity of cues that signal positive ingestive consequences. It is only when the parents of the newly hatched squab grasp the beak and hold the squab's head up that the young get fed. Thus, the proprioceptive and/or vestibular cues that accompany feedings will be the best predictors of food at that age. As the squab gets older and is able to hold its own head up and to move it around, the proprioceptive and vestibular cues become less valid predictors of food. However, at that age, only when the squab's beak is touched by the parents during regurgitative feeding does ingestion occur. Hence, tactile cues are likely to be the most valid predictor of food. As the squab's motor competence increases and it leaves the nest, begins to preen, and to push its beak at the parents beak during begging episodes, there is likely to be much tactile stimulation of the beak that is not followed by feedings. At the same time that the predictive validity of tactile cues is decreasing, the sight of the parent (perhaps in particular positions or postures) is likely to be the cue most predictive of feedings. Finally, as parents become less likely to feed squab and the squab become more efficient at seed ingestion, the seed itself becomes the cue most predictive of positive ingestional consequences. Hence, the changing nature of the underlying Pavlovian contingencies may be responsible for the developmental changes in the sensory controls of feeding and for the dominance of visual cues in guiding feeding behavior in adults.

The specific cues that guide adult food search may also acquire their potency through experiences during the transition from dependent to independent feeding. For example, one cue that the pigeon uses in identifying feeding sites is the behavior of other birds. The sight of a bird pecking at the ground is very likely to attract other pigeons to the feeding site.[30] Experiences during ontogeny may make this an effective signal for food. As squab age, the parents will retreat from the young (see FIGURE 9, left panel) rather than feed them when they beg.[12,15] The parents frequently peck at seed at this stage (FIGURE 9, center panel). It is during these days that squab frequently make their early contacts with seed. Consistent with this hypothesis, FIGURE 9 (right panel) shows that during the first week after squab start pecking, 80% or more of their pecks occur proximally to parent pecking. As they mature this co-occurrence of parent and squab pecking becomes less frequent but still occurs 20–60% of the time on PD 28. These early associations between the sight of a pecking parent and the successful acquisition of food may make the sight of another pecking bird a potent signal for food availability. This signal may continue to be a valid predictor of food availability throughout the lifetime of the bird.

Additionally, the squab's experience of finding food in the presence of a pecking parent may be necessary for more general social facilitation effects. Adult members of the Columbidae will peck more in the presence of other adults who are pecking.[12,29,30] The facilitation of this specific behavior may

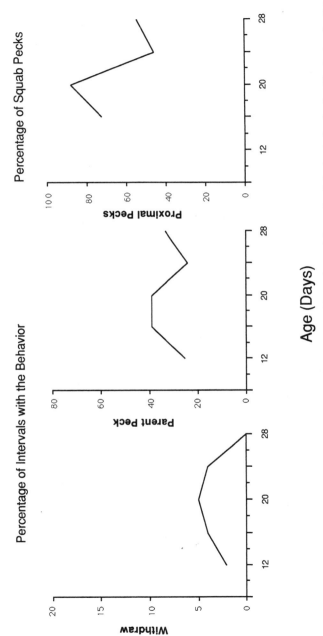

FIGURE 9. Squab 7. The left and center panels show the percent of 10-second intervals containing a given behavior during the first 60 minutes after lights came on in the morning. The left panel shows parent withdrawal from begging squab. The center panel shows intervals in which parents peck at seed. The right panel shows the percentage of squab pecks made in the same or subsequent 10-second observation interval as a parent peck.

conceivably depend on the early experience of squab that are rewarded for pecking in the presence of their pecking parents.

Finally, the search strategies themselves may be molded by specific experiences during ontogeny. There are indeed differences in foraging strategies between juveniles and adults,[28,29,31,32] and many features of foraging patterns are modified by experience. In adult birds, the pattern of movement through a feeding site,[33,34] the number of potential feeding sites,[17] and the specific criteria used to decide whether or not to move on to a new search site[35-37] are all modified by experience. This experience-based flexibility in adults raises the possibility that early experiences exert a substantial influence on the development of foraging strategy.

CONCLUSIONS

Experience has a considerable impact on the ontogeny of independent feeding in ring doves. As the squab get older, the parents become less likely to feed them when they beg. Concomitantly, there is an increase in pecking which we suggest is the result of an increasing efficacy of that response in obtaining food. This increased efficacy is the result of learning where to search for food, learning to identify it, and learning to ingest it efficiently. We have begun to analyze the specific experiences that are responsible for this learning and have found that conditioning processes appear to play a significant role.

Because of Pavlovian pairings of seed and positive ingestional consequences, squab come to direct their pecks at seed. The gape component of the peck and the coordination of the gape and thrust come to be more refined and effective as a consequence of feedback from successful and unsuccessful pecking movements. These Pavlovian and operant contingencies probably continue to be effective at modifying feeding behavior throughout the life of the animal as new food types are encountered.

We also suggest that once there is a repertoire of effective feeding responses, successes and failures direct the animal to proven feeding sites or to search for new ones. This foraging is guided by cues that may owe their effectiveness to experiences during the transition to independent feeding. The cues that signal food availability to the young squab may be the ones that are later used by adults. Furthermore, foraging strategies may also be acquired and influenced by early ontogenetic experience.

Though our analysis has focused on Columbidae and ring doves in particular, the roles that we have described for experience may be important in the ontogeny of many species. It has been suggested that altricial development is an adaptation to limited or highly variable food sources.[38] Thus the development of adult feeding behavior may depend on individual experience in many of these species. The specific operant and Pavlovian contingencies that underlie the transition from dependent to independent feeding in ring doves may play similar roles in the ontogeny of feeding in many species.

For example, as is the case for the ring dove, the rate of changeover from dependent to independent feeding may be influenced by the relative success of juvenile and adult feeding responses. If this is the case, a decrease in the food supplied by the parent would be expected to occur during the transition to independent feeding. Such a decrease seems common across a wide range of altricial species including macaques,[39] domestic cats,[40] white-tailed and fallow deer,[41] and rats.[42] Furthermore, the decrease in parental feeding has been shown to relate to an increase in independent feeding in several species.[43,44] Lastly, in experimental manipulations of the availability of parentally supplied food, it has been shown that the transition to independent feeding occurs at an earlier age when the parentally supplied food is more limited or difficult to obtain.[45-47] Thus the relative payoffs for juvenile and adult feeding responses may play an important role in the transition to independent feeding across a wide range of species.

In many species, the cues that guide foraging behavior change during ontogeny. Porter and Sealy found that in mixed flocks of seabirds, juveniles are attracted to the sight of other birds.[29] Adults are only attracted to the sight of feeding birds and ripples on the surface of the water as indications of good places to search for food. It seems likely that the correlation of these cues with feeding outcomes is responsible for the age-related difference in the feeding cues. In pigeons, new food locations have been shown to be acquired through individual experience.[4,17]

There are also many examples that make it clear that specific feeding behaviors are acquired and improved through experience. For example, the specific feeding responses of oystercatchers[8] are learned through experiences provided by the parents. Robins are able to capture earthworms with increased efficiency as a function of experience.[31] Sticklebacks modify their reaction distance, attack speed, and handling time as a function of successful encounters with different prey types.[48] In mixed flocks of seabirds, Porter and Sealy observed that juveniles showed no surface seizing or stealing as did adults.[29] Furthermore, the young seabirds made many more abortive dives than adults and they did not avoid fishing lines. These differences between juvenile and adult behavior seem likely to be the result of the difference in experience.

In sum, the rate of transition to independent feeding, specific feeding behaviors, and foraging strategies are all influenced by the experiences of individuals during development. The analysis of these experiences in terms of the operant and Pavlovian contingencies embedded in developmental experiences appears to provide an excellent analytic tool for understanding precisely how experience molds these aspects of behavior during ontogeny.

ACKNOWLEDGMENTS

We thank Michael Mondloch and Sara Shettleworth for directing us to some research that was new to us, and we thank Katharine Iskrant, Anat

Reschke, Pat Stokes, and Christina Williams for comments on and help with the manuscript.

REFERENCES

1. GALEF, B. G., JR. 1990. The ecology of weaning: parasitism and the achievement of independence by altricial animals. *In* Interpretation and Explanation in the Study of Behavior. M. Bekoff & D. Jamieson, Eds. **1:** 74–95. Westview Press. Boulder, Colo.
2. FISHER, J. & R. A. HINDE. 1949. The opening of milk bottles by birds. Br. Birds **42:** 347–357.
3. KAWAMURA, S. 1959. The process of sub-culture propogation among Japanese macaques. Primates **2:** 43–54.
4. GIRALDEAU, L. A. & L. LEFEBVRE. 1987. Scrounging prevents cultural transmission of food-finding behaviour in pigeons. Anim. Behav. **35**(2): 387–394.
5. HODGES, C. M. 1981. Optimal foraging in bumblebees: hunting by expectation. Anim. Behav. **29**(4): 1166–1171.
6. MENZEL, C. R. 1991. Cognitive aspects of foraging in Japanese monkeys. Anim. Behav. **41**(3): 397–402.
7. MURTON, R. K. 1971. The significance of a specific search image in the feeding behaviour of the wood-pigeon. Behaviour **40:** 10–42.
8. NORTON-GRIFFITHS, M. 1967. Some ecological aspects of the feeding behavior of the oystercatcher (*Haematopus ostralegus*) on the edible mussel *Mytilus edulis*. Ibis **109:** 412–424.
9. GOODWIN, D. 1983. Pigeons and doves of the world. 3rd Edit. Cornell University Press. Ithaca, N.Y.
10. LEHRMAN, D. S. 1955. The physiological basis of parental feeding behavior in the ring dove (*Streptopelia risoria*). Behaviour **7:** 241–286.
11. SILVER, R. 1978. The parental behavior of ring doves. Am. Sci. **66**(2): 209–215.
12. WORTIS, R. P. 1969. The transition from dependent to independent feeding in the young ring dove. Anim. Behav. Monogr. **2:** 1–54.
13. PATEL, M. D. 1936. The physiology of the formation of "pigeon milk." Physiol. Zool. **9:** 129–152.
14. GRAF, J. G., P. D. BALSAM & R. S. SILVER. 1985. Associative factors and the development of pecking in the ring dove. Dev. Psychobiol. **18:** 447–460.
15. HIROSE, R. & P. D. BALSAM. Parent-squab interaction during the transition from dependent to independent feeding in the ring dove (*Streptopelia risoria*). (Submitted.)
16. HIGUCHI, H. & H. MOMOSE. 1981. Deferred independent and prolonged infantile behaviour in young varied tits, *Parus Varius*, of an island population. Anim. Behav. **29:** 523–528.
17. LEFEBVRE, L. 1983. Equilibrium distribution of feral pigeons at multiple food sources. Behav. Ecol. Sociobiol. **12:** 11–17.
18. KENWARD, R. E. & R. M. SIBLY. 1978. Woodpigeon feeding behaviour at brassica sites: a field and lab investigation of woodpigeon feeding behaviour during adoption and maintenance of a brassica diet. Anim. Behav. **26**(3): 778–790.
19. WILLIAMS, B. A. 1989. Reinforcement, choice, and response strength. *In* Stevens' Handbook of Experimental Psychology. R. Atkinson, R. Herrnstein, G. Lindzey & R. D. Luce, Eds. 2nd Edit. **2:** 167–244. John Wiley and Sons. New York, N.Y.
20. HOGAN, J. A. 1984. Pecking and feeding in chicks. Learn. Motiv. **15:** 360–376.
21. GARCIA, J., L. P. BRETT & K. W. RUSINIAK. 1989. Limits of Darwinian conditioning. *In* Contemporary Learning Theories: Instrumental Conditioning Theory and the

Impact of Biological Constraints on Learning. S. B. Klein & R. R. Mowrer, Eds.: 181–204. Lawrence Erlbaum Assoc., Pub. Hillsdale, N.J.

22. BALSAM, P. D., J. S. GRAF & R. SILVER. Operant and Pavlovian contributions to the ontogeny of pecking in ring doves. Dev. Psychobiol. (In press.)

23. DEICH, J. D., D. HOUBEN, R. W. ALLAN & H. P. ZEIGLER. 1985. "On-line" monitoring of jaw movements in the pigeon. Physiol. Behav. **35**: 307–311.

24. ZWEERS, G. A. 1982. The feeding system of the pigeon (*Columba livia L.*). Adv. Anat. Embryol. Cell. Biol. **73**: 1–108.

25. DEICH, J. D. & P. D. BALSAM. The form of early pecking in the ring dove squab (*Streptoplia risoria*): an examination of the preformation hypothesis. (Submitted.)

26. TANKOOS, J., J. DEICH, R. HIROSE & P. D. BALSAM. 1990. Effects of experience with seed on the ontogeny of pecking. Paper presented at the Annual Meeting of the Society for the Study of Developmental Psychobiology, Cambridge, England.

27. DEICH, J. D., R. W. ALLAN & H. P. ZEIGLER. 1988. Conjunctive differentiation of gape during food-reinforced keypecking in the pigeon. Anim. Learn. Behav. **16**(3): 268–276.

28. MURTON, R. K., A. J. ISAACSON & N. J. WESTWOOD. 1966. The relationships between wood-pigeons and their clover food supply and the mechanism of population control. J. Appl. Ecol. **3**: 55–95.

29. PORTER, J. M. & S. G. SEALY. 1982. Dynamics of seabird multispecies feeding flocks: age-related feeding behaviour. Behaviour **81**(2–4): 91–109.

30. MURTON, R. K., A. J. ISAACSON & N. J. WESTWOOD. 1971. The significance of gregarious feeding behaviour and adrenal stress on a population of wood-pigeons (*Columba palumbus*). J. Zool. Soc. Lond. **165**: 53–84.

31. GOCHFELD, M. & J. BURGER. 1984. Age differences in foraging behaviour of the American robin (*Turdus migratorius*). Behaviour **88**(3–4): 227–239.

32. GREIG, S. A., J. C. COULSON & P. MONAGHAN. 1983. Age-related differences in foraging success in the herring gull (*Larus Argentatus*). Anim. Behav. **31**(4): 1237–1243.

33. CANNON, C. E. 1983. Descriptions of foraging behaviour of eastern and pale-headed rosellas. Bird-Behav. **4**(2): 63–70.

34. ROBINSON, S. K. & R. T. HOLMES. 1984. Effects of plant species and foliage structure on the foraging behavior of forest birds. Auk **101**: 672–684.

35. CUTHILL, I. C., A. KALCELNIK, J. R. KREBS, P. HACCOU & Y. IWASA. 1990. Starlings exploiting patches: the effect of recent experience on foraging decisions. Anim. Behav. **40**(4): 625–640.

36. GREIG-SMITH, P. W. 1987. Persistence in foraging: when do bullfinches abandon unprofitable seeds? Behaviour **103**(1–3): 203–216.

37. YOERG, S. I. & A. C. KAMIL. 1988. Diet choices of blue jays (*Cyanocitta cristata*) as a function of time spent foraging. J. Comp. Psychol. **102**(3): 230–235.

38. LACK, D. 1968. Ecological Adaptations for Breeding in Birds. Menthuen and Co. London, England.

39. KAUFMAN, C. & L. A. ROSENBLUM. 1969. The waning of the mother-infant bond in two species of macaque. *In* Determinants of Infant Behavior IV. B. M. Foss, Ed. Menthuen and Co. London, England.

40. MARTIN, P. 1986. An experimental study of weaning in the domestic cat. Behaviour **99**(3–4): 221–249.

41. GAUTHIER, D. & C. BARRETTE. 1985. Suckling and weaning in captive white-tailed and fallow deer. Behaviour **94**(1–2): 128–149.

42. REISBICK, S., J. S. ROSENBLATT & A. D. MAYER. 1973. Decline of maternal behavior in the virgin and lactating rat. J. Comp. Psychol. **89**: 722–732.

43. DAVIES, N. B. 1976. Parental care and the transition to independent feeding in the young spotted flycatcher (*Muscicapa striata*). Behaviour **59**: 280–295.

44. MORENO, J. 1984. Parental care of fledged young, division of labor, and the development of foraging techniques in the northern wheatear (*Oenathe oenathe L.*). Auk **101**(4): 741–752.

45. DAVIES, N. B. 1978. Parental meanness and offspring independence: an experiment with hand-reared great tits (*Parus major*). Ibis **120**: 509–514.

46. STERN, J. M. & L. ROGERS. 1988. Experience with younger siblings facilitates maternal responsiveness in pubertal Norway rats. Dev. Psychobiol. **21**: 575–589.

47. THIELS, E. & J. R. ALBERTS. 1985. Milk availability modulates weaning in the Norway rat (*Rattus norvegicus*). J. Comp. Psychol. **99**(4): 447–456.

48. CROY, M. I. & R. N. HUGHES. 1991. The role of learning and memory in the feeding behaviour of the fifteen-spined stickleback, *Spinachia spinachia L.* Anim. Behav. **41**(1): 149–159.

Weaning from Mother's Milk to Solid Foods

The Developmental Psychobiology of Self-Selection of Foods by Rats

BENNETT G. GALEF, JR.[a]

Department of Psychology
McMaster University
Hamilton, Ontario L8S 4K1, Canada

DIET SELECTION AS A PROBLEM IN DEVELOPMENT

Developmental psychobiologists have not been much involved in studies of how animals come to eat foods providing all of the varied nutrients needed for normal growth and development. The lack of attention paid by developmental psychobiologists to food selection is somewhat surprising, because choosing the right foods to eat poses one of the most severe challenges faced by juvenile animals in their struggle to survive.

For the first weeks or months following birth, all young mammals are sustained by mother's milk, a single, nutritionally adequate food. However, at some point in development, the needs of young outstrip either the energy-transducing capacity of their dam[1] or her willingness to invest additional resources in her offspring[2] and young mammals must then undertake the arduous task of finding a nutritionally adequate diet of solid foods. To survive, each weanling must select a balanced diet from among a plethora of substances—some beneficial, some harmless, and some dangerous—that it encounters in its attempt to find adequate rations.

Understanding how weaning animals manage this critical developmental transition from total dependence on mother's milk to self-maintenance on solid foods would seem a natural focus of attention for students of animal development. However, it has not proven so. Study of diet selection has been seen as a problem appropriate to regulatory physiologists rather than to developmental psychobiologists.

[a] Supported by grants from the Natural Sciences and Engineering Research Council of Canada and the McMaster University Research Board.

IMPEDIMENTS TO STUDY OF DIET SELECTION AS A PROBLEM IN DEVELOPMENT

The Fragility of Weanlings

Because of the vulnerability to stress of weanlings, regulatory physiologists interested in diet selection have generally adopted a strategy of extending young animals' dependence on others for their diet composition by weaning juveniles to a nutritionally adequate chow. Weaning from milk to chow maintains animals in a state of naiveté with respect to nutrient selection. Animals maintained on chow and faced for the first time, as adults, with a need to select foods for themselves have served as a model system for studying processes that normally occur in the course of weaning from mother's milk. The experimental convenience of adult animals as model systems has, however, obscured the importance of diet selection at weaning and, as I shall argue below, may have limited understanding of processes important in diet selection.

ABSENCE OF A PROBLEM

Until recently, it was not apparent that there really was a problem of diet selection for developmental psychobiologists to address: Clara Davis was widely,[3] through inaccurately,[4] cited as having shown that human infants can compose an adequate diet by selecting items for themselves from a cafeteria of foods. Curt Richter and his coworkers[5,6] were generally believed to have demonstrated that rats in cafeteria feeding situations could self-select a balanced diet without difficult. Richter,[5] Rozin,[7] Booth,[8] and others provided evidence of behavioral processes that would suffice to explain development of the adaptive patterns of dietary choice that Davis and Richter were said to have demonstrated. Nothing appeared to remain for developmental psychobiologists to study.

A NEW APPROACH TO DIETARY SELF-SELECTION

My own interest in the problem of food selection at weaning arose from the realization that neither human infants[4,9,10] nor rats of any age[9,10] had been shown to be particularly adept at self-selecting an adequate diet from a cafeteria of foods. If, as recent reviews of the literature suggest,[4,9,10] (1) animals have great difficulty selecting a nutritionally adequate diet, and (2) selection of appropriate foods is a major problem facing all weanlings, then there is an important question for developmental psychobiologists to answer. How do weanlings succeed in making the life-threatening transition from mother's milk to solid foods?

TWO EXPERIMENTAL PROCEDURES FOR STUDYING DIETARY SELF-SELECTION

Choosing a Diet

In some studies of dietary self-selection, a subject is faced with an array of two or more foods only one of which is a nutritionally balanced diet containing, in proper proportion, all nutrients needed to sustain normal growth. In such situations, the subject's task is to focus its intake on the nutritionally balanced diet and reduce intake of deficient or imbalanced alternatives. The work of Harris *et al.* [11] and of Rozin [12] provides examples of experiments of this type.

Composing a Diet

In other studies of dietary self-selection, subjects are presented with an array of foods no one of which is nutritionally adequate. In such situations, a subject must compose a balanced diet by eating a mixture of foods from the array presented to it. Richter's studies of total dietary self-selection are the best known experiments of this type. [5,6,13]

Although dietary generalists in natural habitat are probably more likely to face the problem of composing a diet than that of choosing a diet, my students and I began by studying diet choice, rather than diet composition, because evaluation of animals' performance in diet choice tasks is relatively straightforward; greater success can be defined as greater intake of the sole nutritionally adequate diet present. Criteria of success are not so easy to specify in diet-composition situations. Nevertheless, we have also begun to look at how animals come to compose nutritionally adequate diets, and I will mention our preliminary findings in this area at the end of the present chapter.

DIET SELECTION: A CONTRIBUTION OF DEVELOPMENTAL PSYCHOBIOLOGY

As mentioned above, self-selection of foods has, historically, been considered a problem in regulatory physiology. Consequently, focus in studies of diet selection has been on how individual animals recognize internal deficiency states and alter either their behavior or physiology so as to redress any internal imbalance. Looking at selection of foods as a developmental problem suggests additional processes that might promote adaptive patterns of food choice in animals.

Infant animals are, obviously, not capable of independent life; they require social support to solve most of life's more pressing problems. For example, infant rats depend on their dams for sustenance and on both their

dams[14] and peers[15] for assistance in thermoregulation. One might, therefore, suspect that weaning rat pups might similarly depend on others for assistance in making the difficult transition from dependence on mother's milk
to independent acquisition of a diet of solid foods.

By their very existence, adult rats demonstrate the adequacy of their food
choices. For a weanling to choose an adequate diet, all it need do is learn
to eat the food or foods that an adult is eating. Thus, there is a potential social
(as well as a physiological) solution to the problem of diet choice. The social
solution may be more salient from the perspective of a developmental psy-
chobiologist, used to observing dependent infants, than from that of a regulatory physiologist, focused on physiological processes controlling the
internal milieu.

LABORATORY STUDIES OF SOCIAL INFLUENCE ON SELECTION OF FOODS

Demonstration of an Effect

In our first experiment, we established rats of weaning age in individual
cages (1 × 1 m), each containing four food bowls (see FIGURE 1).[16] Three
of these four bowls contained diets (cinnamon-flavored diet: Diet Cin, cocoa-
flavored diet: Diet Coc, or thyme-flavored diet: Diet Thy) that were both relatively palatable and relatively protein poor (4.4% protein by weight). The
fourth bowl contained a diet (nutmeg-flavored diet: Diet Nut) that was both
relatively rich in protein (17.5% protein by weight) and relatively unpalatable
to rats. As can be seen in FIGURE 2, individual weanling rats maintained for

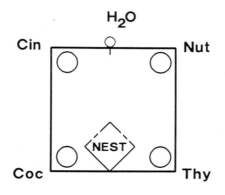

FIGURE 1. Overhead schematic of apparatus
used in the first experiment. (Nut = nutmeg-
flavored diet; Thy = thyme-flavored diet; Cin =
cinnamon-flavored diet; Coc = cocoa-flavored
diet). (From Reference 16. Copyright 1989 by
the American Psychological Association. Reprinted by permission of publisher and authors.)

.3 m

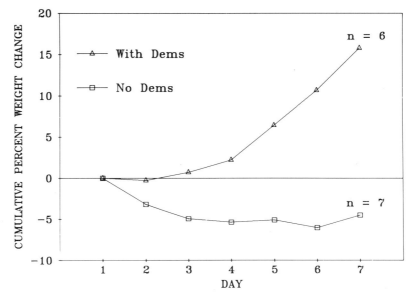

FIGURE 2. Mean cumulative percent weight change of weanling pups. (Dem = demonstrator.) (From Reference 16. Copyright 1989 by the American Psychological Association. Reprinted by permission of publisher and authors.)

6 days under such circumstances did very poorly, and were well on their way to a premature demise when, for ethical reasons, we terminated the experiment.

Weanling subjects in a second group each shared their respective enclosures with an adult rat trained to eat the protein-rich Diet Nut and to avoid eating protein-poor diets Cin, Coc, and Thy. As can also be seen in FIGURE 2, following a brief hiatus in growth, subjects that had access to social information thrived in the experimental situation.

Analysis of an Effect

Possibilities

The results of the experiment described above raise more questions than they answer. In particular, they offer little clue as to how it is that the trained adult rats influenced the food choices of their juvenile cage mates. Results of previous studies of social influences on rats' food choices (see References 17–19 for reviews) provide evidence of several different ways in which food preferences of weaning rats can be modified by interaction with conspecifics: (1) Juvenile rats prefer to eat at locations where other rats are eating rather than at locations where no other rats are to be found.[20-22] (2) Adult rats scent mark both feeding sites and foods they are exploiting thus increasing the attractiveness of those foods and feeding sites to conspecifics.[23-25] (3) After a naive rat interacts with a conspecific that has recently eaten some food, the naive rat exhibits a substantially enhanced preference for whatever food the conspecific with which it interacted has eaten.[26-30]

Realities

To investigate processes promoting adaptive food choice by weanling rats, we needed to gain control over the interactions of weanlings with adults. To that end, we placed weaning rats and their adult demonstrators in enclosures like that illustrated in overhead schematic in FIGURE 3. In these enclosures, a naive juvenile subject was separated from its adult demonstrator by a screen partition. Because adults could not eat from the food cups available to juveniles, we could measure directly intake of the foods available to each juvenile, and, because adults could not contact juveniles' food cups, adults could not scent mark either foods or feeding sites available to their cage mates. Last, and most important, by varying both the location and type food in the food cup on the adult's side of each enclosure, we could distinguish between effects of physical presence of an adult demonstrator in the vicinity of a food cup and effects of the smell of a food eaten by an adult on the food choices of juvenile subjects.

Methods

The arrangements of food cups used in the experiment are illustrated in FIGURE 4. Subjects assigned to the Same-Food, Same-Place group each

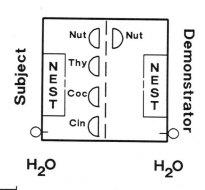

FIGURE 3. Overhead schematic of apparatus used to examine social effects on diet selection. See FIGURE 1 caption for abbreviations. (From Reference 16. Copyright 1989 by the American Psychological Association. Reprinted by permission of the publisher and authors.)

.3 m

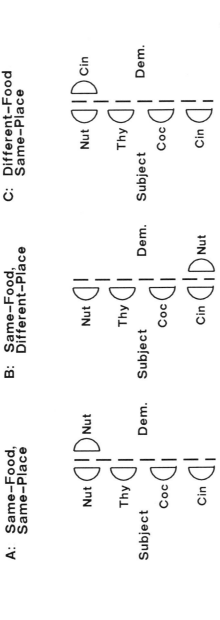

FIGURE 4. Overhead schematic of the positions and contents of food cups presented to subjects. (Nut = nutmeg-flavored diet; Thy = thyme-flavored diet; Coc = cocoa-flavored diet; and Dem = demonstrator. (From Reference 16. Copyright 1989 by the American Psychological Association. Reprinted by permission of publisher and authors.)

shared an apparatus with a demonstrator that had access to a single food cup containing Diet Nut and each demonstrator's food cup containing Diet Nut was placed directly across the screen partition from each subject's food cup containing Diet Nut (see FIGURE 4A). Subjects assigned to the Same-Food, Different-Place group interacted with a demonstrator rat eating Diet Nut from a food cup located directly across the screen partition from each subject's food cup containing Diet Cin (see FIGURE 4B). Last, subjects assigned to the Different-Food, Same-Place Group each shared an apparatus with a demonstrator rat eating Diet Cin directly across the screen partition from a subject's food cup containing Diet Nut (see FIGURE 4C). The experiment lasted 1 week, and during that week subjects and demonstrators were left undisturbed except for daily weighings of both food cups and subjects.

Results

The main results of the second experiment are presented in FIGURE 5, which shows the mean amount of Diet Nut (the diet containing adequate protein) eaten by subjects. As can be seen in FIGURE 5, subjects in Same-Food,

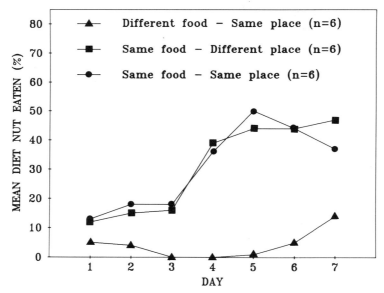

FIGURE 5. Mean amount of protein-adequate, nutmeg-flavored diet (Diet Nut) ingested as a percentage of total amount eaten by subjects in Same-Food, Same-Place (circles), Same-Food, Different-Place (squares), and Different-Food, Same-Place groups (triangles). (From Reference 16. Copyright 1989 by the American Psychological Association. Reprinted by permission of publisher and authors.)

Same-Place and Same-Food, Different-Place groups ate significantly more Diet Nut than did subjects in the Different-Food, Same-Place group and subjects assigned to Same-Food, Same-Place and Same-Food, Different-Place groups did not differ from one another in the amount of Diet Nut that they ate. This finding is consistent with the view that the flavor of the food that a demonstrator ate was more important than the location where it ate in influencing subjects' choices of foods.

It is, perhaps, worth noting in passing that, if the flavor of the food a demonstrator ate was the predominant factor biasing subjects' food selections, then subjects assigned to the Different-Food, Same-Place group [i.e., those subjects whose demonstrators ate Diet Cin (see Figure 3C)] should have exhibited an enhanced preference for Diet Cin, in comparison with subjects in the other two groups. As can be seen in FIGURE 6: (1) subjects in the Different-Food, Same-Place group did, in fact, eat a significantly greater percentage of Diet Cin from among the three available protein-poor diets than did subjects in either of the other two groups, and (2) subjects in the other two groups did not differ significantly from·one another in their intake of Diet Cin.

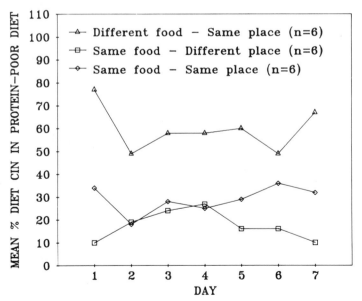

FIGURE 6. Mean amount of cinnamon-flavored diet (Diet Cin) ingested as a percentage of total amount of protein-poor, cinnamon-, cocoa-, and thyme-flavored diets eaten by three groups of subjects. (From Reference 16. Copyright 1989 by the American Psychological Association. Reprinted by permission of publisher and authors.)

A CONUNDRUM

When considered in functional context, the ability of rats to bias conspecifics to eat foods that they have eaten poses something of a problem. Imagine two rats: α and β. α is a healthy individual that has been eating protein-rich food A; β has been subsisting on protein-poor food B and is malnourished. Following a brief period of interaction between α and β, β's probability of eating nutritious food A should be increased, but then so should α's probability of eating substandard food B. Superficially, social influence appears of little use; β's gain is α's loss.

More realistically, the long-term cost to the healthy α of eating an inadequate food (which it could learn to avoid) is surely less than the long-term benefit to the sickly β of being induced to sample a nutritious food (which it could learn to eat). Still, one feels some unease at proposing a process inducing development of adaptive patterns of food selection that, of itself, has equal potential for good and ill.

If it were the case that healthy rats influenced conspecifics to eat foods that they were eating, while sickly rats influenced conspecifics to avoid foods that they were eating, then there would be no problem. However, evidence from several studies indicates that healthy and sickly demonstrators are equally effective in enhancing their respective observers' preferences for foods.[31-33] Rats develop preferences for, not aversions to, foods after interacting with either ill rats[31-33] or unconscious rats[29] that have eaten those foods. Consequently, differences in the response of observer rats to healthy and ill demonstrators do not appear to provide a solution to the conundrum.

The probability of socially acquired food preferences interfering with, rather than enhancing, adaptive food choices could also be reduced if the susceptibility of individual rats to social influence on their diet selection varied as a function of their internal states. For example, if rats that were doing well selecting foods (i.e., well-nourished rats) were relatively resistant to social influence on their food choices, while rats that were doing poorly selecting foods (i.e., malnourished or sickly rats) were relatively susceptible to social influence, then the immediate benefits of social influence would tend to be greater than the immediate costs.

An Experiment

Determining whether deficient rats are more susceptible than replete rats to social influences on their food choices is not so straightforward a matter as it might appear at first glance. In particular, one cannot simply pair naive-deficient and naive-replete rats with demonstrators trained to select a nutritionally adequate food from among an array of foods and then see whether deficient subjects eat more nutritionally adequate food than do replete subjects.

First, and trivially, unless each subject is physically separated from its respective demonstrator, there is no way to determine how much of each food was eaten by subjects and how much was eaten by their demonstrators. Second, and less trivially, deficient subjects might experience greater reward than replete subjects as a result of eating nutritionally adequate food. Consequently, deficient subjects might learn to select a nutritionally adequate food from an array of foods more rapidly than would replete subjects[34] even if deficient subjects were no more susceptible to social influences on their food choices than were replete subjects. Last, it is always possible that deprivation might cause changes in flavor preferences that only accidentally resulted in increased preference for a nutritionally adequate food.[5]

Methods

Our experimental design[35] ensured that (1) both demonstrators and the subjects with which demonstrators were paired fed from separate feeding sites, (2) each of the foods among which replete and deficient subjects chose were equally ineffective in alleviating the deficiency state that had been induced in deprived subjects, and (3) there were no significant changes in the food preferences of subjects as a function of their deprivation states. Condition 1 was met by physically separating demonstrators from observers (see FIGURE 1B); condition 2 by providing subjects with four deficient foods to choose among (consequently they could not learn from postingestional consequences which food to eat), and condition 3 by examining the food choices of replete and deficient subjects in the absence of social influence.

The experiment was conducted in the apparatus illustrated in FIGURE 1B. Subjects chose among four protein-deficient diets (5% by weight casein) flavored with either cinnamon, cocoa, thyme, or nutmeg, and subjects were either protein replete or had been protein deprived for 7 days immediately before the start of the experiment.

Results

The main results of the experiment are presented in FIGURE 7, which shows the mean amount of nutmeg-flavored diet (the diet eaten by demonstrator rats) eaten by subjects during the 7 days of the experiment. As would be expected on the basis of the results of the first two experiments described above, subjects interacting with demonstrators ate more of the relatively unpalatable nutmeg-flavored diet than did subjects without demonstrators. More important for the hypothesis under investigation here, there was a significant interaction between deprivation state and presence of a demonstrator in determining the amount of nutmeg-flavored diet eaten by subjects. Protein-deprived subjects with demonstrators ate significantly more nutmeg-flavored diet than did protein-replete subjects with demonstrators, while

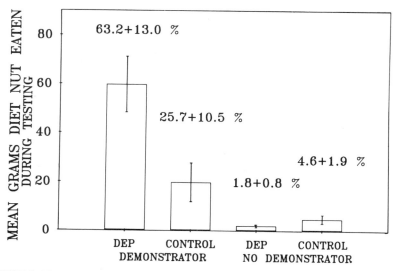

FIGURE 7. Mean total amount of protein-deficient nutmeg-flavored diet (Diet Nut) eaten during 7 days by subjects in each of four groups. Numbers above the histograms indicate the mean percent Diet Nut eaten during 7 days by subjects in each group. Flags = ± 1 standard error of the mean (SEM); Dep = deprived. From Reference 35. Copyright 1991 by the American Psychological Association. Reprinted by permission of publisher and authors.)

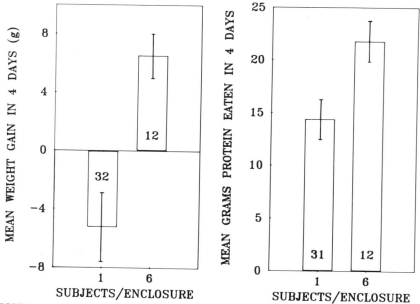

FIGURE 8. A: Mean cumulative weight change exhibited by subjects housed either individually or in groups of 6. B: Mean protein intake of subjects housed either individually or in groups of 6. Flags = ± 1 SEM.

protein-replete and protein-deprived subjects without demonstrators did not differ significantly in their intake of nutmeg-flavored diet. This last result indicates that protein deprivation affected the susceptibility of young rats to social influence, not their preference for protein.

A Resolution

If the present laboratory experiments reflect difficulties weanling rats experience when attempting to choose an appropriate diet outside the laboratory, then weanlings are likely to get into serious nutritional trouble when they choose foods for themselves. As the physical condition of weanlings deteriorates, they should become increasingly susceptible to social influences on their food choices. On the other hand, healthy adults should be less influenced to select the inadequate rations of juveniles with which they interact. Thus, adults might induce juveniles to choose an adequate diet without seriously compromising the integrity of their own diet selection.

SOCIAL INFLUENCES ON DIET COMPOSITION

My coworkers and I have only just started to explore the role of social influence in the weaning of rat pups living in environments where constructing a balanced diet requires composing an appropriate mixture of foods rather than choosing a single food. However, our early data are so surprising (and so promising), that they deserve some mention despite their preliminary nature.

In 1963, McDonald, Stern, and Hahn reported results of a study in which a group of 12 juvenile rats were placed together in an enclosure and the members of a second group of 12 juvenile rats were each placed in an individual cage.[36] All 24 animals had to compose a diet by eating from four containers which contained either casein, sugar, fat, or mineral mix (vitamins were provided in drinking water). McDonald et al. found that, although the isolated rats failed to gain weight, the rats living together in the group of 12 grew as rapidly as did control rats fed a nutritionally balanced chow.[36]

We have repeated McDonald et al's. study using as subjects both individual juvenile rats ($n = 12$) and juvenile rats in groups of six ($n = 8$ groups). FIGURE 8 provides data describing both the rate of weight gain and protein intake of juvenile rats feeding either in isolation or in groups. As can be seen in FIGURE 8, individually housed rats ate less protein and grew more slowly than did rats housed in groups of six. In fact, isolated rats lost weight, while group-housed rats gained weight during their week in the test situation.

At the present time, we have no information as to how group living facilitates diet composition. However, whatever the mechanism, this social facilitation of food selection demonstrates a role of peer interaction in the weaning process. These data provide further evidence that understanding weaning will require attention to the role of social interactions in the development of nutritionally adequate diets.

CONCLUSIONS

Developmental psychobiologists studying rodents have focused their attention on the relationship of adult mammals and their young during the period when young are dependent on mother's milk for survival. The results of the present series of studies suggest that during weaning, as during suckling, social interactions, both between adults and weanlings and among the members of weaning peer groups, may be critical to survival.

Approaching diet selection and diet composition as acute problems facing weanlings, and consequently, as problems in developmental psychobiology,[37] suggested the need to examine the impact of social influences on the development of adaptive patterns of food choice. The data reviewed here suggest that studying social aspects of diet selection and diet composition may provide part of the answer to a classic question in regulatory physiology. How do animals living in natural circumstances learn to eat nutritionally adequate diets?

REFERENCES

1. BABICKY, A., I. OSTRADOLOVA, J. PARIZEK, J. KOLAR & B. BIBR. 1970. Use of radio-isotope techniques for determining the weaning period in experimental animals. Physiol. Bohemoslov. **19:** 457–467.
2. TRIVERS, R. L. 1974. Parent-offspring conflict. Am. Zool. **14:** 249–264.
3. DAVIS, C. M. 1928. Self-selection of diet by newly weaned infants: an experimental study. Am. J. Dis. Child. **36:** 651–679.
4. STORY, M. & J. E. BROWN. 1987. Do young children instinctively know what to eat? The studies of Clara Davis revisited. N. Engl. J. Med. **316:** 103–106.
5. RICHTER, C. P. 1938. Nutritional requirements for normal growth and reproduction in rats studied by the self-selection method. Am. J. Physiol. **122:** 734–744.
6. RICHTER, C. P. 1943. Total self regulatory functions in animals and human beings. Harvey Lect. **38:** 63–103.
7. ROZIN, P. 1976. The selection of foods by rats, humans and other animals. In Advances in the Study of Behavior. J. S. Rosenblatt, R. A. Hinde, E. Shaw & C. Beer, Eds. **6:** 21–76. Academic Press. New York, N.Y.
8. BOOTH, D. A. 1985. Food-conditioned eating preferences and aversion with interoceptive elements: conditioned appetites and satieties. Ann. N.Y. Acad. Sci. **443:** 22–41.
9. GALEF, B. G., JR. & M. BECK. 1990. Diet selection and poison avoidance by mammals individually and in social groups. In Handbook of Behavioral Neurobiology. E. M. Stricker, Ed. **11:** 329–349. Plenum Press. New York, N.Y.
10. GALEF, B. G., JR. 1991. A contrarian view of the wisdom of the body as it relates to food selection. Psychol. Rev. **98:** 218–223.

11. HARRIS, L., J. CLAY, F. HARGREAVES & A. WARD. 1933. The ability of vitamin B deficient rats to discriminate between diets containing and lacking the vitamin. Proc. R. Soc. Lond. Biol. **113:** 161–190.
12. ROZIN, P. 1969. Adaptive food sampling patterns in vitamin deficient rats. J. Comp. Physiol. Psychol. **69:** 126–132.
13. RICHTER, C. P., L. HOLT & B. BARELARE. 1938. Nutritional requirements for normal growth and reproduction in rats studied by the self-selection method. Am. J. Physiol. **122:** 734–744.
14. LEON, M., P. G. CROSSKERRY & G. K. SMITH. 1978. Thermal control of mother young contact in rats. Physiol. Behav. **21:** 793–811.
15. ALBERTS, J. R. 1978. Huddling by rat pups: group behavioral mechanisms of temperature regulation and energy conservation. J. Comp. Physiol. Psychol. **92:** 231–240.
16. BECK, M. & B. G. GALEF, JR. 1989. Social influences on the selection of a protein-sufficient diet by Norway rats (*Rattus norvegicus*). J. Comp. Psychol. **103:** 132–139.
17. GALEF, B. G., JR. 1977. Mechanisms for the social transmission of food preferences from adult to weanling rats. *In* Learning Mechanisms in Food Selection. L. M. Barker, M. Best & M. Domjan, Eds.: 123–150. Baylor University Press. Waco, Tex.
18. GALEF, B. G., JR. 1986. Olfactory communication among rats of information concerning distant diets. *In* Chemical Signals in Vertebrates. D. Duvall, D. Müller-Schwarze & R. M. Silverstein, Eds. **4:** 487–505. Plenum Press. New York, N.Y.
19. GALEF, B. G., JR. 1988. Communication of information concerning distant diets in a social, central-place foraging species: *Rattus norvegicus. In* Social Learning: Psychological and Biological Perspectives. T. R. Zentall & B. G. Galef, Jr., Eds.: 119–139. Lawrence Erlbaum. Hillsdale, N.J.
20. GALEF, B. G., JR. 1978. Differences in affiliative behavior of weanling rats selecting eating and drinking sites. J. Comp. Physiol. Psychol. **92:** 431–438.
21. GALEF, B. G., JR. & M. M. CLARK. 1971. Parent-offspring interactions determine time and place of first ingestion of solid food by wild rat pups. Psychon. Sci. **25:** 15–16.
22. GALEF, B. G., JR. & M. M. CLARK. 1971. Social factors in the poison avoidance and feeding behavior of wild and domesticated rat pups. J. Comp. Physiol. Psychol. **75:** 341–357.
23. GALEF, B. G., JR. & M. BECK. 1985. Aversive and attractive marking of toxic and safe foods by Norway rats. Behav. Neural Biol. **43:** 298–310.
24. GALEF, B. G., JR. & L. HEIBER. 1976. The role of residual olfactory cues in the determination of feeding site selection and exploration patterns of domestic rats. J. Comp. Physiol. Psychol. **90:** 727–739.
25. LALONDE, K. N. & H. C. PLOTKIN. 1991. Excretory deposits surrounding food sites facilitate social learning of food preferences in Norway rats. Anim. Behav. **41:** 997–1005.
26. GALEF, B. G., JR., D. J. KENNETT & S. W. WIGMORE. 1984. Transfer of information concerning distant foods in rats: a robust phenomenon. Anim. Learn. Behav. **12:** 292–296.
27. GALEF, B. G., JR. & M. STEIN. 1985. Demonstrator influence on observer diet preference: analyses of critical social interactions and olfactory signals. Anim. Learn. Behav. **13:** 31–38.
28. GALEF, B. G., JR. & E. E. WHISKIN. 1992. Social transmission of information about multiflavored foods. Anim. Learn. Behav. **20:** 56–62.
29. GALEF, B. G., JR. & S. W. WIGMORE. 1983. Transfer of information concerning dis-

tant foods: a laboratory investigation of the "information-centre" hypothesis. Anim. Behav. **31**: 748–758.

30. POSADAS-ANDREWS, A. & T. J. ROPER. 1983. Social transmission of food preferences in adult rats. Anim. Behav. **31**: 265–271.

31. GALEF, B. G., JR., L. M. McQUOID & E. E. WHISKIN. 1990. Further evidence that Norway rats do not socially transmit learned aversions to toxic baits. Anim. Learn. Behav. **18**: 199–205.

32. GALEF, B. G., JR., S. W. WIGMORE & D. J. KENNETT. 1983. A failure to find socially mediated taste aversion learning in Norway rats (*R. norvegicus*). J. Comp. Psychol. **97**: 358–363.

33. GROVER, C. A., J. S. KIXMILLER, C. A. ERICKSON, A. H. BECKER, S. F. DAVIS & G. B. NALLAN. 1988. The social transmission of information concerning aversively conditioned liquids. Psychol. Rec. **38**: 557–566.

34. GIBSON, E. C. & D. A. BOOTH. 1986. Acquired protein appetite in rats: dependence on a protein-specific need state. Experientia **42**: 1003–1004.

35. GALEF, B. G., JR., M. BECK & E. E. WHISKIN. 1991. Protein deficiency magnifies social influence on the food choices of Norway rats (*Rattus norvegicus*). J. Comp. Psychol. **105**: 55–59.

36. McDONALD, D. G., J. A. STERN & W. W. HAHN. 1963. Effects of differential housing and stress on diet selection, water intake and body weight in the rat. J. Appl. Physiol. **18**: 937–942.

37. GALEF, B. G., JR. 1991. Innovations in the study of social learning in animals: a developmental perspective. *In* Developmental Psychobiology: New Methods and Changing Concepts. H. N. Shair, G. A. Barr & M. A. Hofer, Eds.: 114–125. Oxford University Press. New York, NY.

The Emergence of Behavioral Regulation during Fetal Development[a]

SCOTT R. ROBINSON AND
WILLIAM P. SMOTHERMAN

Laboratory for Perinatal Neuroethology
Center for Developmental Psychobiology
Department of Psychology
Post Office Box 6000
State University of New York at Binghamton
Binghamton, New York 13902-6000

The past decade has seen a renaissance of interest in prenatal behavior in fields that are dedicated to understanding brain-behavior relationships, such as psychobiology and behavioral neuroscience. The growth in fetal research has been accompanied by changes in the way prenatal development is viewed by many investigators. From the perspective of development, it has become manifest that newborn mammals exhibit sophisticated behavioral capacities within minutes or hours of birth, and that the mechanisms underlying this early behavioral organization must either appear *de novo* at the moment of birth, or extend their roots into the prenatal period.[1] From the perspective of understanding the neural control of behavior, the fetus provides a relatively simpler system in which to investigate the emergence of coordinated action and behavioral regulation.[2] Further, the simpler systems subserving fetal behavior are directly relevant and ultimately give rise to the behavioral complexity associated with the infant, juvenile, and adult mammal.

From the perspective of the experimenter, investigation of behavior during the fetal period also provides certain methodological advantages over early postnatal study. Newborn mammals, especially the offspring of altricial species with poorly developed motor skills at birth (e.g., rats and other Murid rodents), are highly dependent upon the behavior of the mother as a source of nutrition, water and salt balance, heat, and protection. Through their behavioral interactions, the mother and neonate form a dyadic relationship that is the ultimate source of behavioral and physiological regulation during the early postnatal period.[3] Consequently, experiments intended to

[a] The original research reported in this paper is supported by the National Institute of Child Health and Human Development (National Institutes of Health) grants HD 16102 and Research Career Development Award HD 00719 to WPS, and HD 28231 to SRR and WPS. WPS also is supported by the NATO Collaborative Research Grants Program (0551/90).

investigate neonatal behavior must risk maternal interference with the test situation when the mother is present, or eliminate the primary regulatory source for the neonate when the mother is absent.

In contrast to the newborn, the fetus relies upon its umbilical connection to the placenta and access to the maternal circulatory system to provide for its nutritional, osmotic, immunological, and excretory needs, and upon its physical location within the concentric envelopes of amniotic fluid, extra-embryonic membranes, uterus, and maternal abdomen to provide thermoregulation and protection. Although the mother is still indispensable to meet these needs, it is her physiology, and not her behavior, that provides the principal extrinsic regulatory influence during the prenatal period. The advantage of fetal study accrues from technologies that maintain the fetal system of life support without permitting direct behavioral interference by the mother.

METHODS OF FETAL STUDY

Investigation of the behavioral capacities of the fetus historically has been dependent upon technologies for detecting and characterizing fetal activity. Much of the early work by behavioral embryologists in the 1920s and 1930s was subsequently criticized for failing to provide adequately for fetal life support.[4] Inferences drawn from nonviable human fetuses obtained from premature delivery or therapeutic abortion[5,6] suffer from the same difficulty: subjects are physiologically compromised or moribund at the time of behavioral assessment. Much of the recent progress in understanding fetal behavior thus has been dependent upon technical advances in our ability to gain access to healthy fetal subjects *in utero*.

Two important technologies are routinely used in hospitals and other clinical settings for characterizing fetal activity in humans. External fetal monitoring, in which sensory transducers are placed around the abdomen of a pregnant woman, permit measurement of fetal heart rate and gross fetal body movements as well as uterine contractions. Such records permit assessment of temporal patterns in overall fetal activity,[7,8] but the inability to visualize the fetus prevents more detailed analysis of the individual movements that comprise activity. Real-time ultrasonography, in which video images of the contours and surfaces of the fetus are defined by the echoes of high-frequency sound pulses, can provide more detailed information about the topography of fetal movements.[9] Ultrasound technology has proven useful for describing the behavioral repertoire of the human fetus,[10,11] but typically provides a noncontinuous, restricted field of view of the fetus that is inadequate to characterize temporal, sequential, and coordinative patterns in fetal behavior.

The need for continuous, fine-grained records of fetal behavior is best met by direct observation of the fetus, which is practicable only through comparative study of nonhuman animal subjects. Surgical and experimental procedures are available that permit observation of rodent fetuses after spinal anesthesia of the pregnant female and surgical externalization of the uterus and fetuses into an isotonic fluid maintained at body temperature.[12] Because the umbilical cord and placental connection of the fetus to the uterus remain intact, fetal motor activity can be observed directly or videotaped from the earliest expressions of movement through term. These surgical techniques also allow experimental access to the fetus, permitting controlled manipulation of the fetus's sensory experience and nervous system. To describe and quantify developmental changes in fetal activity, individual fetal movements may be categorized on the basis of the region of the body responsible for the movement (e.g., head, mouth, forelimb, rearlimb, and body trunk). This coding scheme permits discrimination of simple movements, which involve just one body region, and synchronous or concurrent movements, which involve simultaneous movements of two or more regions. Overall fetal activity can be estimated conveniently by summing across all individual movement categories. This combination of surgical access and behavioral coding provides reliable and detailed records of fetal behavior that preserve information about the abundance of fetal movements in time, sequence, and space. Using this research strategy, our laboratory and others have obtained evidence for the temporal and spatial organization of nonevoked motor activity in rodent fetuses,[13,14] the prenatal expression of species-typical behavior patterns in response to sensory stimulation,[15,16] and the capacity to acquire and express learning *in utero.*[17,18] Additional details regarding these technical and observational procedures have been reported previously.[12]

FETAL ACTIVITY AS A PROBLEM IN REGULATION

Mammalian fetuses, and vertebrate embryos in general, begin to exhibit motor activity during the period of embryonic organogenesis soon after the appearance of functional neuromuscular junctions in skeletal muscles. The earliest age at which fetuses may be observed to move, which corresponds to embryonic day 15.5–16 (designated E16, with the day of conception defined as E0) in laboratory rats[13,19,20] and week 7–8 in humans[5,10] will be referred to as the "inception" of movement. In the 10–12 species of placental mammals studied to date, fetuses exhibit motor activity continuously from inception through term (the day of birth). An important property of this activity is its spontaneous expression, which has been noted by virtually all fetal observers since the early work of Preyer[21] and Brown.[22] In the context of fetal movement, the term "spontaneous" usually refers in a general sense to the absence of explicit sensory stimulation by the experimenter, and to the lack of obvious cues in the fetal environment temporally associated with movement (i.e., nonevoked activity).

However, at least some embryonic movements have been demonstrated to be spontaneous in a more technical, narrow sense of the term. Now-classic experiments with domestic chicken embryos, conducted by Hamburger, Op-

penheim and others,[23-25] revealed that motor activity can be expressed in
the absence of sensory feedback from the periphery. Further, motor activity
in the limbs can be generated by relatively small, isolated segments of the
spinal cord alone. In one representative experiment, a small segment of lumbosacral spinal cord in the chick embryo, isolated from more rostral influences by surgical removal of another section of the cord, and isolated from
sensory influences by deafferentation, nonetheless exhibited patterned
neuronal activity. The hindlimbs of the embryos, which were innervated by
this section of the cord, exhibited relatively high levels of movement associated with this neural activity.[26] Although avian embryos may exhibit a
brief period of myogenic activity prior to functional innervation of the muscles, all motor activity subsequent to primary innervation appears to be neuro-
genic: curare, which eliminates transmission at the neuromuscular junction
of skeletal muscles, abolishes spontaneous motor activity.[27] Experiments
that employ direct manipulation of the central and peripheral nervous systems
have provided the conclusive evidence that fetal motor activity is the consequence of neural activity generated spontaneously (i.e., in a nonreflexogenic
manner) in local areas of the spinal cord.

Although the activity expressed by fetuses occurs spontaneously and continuously (in a developmental frame of reference), it does not occur at a constant rate. Fetal movements, whether measured by external strain gauges or
direct observation, exhibit a typical burst-pause pattern that may involve one,
two, or many different parts of the body. On a very brief time scale (about
10 seconds), activity can vary from the absence of any movement to a maximum of about 1–2 events/second. Over a longer time scale (about 10 minutes), much of the variability in nonevoked fetal activity is diminished and
highly replicable rates of movement become apparent; for example, fetal rats
consistently exhibit activity at a rate of 10–12 events/minute over the last three
days of gestation.[13] Maximal rates of fetal activity are rarely sustained for
more than a few seconds in the absence of explicit sensory stimulation, or
for more than 15–20 seconds in the absence of exogenous pharmacological
manipulation.[28] However, administration of various drugs, including dopaminergic and opioid agonists, can produce sustained high levels of fetal activity (70–90 events/minute), indicating that fetuses have the capacity to support
constant, vigorous activity over a period of 30–60 minutes or longer.[29,30]
The characteristic tendency of fetuses to exhibit nonevoked movement, which
fluctuates on a short time scale and is maintained, on average, at a level
10–15% of maximum on a longer time scale, suggests that fetal motor activity
is somehow regulated.

The fact that nonreflexive motor output can be generated by the fetal central nervous system (CNS), and that it is expressed in consistent patterns, has
suggested that measurement of organized motor activity may provide a means
for assessing normal CNS function and detecting anomalies during fetal development.[31,32] This interpretation implies that the quantitative measures of
organization apparent in nonevoked motor activity, which will be described

in more detail below, are the consequence of central processes that regulate the level (amount of activity) and kind (regional distribution) of fetal behavior. Further, it emphasizes the apparent discontinuity in the outwardly "purposeless" and "aimless" movements of the fetus[23] and the orderly, goal-directed behavior one typically associates with the postnatal period. An alternative to this centralized view of behavioral regulation emphasizes the need to understand how order can emerge from apparently random interactions. Several parallel lines of research recently have documented the tendency for complex systems to exhibit self-organization in the absence of an explicit blueprint or plan.[33-35] From this perspective, the evident regulation of fetal activity is decentralized or distributed, emerging from the interactions among smaller, localized subunits of the intrinsic neuromotor system and the extrinsic environment. These central and distributed conceptions of behavioral regulation in the fetus have important and different implications for the control and development of motor behavior. In the following sections, these implications will be explored for different measures of organization in fetal motor activity, with a focus on the following questions: (a) What is the evidence for behavioral regulation during the prenatal period? (b) Does unpatterned (i.e., chance) expression of motor activity play a role in fetal development? and (c) Does the emergence of nonrandom behavior reflect central regulation or distributed interaction?

ENVIRONMENTAL DETERMINANTS OF FETAL MOTOR ACTIVITY

During the first 24–48 hours after the inception of movement, fetal rats exhibit a general increase in the overall level of motor activity *in utero* and the number of regions of the body involved in movement. The first movements of the fetus are brief in duration and simple in topography; most movements on E16 are unidirectional and involve simple flexion or extension at a single joint. During this early period, movements by the forelimbs predominate (70% of all movements on E16), with moderate levels of head (13%) and trunk (15%) activity. Rearlimb movements are very uncommon at inception, but increase steadily through E19, when they constitute 27% of all activity *in utero*.[13,36]

In contrast to the first few days after inception, the rates of movement expressed by fetal rats remain roughly the same over the last three days of gestation (E19–E21). Movements involving the head, forelimbs, or rearlimbs are all relatively common. Synchronous activity, involving the simultaneous movement of two or more body regions, also reaches its peak expression during the prenatal period, and fetuses begin to exhibit clearly coordinated, species-typical motor patterns that appear to foreshadow postnatal grooming, suckling, righting, and locomotor responses.[2] Comparison of fetuses near term with fetuses soon after the inception of movement in many respects reveals more profound behavioral changes that occur during gestation than are apparent between prenatal and postnatal life.

A number of environmental factors can affect the expression of motor activity in the rat fetus from the general pattern described above. One of the most profound influences on early motility is the physical restraint created by the uterus and embryonic membranes. During the last third of gestation, the volume of amniotic fluid surrounding each fetus slowly increases to a peak (E19), then diminishes and virtually disappears before parturition. Over this same period of gestation, fetal body mass increases at nearly an exponential rate (from 0.6 g on E16 to 5.5 g on E21). The combined effect of increasing body size and decreasing fluid volume is a dramatic reduction in the free space surrounding the fetus *in utero*: on E21, rat fetuses have about 3% of their own body volume within which to move.[37] Comparison of the behavior of fetuses exposed to such cramped conditions *in utero* with fetuses observed *ex utero*, after externalization into an unbounded fluid medium, has revealed that physical restraint induced by diminished free space *in utero* exerts differential effects on various kinds of fetal movement. After delivery *ex utero*, fetuses exhibit a general increase in the level of motor activity (FIGURE 1, left). Changes are apparent in the relative contribution of different body regions to overall activity (FIGURE 1, right). Fetuses *ex utero* also exhibit a sharp increase in the incidence of synchronous activity (FIGURE 1, left). Behavioral differences between fetuses observed *in utero* and *ex utero* are apparent as early as E17, only 24 hours after the inception of movement, but are most dramatic near term, when intrauterine restraint presumably is most extreme.

Behavioral changes promoted by reducing intrauterine restraint argue that fetuses are responsive to features of their immediate environment. This responsiveness is evident not only in the general level of nonevoked activity and degree of behavioral organization, but also in the expression of discrete motor patterns following explicit stimulation. For instance, moderate physical restraint *in utero* on E19 facilitates paw-face contact during facial wiping behavior (a fetal action pattern similar to postnatal face grooming), but the extreme intrauterine restraint that occurs naturally on E21, or which can be induced on E19 by experimental oligohydramnios (removal of amniotic fluid), eliminates the expression of this behavior.[2,38] In this sense, molar changes in environmental conditions induce an alteration in the regulation of fetal motor activity. However, it is equally apparent that fetal activity is not merely increased or decreased in level or intensity by gross environmental manipulations. Rather, removal of the confining influences of the uterus and amnion alters the distribution of fetal activity among various regions of the body. For example, movements involving the extremes of the body's long axis—the head and rearlimbs—are most affected: on E21 the rate of head movement increases by 215% and rearlimb movement by 289% following delivery into the saline bath, compared to an increase of only 67% for forelimbs (FIGURE 1, right). Although all nonevoked fetal activity, whether *in* or *ex utero*, may ultimately

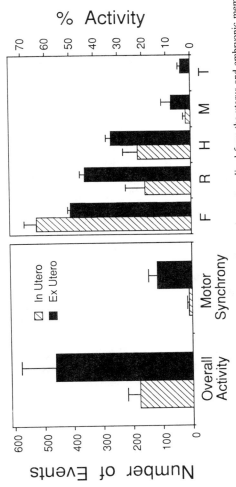

FIGURE 1. Nonevoked behavior of rat fetuses observed within the uterus (*in utero*) or externalized from the uterus and embryonic membranes into a warm saline bath (*ex utero*) on day 21 of gestation (E21). **Left panel:** Incidence of overall activity and motor synchrony *in utero* and *ex utero*; bars depict mean number of movements in a 30-minute period, vertical lines show standard error of the mean (SEM). **Right panel:** Percentage of fetal activity involving different body regions: forelimb (F), rearlimb (R), head (H), mouth (M), body trunk (T).

be generated by spontaneous neural activity, different regional categories of fetal movement appear to be differentially affected by immediate environmental conditions.

THE EMERGENCE OF MOTOR SYNCHRONY

Even to the casual observer, fetal activity does not seem to be distributed uniformly in time. Events appear to occur in bouts or clusters involving multiple events, which in turn are separated by more distinct pauses involving little or no activity. Temporal variation in motor activity is an important characteristic of behavior in mature animals, and various mathematical approaches for detecting and characterizing temporal patterns in fetal activity have proven to be powerful tools for understanding the emergence of behavioral organization.[14,39]

On a fine time scale, temporal patterning is evident in synchronized activation of different muscle groups and body parts, which is fundamental to the coordinated movement involved in all complex behavior. One measure of motor synchrony that changes dramatically during gestation in fetal rodents is the number of instances in which two or more body parts move at the same time, such as concurrent movement of forelimbs and rearlimbs.[40] On E16–E17 in the rat fetus, motor synchrony is relatively uncommon and coordination between different body regions appear random. Indeed, comparison of motor synchrony during the first days after inception with predictions generated by formal stochastic models suggests that the few instances of concurrent movement can be attributed to the accidental or chance coincidence of independent movements. In contrast, the abundance of synchronous movements expressed by fetal rats after E19 far exceeds expected levels of chance association.[14] These findings accord well with experiments involving surgical interruption of intraspinal communication between different body regions. After complete midthoracic spinal transection on E20, fetal rats continue to exhibit nonevoked motor activity both rostral and caudal to the cut, but the incidence of synchronous forelimb-rearlimb activity, which typically is the most common combination of individual movement categories, is virtually eliminated.[41] The emergence of synchronous motor activity during the period E17–E19 represents the earliest evidence for coordinated behavior in the rat fetus.

Comparison of observed motor synchrony to predictions generated by random models also has been used to identify specific patterns of coordinated movement during the prenatal period. The emergence of synchronous movement has been described in both the fetal rat (*Rattus norvegicus*) and Mongolian gerbil (*Meriones unguiculatus*), which are born in a relatively immature (altricial) condition. But the appearance, elaboration, and gradual replacement of different patterns of motor synchrony are especially apparent in species that bear more mature (precocial) offspring. Cotton rats (*Sigmodon hispidus*) and spiny mice (*Acomys cahirinus*) are members of the same family of rodents as rats and gerbils (Muridae), but bear young that are furred, whose eyes open, and who are capable of walking, climbing, and grooming on the day of birth.[42,43] Fetuses of these species exhibit behavior that is qualitatively and quantitatively similar to rats and gerbils at the inception of movement. The initial emergence of synchronous fetal activity also is similar, although it occurs relatively earlier in gestation in precocial species.

During the emergence of motor synchrony, three body regions—head (H), forelimbs (F), and rearlimbs (R)—account for nearly all fetal activity and may be expected to be involved in synchronous movements. These three body regions can be combined in three unique pairs and one triplet, allowing four possible categories of synchronous movement (FH, FR, HR, FHR). In spiny mice, all four categories of motor synchrony are expressed at the level predicted by random association at the inception of movement (E22). Within four days, spiny mouse fetuses exhibit abundant FH and FR movements; however, HR and FHR movements are expressed less often than expected by chance, suggesting that these combinations are actively inhibited at this age. By E30, halfway between inception and term (E38) in these precocial mice, FH and FR movements continue to be expressed more often than expected and HR movements less often. But FHR movements exhibit a reversal from E26 and are expressed more often than chance (FIGURE 2). A similar pattern of development of these four categories of synchronous movement is exhibited by precocial cotton rats.[36]

The discontinuity evident in the expression of FHR movements by pre-

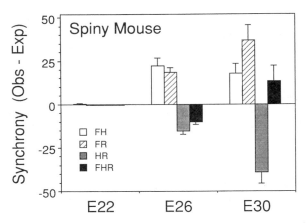

FIGURE 2. Nonrandom expression of motor synchrony in spiny mouse fetuses during the first half of the fetal period (E22–E30). Bars depict the mean difference (± SEM) between the observed incidence of synchronous movements and predictions based on random temporal association of independent events (shown as the horizontal zero line). Four categories of motor synchrony are presented, comprising the possible combinations of head (H), forelimb (F), and rearlimb (R) activity.

cocial fetuses implies that different mechanisms are responsible for generating this category of motor synchrony at each of three points during gestation. On E22, random association of independent movement events is fully sufficient to account for the occasional occurrence of FHR combinations. On E26, pairwise movements involving the forelimbs (FH and FR) appear to be promoted. The reduction in FHR movements at this age, which cannot be accounted for by chance occurrence, may reflect behavioral inhibition by the same mechanism responsible for suppressing synchronous head and rearlimb activity (HR), which shares two of the same motor components. By E30, the pronounced suppression of HR movements continues to be expressed, but is dissociated from FHR activity, indicating the emergence of a third source of regulation that specifically stimulates FHR activity above chance levels. Quantitative analyses such as these, which are based solely upon observational data, appear to reflect a general developmental trend from randomly associated independent movements to increasing specification of synchronized activity. Further, the existence of discontinuous patterns of expression and the different developmental timetables for various categories of concurrent movement imply that this specification emerges from interactions among multiple sources of behavioral regulation, not from the maturation of a single centralized activity generator.

BOUTS AND CYCLICITY IN FETAL MOVEMENT

Another dimension of temporal patterning in fetal behavior is the clustering of movements. As mentioned earlier, fetal motor activity fluctuates over the course of an observation session, with the intervals between successive movement events varying from less than 1 second to more than a minute. Much of the apparent randomness in this temporal variation belies an underlying orderliness: quantitative analysis has revealed the tendency for fetal movements to occur in temporal clusters or bouts.[14] A bout may be defined as a collection of movements that follow one another by brief intervals, but which are separated from other movements by relatively longer pauses. Bouts often are described subjectively, but may be characterized objectively by examination of the overall distribution of interevent intervals. If movements occur randomly in time, then a large sample of interevent intervals may be described by a negative exponential distribution, which will appear as a straight line on a log survivor plot of the cumulative interval distribution.[44] Log survivor analysis indicates that fetal activity is randomly distributed in time at the inception of movement in all species studied to date. Within 1–2 days of inception, however, fetal movements show an increasing tendency to cluster at short interevent intervals. This analytic approach suggests that two underlying processes are responsible for generating fetal movements in real time: (a) a time-independent process, in which the probability of adding an additional second to the interval between events is constant and independent of the elapsed time since the last movement, and (b) a time-dependent process in which the probability of movement is much greater than 5 seconds of the preceding movement. Although the relative strength of the time-dependent process increases during gestation, its temporal limits do not; across ages (and species) the influence of preceding movements decays within 5–6 seconds. The tendency for movements to occur in bouts also is enhanced when fetuses are removed from the confinement of the uterus and reaches its maximum extent near term, when more than 90% of all interevent intervals are less than 5 seconds in duration.

The occurrence of temporal clusters of fetal movements is not related in any obvious way to intermittent stimuli in the intrauterine environment. To the contrary, bouts of nonevoked movement tend to be distributed in irregular but recurrent cycles. Spontaneous cyclicity in motor activity (CM) with oscillations of 1–5 minutes have been described in many vertebrate embryos and may reflect a ubiquitous characteristic of early motor development.[39,45] Unlike many other biological cycles (e.g., circadian, lunar, and annual cycles), CM does not appear to be entrained by extrinsic cues and the underlying mechanisms or sources of cyclic regulation remain poorly understood.

CM has been well documented in the human fetus and is consistently expressed from at least midgestation (20 weeks) through term.[8] CM continues to be expressed by the human newborn in both active sleep and waking states, reflecting the underlying continuity between the prenatal and neonatal periods. In addition to the human fetus, CM has been objectively characterized in fetal rats[41] and sheep. Despite the very different methods employed to detect and quantify fetal activity in these three species [external movement sensors in humans, direct observation in rats, pooled electromyographic (EMG) records from limb muscles in sheep], the principal characteristics of CM are remarkably similar. (a) Fourier analyses of movement time series consistently indicate a dominant frequency of CM of about 1 cycle per minute (cpm). The average frequency of CM varies little during gestation in normal fetuses, persists relatively unchanged into the neonatal period, and appears to be little affected by the overall rate of movement.[46] (b) The strength of CM, as indicated by the amplitude of the dominant frequency, also is very stable across species, ages, and experimental conditions. (c) Oscillations in motor activity are irregular, unlike the highly periodic activity of other biological systems. Like other properties of CM, this irregularity in activity, as measured by the dispersion of movement variance around the dominant frequency, is stable and consistent. The fact that CM is not highly rhythmic implies that it is not strongly regulated, at least by a single, centralized source of oscillation. Rather, irregularity in CM may indicate that erratic fluctuations in activity are the result of interactions between distributed sources of oscillation in the nervous system that are incompletely coupled.[39]

The results of spinal transection experiments conducted with fetal rats on E20 may provide support for a multiple source model of CM.[47] CM is evident not only in overall motor activity, which sums across all categories of individual fetal movement, but also in the activity of specific regions of the body. Intact fetuses and fetuses that receive a sham transection treatment exhibit cyclicity in both rostral (head and forelimb) and caudal (rearlimb) movements. The main properties of CM (frequency, strength, and irregularity) as measured independently in rostral and caudal activity are virtually identical in nontransected fetuses. Following complete midthoracic spinal transection, fetuses continue to express spontaneous motor activity rostral and caudal to the cut, and this activity shows evidence of cyclicity. Although the rate of rearlimb movement is reduced, the dominant frequency of caudal CM is virtually unchanged after transection. However, movements rostral to the transection, which are relatively less affected in overall number, show cyclicity with a dominant frequency less than half that of control fetuses (FIGURE 3). This experiment demonstrates two important aspects underlying the regulation of CM. First, at least two sources in the central nervous system (rostral and caudal to a midthoracic spinal transection) are capable of supporting CM in the fetus. Second, these sources interact, producing rostral and caudal activity with similar frequencies of cyclicity in the intact fetus, but diverge toward different preferred frequencies (slower in rostral segments) after interruption of intraspinal communication.

BEHAVIORAL SETS AND STATE ORGANIZATION

In the general sense originally borrowed from cybernetics,[48] a state is an outward manifestation of a stable but reversible pattern of internal conditions

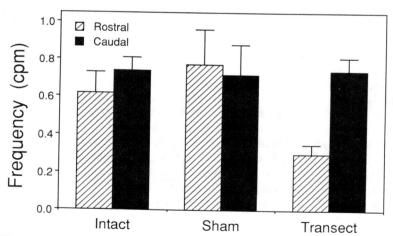

FIGURE 3. Change in the dominant frequency of cyclic motor activity rostral and caudal to a midthoracic spinal transection in E20 rat fetuses. Rostral activity comprises movements of the head, mouth and forelimbs; caudal activity involves movements of the rearlimbs. Spinal transection does not eliminate activity, but induces a change in the temporal patterning of movements rostral to the site of transection.

in an animal. Even within the behavioral literature, the term often has been used in multiple contexts to refer to changes in motivation ("hungry," "aggressive"), phase in a reproductive cycle ("sexually receptive," "nesting"), wakefulness ("asleep," "awake"), arousal ("drowsy," "alert"), and level of activity ("quiet," "active"). States may be defined in terms of external appearance, as in species that change color, shape, posture, or expression, or measurement of neural or physiological variables, such as electroencephalogram (EEG) or electrocorticogram (ECoG), heart rate, respiration, hormone levels, etc. Ultimately, though, the utility of the concept of state depends upon the stable association of an array or set of behavioral variables: identification of an animal's state leads to improved predictability of its behavior.[44,49]

From a methodological standpoint, the most accessible means of gaining information about what an animal is likely to do next is to observe what it has just done. This approach is the essence of sequential analysis, which quantifies the relationship between successive pairs or longer strings of behavioral events. A Markov approach to sequential analysis assumes that a system of interest can exhibit only a finite number of discrete categories of behavior, and that the current behavior of the system is probabilistically related to the next behavior to occur.[50] The degree of serial relationship may be estimated by constructing a matrix comprising the frequencies of transition, or conditional probabilities of transition, between all possible ordered pairs of behavioral events. Information in a complete transition matrix permits specific sequential questions to be addressed, including overall sequential organization as indicated by chi-square or information theory measures,[44] and hypothesis testing of specific behavioral sequences.[50] The transition matrix also provides a basis for measuring the degree of similarity between different behavioral categories: each row of the matrix constitutes an array of probabilities associated with transitions to other categories of behavior, including self-recursion (repetition of the same behavioral event). Behavioral categories that are functionally related or are regulated by a common mechanism should exhibit arrays of transition probabilities that are similar. Specifically, behaviors that tend to occur within a given general state should exhibit frequent transitions to other behaviors within the same state and relatively infrequent transitions to behaviors within different states. Sequential analysis thus can provide clues to how various behavioral categories are organized into associated sets.

An example of this sequential approach to describing state is provided in FIGURE 4. A representative matrix of transition probabilities during non-evoked motor activity is shown (top) for fetal rats observed *ex utero* on E20. For purpose of analysis, eight discrete categories of fetal behavior are distinguished, comprising simple movements of the head (H), mouth (M), forelimbs (F), rearlimbs (R), and body trunk (T), and two categories of synchronous movement (FH and FR); the eighth category comprises all movements not otherwise coded (O), including rare behaviors (e.g., stretch and facial wipe), and other combinations of simple movements (primarily HR, FHR,

TR, and HM). Because these categories are mutually exclusive and exhaustive, all sequential transitions in a given time series can be coded. Each row of the transition matrix then is used to estimate similarity among categories of behavior, with pairwise comparisons of similarity measures subjected to hierarchical cluster analysis using a complete linkage algorithm.[51] Patterns of similarity among clustered behaviors are summarized in the dendrogram (FIGURE 4, bottom), which depicts the degree of similarity (i.e., sequential transition probability) between individual behaviors or clusters of behaviors. Behavioral categories with similar patterns of serial relationship are linked together in tight clusters and are connected more distantly to other clusters with more dissimilar transitional arrays.

Three main clusters of fetal behavior are evident in this example: (a) simple and synchronous fetal movements principally involving rearlimb activity (R, FR, and the heterogenous category O), (b) simple and synchronous movements involving the head and forelimbs (H, F, and FH), and (c) mouth activity. The first two clusters correspond quite closely to the rearlimb-nonrearlimb dichotomy identified in spinal transection studies conducted at the same fetal age. The segregation of head and rearlimb activity into different clusters also may be related to the suppression of fetal activity involving synchronous HR movements evident at this age. The general concordance of these quantitative measures of behavioral organization appears to indicate the existence of at least two neural sources of regulatory influence (rostral and caudal, or more specifically, supraspinal and lumbosacral) on fetal activity. The distinct clusters of different movement categories further suggest that fetal activity is organized in discrete time periods that predominantly comprise only a subset of the fetus's motor repertoire. These periods, which will be referred to as "behavioral sets," may reflect emerging state organization in fetal behavior.

Detailed examination of the behavior of rat fetuses provides additional evidence that fetal motor activity is organized in behavioral sets. Fetal movements involving rostral and caudal elements tend to be poorly associated during periods of nonevoked activity. Further, fetal movements in this rostral-caudal dimension are nonrandomly distributed in time. Time series created by calculating the probability of rearlimb movement (P_R = no. rearlimb events/overall activity) within a 10-event moving window over the course of a 30-minute observation session show periodic fluctuations between high and low probabilities (FIGURE 5, top). Spectral analysis indicates that P_R exhibits cyclic organization with a mean dominant frequency (0.39 ± 0.05 cpm) that is significantly slower than the cyclicity of overall fetal activity (0.67 ± 0.15 cpm). Further, simulations involving Monte Carlo techniques indicate that the average durations of objectively delimited high P_R and low P_R periods differ from random rearrangements of behavioral time series. In other words, the temporal distribution of high and low P_R periods cannot be attributed to the accidental sequencing of random fetal movements. These quantitative analyses suggest that fluctuations in P_R during nonevoked ac-

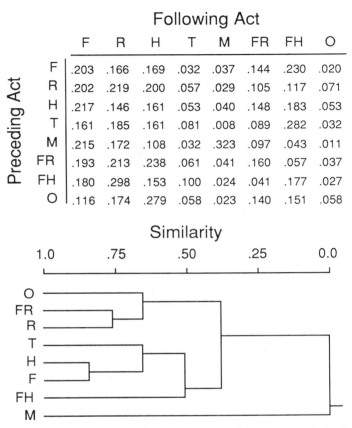

Following Act

	F	R	H	T	M	FR	FH	O
F	.203	.166	.169	.032	.037	.144	.230	.020
R	.202	.219	.200	.057	.029	.105	.117	.071
H	.217	.146	.161	.053	.040	.148	.183	.053
T	.161	.185	.161	.081	.008	.089	.282	.032
M	.215	.172	.108	.032	.323	.097	.043	.011
FR	.193	.213	.238	.061	.041	.160	.057	.037
FH	.180	.298	.153	.100	.024	.041	.177	.027
O	.116	.174	.279	.058	.023	.140	.151	.058

(Preceding Act)

Similarity

FIGURE 4. Sequential organization of motor activity in E20 rat fetuses. **Top:** Matrix of sequential transition probabilities among eight categories of fetal behavior. **Bottom:** Dendrogram depicting the results of hierarchical cluster analysis, using a complete linkage algorithm, of sequential relationships among fetal behaviors. Categories of behavior within the same cluster are more similar in patterns of sequential transition than behaviors in different clusters.

tivity are indicative of persistent, qualitative shifts between behavioral sets in the rat fetus.

P_R is defined solely with reference to the categories of movement expressed by fetuses. Fetal behavioral sets also may be distinguished in the time domain, which is theoretically independent of the categories of behavioral events. Successive fetal movements are separated by intervals of varying duration. Variability in the length of interevent intervals, expressed as the mean difference between successive intervals (D_I) during the same 10-event moving window used in the P_R analysis, also exhibits fluctuation during nonevoked fetal activity. Like P_R, interval variability exhibits alternating high

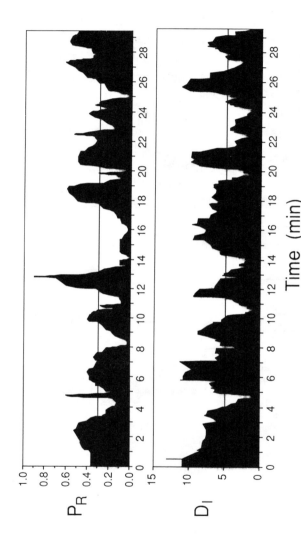

FIGURE 5. A representative time series that illustrates behavioral sets in categorical and temporal measures of fetal activity in an E20 rat fetus. The two graphs depict changes in the probability of rearlimb movement (P_R, top) and variability of interevent intervals (D_I, bottom) within a moving 10-event window during the same 30-minute observation period. Epochs of low and high activity are distinguishable from overall mean activity, shown as a horizontal line on each graph.

and low periods over the course of a 30-minute session. Unlike the rostral-caudal metric, D_I shows no evidence of cyclicity (it does not differ from a spectral distribution of white noise). Monte Carlo techniques confirm that the durations of periods of high and low D_I differ significantly from random time series, suggesting that interval variability also may be used to delineate behavioral sets in the rat fetus.

Although defined by independent behavioral parameters (categorical and temporal), it is reasonable to presume that P_R and D_I are general reflections of the same underlying source of behavioral regulation in the fetus. But these two measures of motor patterning show little evidence of synchronization during periods of nonevoked motor activity on E20. Within an individual fetus, synchronous measurements of P_R and D_I typically are weakly correlated (Pearson r values on E20 generally < 0.15). In some subjects, however, stronger positive correlations are evident at an event lag, with one time series offset by a given number of events relative to the other. FIGURE 5 shows an example of a time series from one fetal subject that exhibits such a delayed temporal relationship between P_R and D_I. Although little relationship between P_R and D_I is evident in measurements within the same time window (lag = 0, $r = 0.028$), the time series shows a significantly stronger relationship with a relative lag of 11 events ($r = 0.351$, $p < 0.001$), which in this subject is equivalent to an average time difference of about 55 seconds. The onset of high levels of rearlimb activity thus is delayed by about 1 minute relative to the onset of periods of high interval variability. This finding suggests that categorical and temporal indices of fetal behavioral sets are not synchronized to a common global source of behavioral regulation. Rather, they seem to reflect independent dimensions of behavioral organization that are weakly coupled during nonevoked activity in the rat fetus.

FETAL BEHAVIORAL STATES

The concept of behavioral state is widely used in a specific, formal context within the fields of pediatrics and child development. In this narrow sense, states were originally described in human infants as recognizable points along a continuum from sleeping to waking.[52] More recently, infant states have been viewed as fundamental dimensions of neurobehavioral organization that are qualitatively distinct and unrelated to a hypothetical continuum of arousal.[53,54] Four principal behavioral states are generally recognized in human neonates: (a) quiet sleep, with eyes closed, regular respiration, and an absence of general motor activity (except for occasional startles); (b) active or REM sleep, with eyes closed, irregular respiration, and small movements of the face, body, and extremities; (c) quiet awake, with eyes open and an absence of motor activity; and (d) active awake, with eyes open and frequent gross motor movements. A fifth state—crying—also may be distinguished. The four basic states, originally described on the basis of observational criteria, are robust and have been shown to be associated consistently with more direct measures of central nervous system activity, such as ECoG and heart rate variability. Infant states exhibit further organization in their temporal and sequential relationships to one another. Newborns spend roughly equal thirds of their time in quiet sleep, active sleep, and awake states. Transitions between states involve simultaneous change in associated state variables. State transitions occur periodically, with quiet and active sleep alternating in a 15-minute cycle, with interruptions every few hours by waking and nursing. As postnatal development proceeds, this sleep-wake cycle becomes increasingly regulated by the infant-mother dyad, principally during feeding interactions.

Because state organization is evident in the human neonate, a number of people have sought to investigate the prenatal roots of sleep-wake states.[55-57] Because of the difficulty in assessing fetal behavior, prenatal behavioral states typically are defined in terms of variables that can be monitored externally, such as gross motor activity and fetal heart rate. Further, to qualify as a behavioral state in the narrow sense employed in pediatrics, patterns of neurobehavioral organization must satisfy three criteria: (a) The putative state must be defined in terms of multiple, independent variables that can be continuously monitored. (b) Changes in all of the defining variables must approximately coincide in time. (c) The state must exhibit a minimum duration of stable association (often defined as 3 minutes).[57]

Some inferences regarding the prenatal development of state organization have been drawn from the study of low-risk preterm infants older than 32 weeks postconception. For example, it is difficult to reliably distinguish quiet and active sleep in preterm infants younger than 38 weeks, although the constellation of variables associated with active sleep can be observed as early as 35 weeks.[53,54] This kind of observation has been interpreted by some investigators as evidence for the gradual maturation of central mechanisms that regulate state organization. Most researchers agree, however, that the parameters used to characterize states exist and exhibit variation in younger infants. In a more recent study, active and quiet sleep were identified consistently on the basis of EEG and eye movement criteria at least as early as 31 weeks postconception. Other variables typically associated with different sleep states in full-term newborns, such as regularity of respiration, expression of limb movements, and tonic chin EMG, were not well associated at younger ages.[58] These findings suggest that recognizable states appear with the concordance of two important parameters, cortical activity and eye movement. Additional variables are successively associated with this stable relationship, gradually building more complex and comprehensive levels of state organization.

Study of premature infants can provide only an imperfect window on the prenatal development of behavioral states, because even at 40 weeks postconception, preterm infants exhibit more poorly developed sleep-wake states than full-term neonates.[59] Disrupted state organization is probably attributable in part to the noisy, invasive conditions that are present routinely in neonatal intensive care units.[60] Direct study of fetal state development has been facilitated by the technical ability to monitor fetal heart rate and detect the presence or absence of eye activity and gross body movements in real-time ultrasound images of human fetuses.[31] Variables such as heart rate and eye movement, which can be monitored in humans, have been augmented with direct EMG and ECoG measurements in experimental preparations of fetal sheep.[61] These approaches have led to proposed definitions for four discrete and recognizable behavioral states in the fetus:[57] (a) state 1F, involving motor quiescence (except for occasional startles), absence of eye movements, and stable heart rate; (b) state 2F, involving frequent and periodic motor activity, continuous eye movements (REM), and a heart rate pattern with wider oscillation and frequent acceleration associated with gross movements; (c) state 3F, involving the absence of motor activity, continuous eye movements, and stable heart rate without frequent accelerations; and (d) state 4F, involving vigorous motor activity, continuous eye movements, and unstable heart rate with frequent and/or lasting episodes of tachycardia. Discrete states may be distinguished by week 32 in human fetuses[57] and day 130 in the fetal sheep (term = 150 days).[61]

As in the studies of preterm infants, different variables used to define behavioral states in the fetus exhibit variation early during gestation, before the emergence of state organization. For example, eye, head, limb, and gross body movements are expressed very early in gestation in the fetal sheep,[62,63] although they are not synchronized within well-defined states. Similarly, the amplitude of ECoG activity in the fetal sheep branches from an early unimodal distribution (evident on day 120) to gradually form a bimodal distribution comprising relatively stable periods of low voltage and high voltage ECoG activity by day 135.[64] More information regarding the direct measurement of state variables in human fetuses and appropriate animal models (such as the sheep) clearly is warranted. The current evidence, though, suggests that periodic variation in state variables emerges earlier in gestation than behavioral states per se. This interpretation is consistent with a hypothesis of multiple sources of behavioral regulation that become temporally coupled, in a fashion analogous to the stochastic synchronization of motor activity in fetal rats, during the development of fetal behavioral states.

STIMULUS-EVOKED CHANGES IN MOTOR ORGANIZATION

The foregoing discussion has focused on various measures of behavioral organization during periods of nonevoked motor activity in the fetus. Although quantitative approaches have successfully documented temporal, sequential, and statelike organization in fetal behavior, much of the activity of fetuses subjectively looks sporadic and unoriented. In contrast, controlled presentation of sensory stimuli to the fetus can elicit striking changes in fetal activity and promote the expression of coordinated behavior patterns. For example, infusion of a small volume (20 µl) of lemon odor extract through a cannula directly into the mouth of the rat fetus consistently evokes a facial wiping response on E20 and E21.[15] Playback of videotaped infusion sequences at reduced speed reveals three distinct phases in the expression of facial wiping behavior. In the first phase (flexion), both forelimbs are drawn inward toward a point under the fetus's jaw. In the second phase (placing), one or both forepaws are moved to a position along the side of the head, generally between the ears and eyes. In the third phase (stroking), the paws make contact with the side of the head and move in a rostral direction, sliding along the face and extending beyond the tip of the nose. The placing and stroke phases together constitute a complete stroke cycle, which lasts about 1 second and is repeated 2–10 times during a single bout of wiping.[38]

The fetal wiping response is a species-typical action pattern that continues to be expressed as face-washing during grooming and aversive response sequences in juvenile and adult rodents.[65-67] In its mature form, facial wiping involves a high degree of coordination between the head (which is held motionless) and both forelimbs (which are synchronized during placing and stroking). One measure of interlimb coordination is the relative phase of each wiping cycle, which may be defined as the absolute difference in time between corresponding points in the strokes of left and right limbs divided by cycle duration. When expressed as a percentage of the stroke cycle, relative phase can vary from 0% (indicating perfect synchronization between limbs) to 50% (indicating strict alternation between left and right strokes). By parsing each bout of wiping into three time segments, each comprising an equal number of strokes, systematic changes in the phase relationships between left and right limbs become apparent (FIGURE 6). During the first third of the bout, phase relationships are distributed uniformly from 0% to 50% (median relative phase = 29.7%), indicating that wiping strokes are random with respect to bilateral coordination. Wiping strokes exhibit nonrandom coordination during the second segment as one limb performs a stroke slightly in advance of the other limb (median relative phase = 15.5%). By the last third of the bout, wiping strokes are nearly synchronized (median relative phase = 6.5%). These findings argue that the coordination evident in facial wiping is not expressed at the beginning of the response, in contrast to the traditional descriptions of adult action patterns in animal behavior[68] and neuroethology.[69] Instead, coordinated facial wiping in the fetus emerges as a product of the interaction between independent motor components, comprising strokes by left and right limbs, as they move during a bout.

The gradual construction of coordinated behavior is even more evident in the fetal response to intraoral delivery of milk. Immediately after birth, newborn mammals must recognize and orient toward the mother, attach to a nipple, and actively suckle to obtain milk. Upon milk letdown by the mother, neonatal rodents exhibit a stretch response, which consists of dorsiflexion and extension of the rearlimbs.[70,71] On E20 and E21, intraoral infusion of milk (bovine light cream) reliably elicits stretching behavior in the

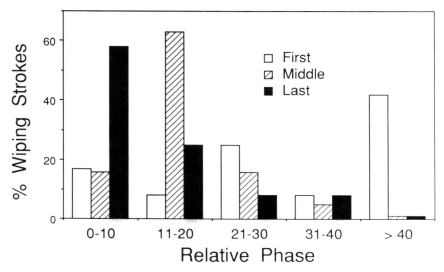

FIGURE 6. Distribution of differences in relative phase between left and right strokes during bouts of facial wiping in E20 rat fetuses. Relative phase, which indicates the degree of synchronization between forelimbs, is expressed as a percentage of the overall facial wiping cycle. Changes in relative phase are evident across three equal time segments (first, middle, and last) within wiping bouts.

fetal rat that is very similar in form to the neonatal response at the nipple.[15] Unlike the neonatal stretch, though, the fetal stretch occurs with a characteristic latency of 1–5 minutes after milk infusion (mean latency = 175 ± 12 seconds). During the intervening minutes between milk delivery and expression of the stretch, fetal behavior undergoes systematic changes in organization that culminate in the stretch.[72] In a typical sequence, the fetus exhibits a brief bout of mouthing activity immediately after milk infusion, which probably reflects a period of sampling of the chemosensory stimulus.[73] As mouthing diminishes, fetal activity gradually changes from the head and forelimb movements that are common before infusion to activity predominated by rearlimb movements. Rearlimb activity, which comprises about 25% of all fetal movements before milk infusion, accounts for more than 75% of all movements during the minute before the stretch (FIGURE 7). This reorganization of fetal activity is necessary for expression of the stretch response: perioral tactile stimulation administered 1 minute after milk infusion disrupts the transition to rearlimb activity and eliminates expression of the stretch. These data imply that the fetal stretch response is not simply triggered by milk, but is expressed as the culmination of a cascade of behavioral changes initiated by milk infusion.

Neonatal rats also exhibit a characteristic sequence of behavioral changes associated with ordinary suckling behavior and milk letdown at the nipple.

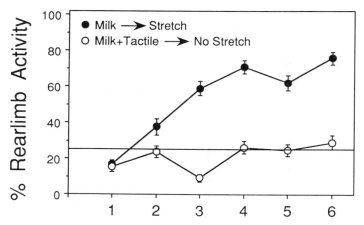

FIGURE 7. Changes in the abundance of rearlimb movements, expressed as a percentage of overall fetal activity, during six consecutive time segments between milk infusion and the stretch response (Stretch), or during an equivalent period of time after milk infusion in fetuses receiving perioral tactile stimulation (Tactile). The shaded area represents the 99% confidence intervals around mean rearlimb activity during the baseline period before milk infusion. Points show mean activity (± SEM) of E20 and E21 rat fetuses.

Rhythmic sucking and rearlimb treadling movements are expressed by rat pups in advance of milk delivery.[70] EEG measurements conducted with 10-day-old pups have revealed that this period of rhythmic sucking takes place while the pup is in a quiet or active sleep state. Milk letdown by the mother results in distension of the nipple, which makes milk available to the pup. At this moment the pup awakens, exhibits a sharp increase in motor activity which includes vigorous rearlimb movements, extracts milk from the nipple, and expresses the stretch response. Within 30–60 seconds of milk delivery, the awake pup reattaches to a nipple and returns to a sleep state.[74] Many of the behavioral effects promoted by milk in a normal, postnatal suckling context also are expressed by fetal rats, but in different temporal relation to the moment of milk delivery: changes in motor behavior that occur in advance of milk letdown in the pup are initiated by milk infusion in the fetus. The underlying continuity between prenatal and postnatal expression of the stretch response is consistent with the interpretation that stretching emerges from a process of behavior reorganization associated with suckling and milk delivery.

Behavioral states traditionally are associated with different patterns of responsiveness to sensory stimulation.[57] A single exposure to milk has been shown to alter the responsiveness of neonatal rats to various forms of cutaneous stimulation,[75,76] which is consistent with the hypothesis that milk promotes a change in state. Untreated rat fetuses reliably respond to a Von Frey bristle applied to the perioral region with a unilateral wiping response.[77] When tested 60–300 seconds after milk infusion, however, fetuses rarely express this behavioral response. The effects of milk on sensory responsiveness recently have been shown to be mediated by the fetus's endogenous opioid system.[29] Pretreatment of fetal subjects with naloxone, a nonspecific opioid antagonist, reinstates wiping responses to tactile stimulation following milk infusion. Nor-binaltorphimine, an antagonist specific to the kappa subclass of opioid receptors, also is effective in reversing the influence of milk on sensory responsiveness. These findings imply that milk infusion is effective in promoting endogenous opioid activity, which in turn may influence a number of behavioral variables in the fetus and neonate.[78,79]

A brief exposure to milk exerts concurrent, lasting effects on fetal physiology as well. On E21, fetal heart rate before milk infusion exhibits considerable variability between successive 5-second intervals; baseline heart rate changes about 15 bpm (5% of average heart rate on E21) from one interval to the next. In contrast, a single 20-µl infusion of milk sharply reduces heart rate variability, with the mean interval-to-interval change lowered to about 6 bpm.[80] The reduction in heart rate variability is expressed by fetuses that ultimately perform the stretch response and fetuses that do not. However, fetuses that stretch uniquely exhibit a patterned bradycardia, which amounts to nearly 60 bpm, that begins about 30 seconds before and returns to baseline at the moment the stretch occurs. Bradycardia also is expressed by suckling rat pups during the transition from sleep to waking triggered by milk letdown.[81] The occurrence of delayed bradycardia in the fetus suggests that a secondary neurobehavioral event, such as the transition between behavioral states, may be proximately responsible for evoking the fetal stretch.[80]

It remains uncertain whether the persistent behavioral and physiological effects promoted by milk, such as reduced heart rate variability and the delayed stretch response, are related to changes in underlying state organization. However, new data from the fetal rat suggest that a single infusion of milk can facilitate the coupling of state variables, such as the categorical and temporal behavioral sets described earlier. During a 30-minute period before milk delivery the probability of rearlimb movement (P_R) and interval variability (D_I) exhibit a weak cross-correlation (mean $r = 0.135$). Epochs of high and low sets within each variable are relatively brief, with mean durations of 1–2 minutes. After milk infusion, the duration of high P_R periods increases significantly, while the length of low P_R periods does not change (FIGURE 8). This finding, which is based on a different method of measuring changes in rearlimb activity from that used in previous studies,[72] documents that low P_R epochs are not eliminated after milk infusion, but merely are separated by longer periods of high P_R.

Although low and high P_R epochs exhibit striking changes in relative duration, the general organization of interval variability does not appear to be affected by milk infusion (FIGURE 8). The relationship between categorical and temporal sets is altered by infusion, though, with significantly stronger correlations within the same time window (event lag = 0, mean $r = 0.205$).

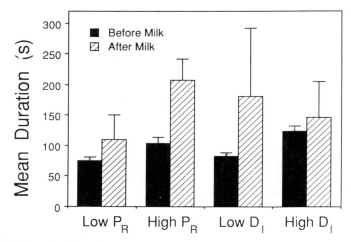

FIGURE 8. Mean duration (± SEM) of categorical and temporal behavioral sets before and after milk infusion in E20 rat fetuses. Categorical sets are defined as sustained periods of low or high probability of rearlimb movement (P_R). Temporal sets are defined as periods of low or high variability of interevent intervals (D_I). Although milk infusion promotes a doubling in the length of high P_R epochs, it does not result in significant cha.ges in the duration of low or high D_I epochs.

Further, the relationship between P_R and D_I at varying event lags also changes. The strongest correlations before milk infusion (mean $r = 0.210$) occur with P_R lagged by an average of 13.3 ± 1.8 events relative to D_I, indicating that fluctuations in P_R tend to follow fluctuations in D_I. After milk infusion, the strongest correlations between P_R and D_I (mean $r = 0.222$) occur with an average lag of 2.5 ± 2.2 events. The shift in peak correlation lags implies that the two variables are becoming synchronized. This synchronization is visually apparent in the time series portrayed in FIGURE 9, which depicts P_R and D_I in an E20 rat fetus observed for one hour with a milk infusion delivered midway through the session. The temporal coupling of two independent behavioral variables promoted by a sensory event argues that milk-induced changes in behavioral sets can provide a useful model for understanding the prenatal development of behavioral state organization.

IMPLICATIONS FOR THE PRENATAL DEVELOPMENT OF BEHAVIORAL REGULATION

Although they occur on different time scales, a number of the foregoing examples may illustrate a fundamental process of behavioral development during the prenatal period. On a scale of seconds, coordinated facial wiping behavior emerges from more generalized fetal activity evoked by chemosensory infusion. The forelimb strokes initially occur with random interlimb co-

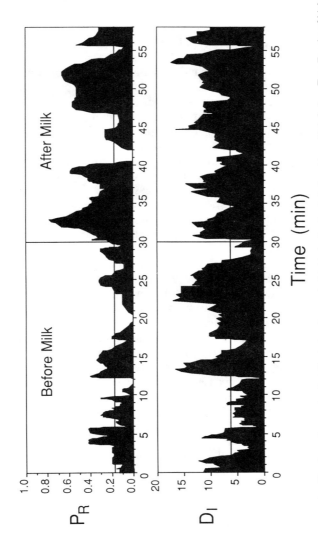

FIGURE 9. A representative 60-minute time series that illustrates changes in fetal behavioral sets induced by milk infusion. **Top:** Epochs of high P_R increase in duration after infusion, but do not eliminate periodic transitions to low P_R epochs. **Bottom:** Milk also promotes a stronger temporal relationship between fluctuations in D_I and P_R.

ordination, but become synchronized as successive wiping cycles are performed. On a scale of minutes, delivery of milk to the fetus promotes lasting changes in physiology and behavioral organization. Among these changes, independent temporal and categorical variables that spontaneously fluctuate but bear little relationship to one another before infusion become more closely coupled in time after milk exposure. On a scale of days, patterns of motor synchrony that initially are expressed as random coincidence are differentiated and generated in relative abundance or almost completely suppressed. On a scale of weeks, organized behavioral states emerge in the preterm infant and human fetus from a constellation of behavioral and physiological variables that are expressed, but not associated, at earlier ages.

Examples such as these emphasize the principal problem of developmental science: the emergence of organization, regulation, orderliness — in short, how one gets something from nothing. But they also focus attention on the process whereby organized behavior is preceded, in real time or developmental time, by simpler components that exhibit spontaneous activity and random interaction. In its earliest expression, fetal motor activity does not appear to exhibit regulation. Rather, convergent evidence indicates that early movements are influenced by multiple sources both intrinsic (e.g., spontaneous neural activity within the spinal cord) and extrinsic to the fetus (e.g., environmental facilitation or constraint of movement). As gestation proceeds, fetal behavior comes to exhibit greater organization, which is reflected in quantitative measures of temporal, sequential, spatial, and statelike relationships between behavioral variables. Behavioral organization thus is not expressed at the inception of movement, but gradually emerges to replace stochastic interactions during spontaneous motor activity.[14]

Although changes in behavioral organization can be discerned in the nonevoked activity of fetuses *in utero*, investigation of the process of emerging organization is greatly enhanced by experimental presentation of sensory stimulation to the fetus. In the cases of facial wiping evoked by lemon odor and the multiple behavioral effects induced by milk, challenging the fetus with a chemosensory stimulus is effective in promoting both local and global changes in behavioral organization within a time frame suitable for analysis. Although fetuses are not exposed to lemon or milk during normal development *in utero*, presentation of these stimuli can provide a powerful tool for measuring the capacity of behavioral systems at various ages during gestation. Fetal stimulation has the additional advantage of allowing control over sensory experience across a range of ages; fetuses exhibit responsiveness to many stimuli in the absence of previous specific experience.

Typically, various measures of behavioral organization are strengthened or enhanced following sensory stimulation in the fetus. This is most evident in the case of milk, which promotes changes in temporal and sequential patterning of motor activity, the distribution of activity among different regions of the body, the expression of variability in heart rate and the timing of movements, and the temporal relationships among these independent variables. Sensory stimulation thus promotes the emergence of behavioral regulation within a span of minutes. It is not intuitively obvious why this should be so. One can readily imagine a developmental system in which specific behavioral responses are triggered by stimulation without general changes in overall behavioral organization. In fact, the opposite pattern appears to be characteristic of fetal responses to sensory stimuli: the stimulus first promotes changes in motor activity, which lead to more interactions between independent behavioral components and eventually culminate in seemingly global shifts in overall behavioral organization and the expression of coordinated action patterns. It is possible that the chemosensory event, which is sharply contrasted against the slowly fluctuating chemical milieu within the amniotic fluid *in utero*, provides a temporal reference point that serves as the center of focus for coupling independent behavioral variables. Subsequent changes in behavior may be viewed as a self-organizing cascade from this initial point of stable association.

A similar interpretation recently has been offered by Thelen[35] for the progressive elaboration of behavioral states reported in preterm infants.[58] In effect, an initial association between variables, such as EEG activity and eye movements, provides a stable attractor that permits the temporal coupling of additional variables associated with behavioral state. Rather than representing the maturation of a global source of behavioral regulation, the development of behavioral states may entail a process of self-organization around an initial, stable cluster of variables. A dynamical systems perspective such as this is gaining currency in developmental studies,[82] but will require additional study to be adequately evaluated.

Concepts such as spontaneous activity, stochastic interaction, and self-organization within dynamical systems contrast sharply with a more conventional view of regulation as a centrally controlled homeostatic process. However, they may be especially useful when applied to development during the prenatal period. Although fetuses possess a number of functional senses and are exposed during gestation to ambient stimuli in tactile, chemosensory, and acoustic modalities,[83,84] most stimuli that succeed in penetrating the concentric envelopes of the mother, uterus, and amniotic sac are not related in any direct way to the fetus's immediate needs. While we are accustomed to thinking of behavior as goal directed and contingent on specific environmental circumstances, the fetus's requirements for life support are largely met through its physiological connection to the mother and are not dependent upon its behavior (cf., Reference 37). In this context, which is virtually unique to placental mammals, the behavioral systems of the fetus may be especially sensitive to internal contingencies that arise through chance interactions during spontaneous motor activity. What may be referred to as regulation or self-organization thus may simply entail the selective strengthening of these motor contingencies.

REFERENCES

1. HALL, W. G. & R. W. OPPENHEIM. 1987. Developmental psychobiology: prenatal, perinatal, and early postnatal aspects of behavioral development. Annu. Rev. Psychol. **38:** 91–128.
2. ROBINSON, S. R. & W. P. SMOTHERMAN. Fundamental motor patterns of the mammalian fetus. J. Neurobiol. (In press.)
3. ALBERTS, J. R. & C. P. CRAMER. 1988. Ecology and experience: sources of means and meaning of developmental change. *In* Handbook of Behavioral Neurobiology. Developmental Psychobiology and Behavioral Ecology. E. M. Blass, Ed. **9:** 1–39. Plenum Press. New York, N.Y.
4. WINDLE, W. F. 1944. Genesis of somatic motor function in mammalian embryos: a synthesizing article. Physiol. Zool. **17:** 247–261.
5. HOOKER, D. 1952. The Prenatal Origin of Behavior. 18th Porter Lecture Series. University of Kansas Press. Lawrence, Kans.
6. HUMPHREY, T. 1953. The relation of oxygen deprivation to fetal reflex arcs and the development of fetal behavior. J. Psychol. **35:** 3–43.
7. PATRICK, J., K. CAMPBELL, L. CARMICHAEL, R. NATALE & B. RICHARDSON. 1982. Patterns of gross fetal body movements over 24-hour observation intervals during the last 10 weeks of pregnancy. Am. J. Obstet. Gynecol. **142:** 363–371.
8. ROBERTSON, S. S. 1985. Cyclic motor activity in the human fetus after midgestation. Dev. Psychobiol. **18:** 411–419.
9. BIRNHOLZ, J. C. 1988. On observing the human fetus. *In* Behavior of the Fetus. W. P. Smotherman & S. R. Robinson, Eds.: 47–60. Telford Press. Caldwell, N.J.
10. DEVRIES, J. I. P., G. H. A. VISSER & H. F. R. PRECHTL. 1982. The emergence of fetal behavior. I. Qualitative aspects. Early Hum. Dev. **7:** 301–322.
11. DEVRIES, J. I. P., G. H. A. VISSER & H. F. R. PRECHTL. 1985. The emergence of fetal behavior. II. Quantitative aspects. Early Hum. Dev. **12:** 99–120.
12. SMOTHERMAN, W. P. & S. R. ROBINSON. 1991. Accessibility of the rat fetus for psychobiological investigation. *In* Developmental Psychobiology: New Methods and Changing Concepts. H. Shair, G. A. Barr & M. A. Hofer, Eds.: 148–166. Oxford University Press. New York, N.Y.
13. SMOTHERMAN, W. P. & S. R. ROBINSON. 1986. Environmental determinants of behaviour in the rat fetus. Anim. Behav. **34:** 1859–1873.
14. ROBINSON, S. R. & W. P. SMOTHERMAN. 1988. Chance and chunks in the ontogeny of fetal behavior. *In* Behavior of the Fetus. W. P. Smotherman & S. R. Robinson, Eds.: 95–115. Telford Press. Caldwell, N.J.
15. SMOTHERMAN, W. P. & S. R. ROBINSON. 1987. Prenatal expression of species-typical action patterns in the rat fetus (*Rattus norvegicus*). J. Comp. Psychol. **101:** 190–196.
16. SMOTHERMAN, W. P. & S. R. ROBINSON. 1989. Cryptopsychobiology: the appearance, disappearance and reappearance of a species-typical action pattern during early development. Behav. Neurosci. **103:** 153–160.
17. SMOTHERMAN, W. P. & S. R. ROBINSON. 1985. The rat fetus in its environment: behavioral adjustments to novel, familiar, aversive and conditioned stimuli presented in utero. Behav. Neurosci. **99:** 521–530.
18. SMOTHERMAN, W. P. & S. R. ROBINSON. 1987. Psychobiology of fetal experience in the rat. *In* Perinatal Development: a Psychobiological Perspective. N. A. Krasnegor, E. M. Blass, M. A. Hofer & W. P. Smotherman, Eds.: 39–60. Academic Press. Orlando, Fla.
19. ANGULO Y GONZALEZ, A. W. 1932. The prenatal development of behavior in the albino rat. J. Comp. Neurol. **55:** 395–442.

20. NARAYANAN, C. H., M. W. FOX & V. HAMBURGER. 1971. Prenatal development of spontaneous and evoked activity in the rat. Behavior 40: 100–134.
21. BROWN, T. G. 1915. On the activities of the central nervous system of the unborn foetus of the cat; with a discussion of the question whether progression (walking, etc.) is a "learnt" complex. J. Physiol. Lond. 49: 208–215.
21. PREYER, W. 1885. Specielle Physiologie des Embryo. Untersuchungen uber die Lebenserscheinungen vor der Geburt. Grieben. Leipzig, Germany.
23. HAMBURGER, V. 1973. Anatomical and physiological basis of embryonic motility in birds and mammals. In Behavioral Embryology. G. Gottlieb, Ed.: 51–76. Academic Press. New York, N.Y.
24. OPPENHEIM, R. W. 1982. The neuroembryological study of behavior: progress, problems, perspectives. In Current Topics in Developmental Biology. Neural Development. R. K. Hunt, Ed. 17(Part 3): 257–309. Academic Press. New York, N.Y.
25. PROVINE, R. R. 1986. Behavioral neuroembryology: motor perspectives. In Developmental NeuroPsychobiology. W. T. Greenough & J. M. Juraska, Eds.: 213–239. Academic Press. New York, N.Y.
26. HAMBURGER, V., E. WENGER & R. W. OPPENHEIM. 1966. Motility in the chick embryo in the absence of sensory input. J. Exp. Zool. 162: 133–160.
27. RIPLEY, K. L. & R. R. PROVINE. 1972. Neural correlates of embryonic motility in the chick. Brain Res. 45: 127–134.
28. SMOTHERMAN, W. P. & S. R. ROBINSON. 1988. Behavior of rat fetuses following chemical or tactile stimulation. Behav. Neurosci. 102: 24–34.
29. SMOTHERMAN, W. P. & S. R. ROBINSON. 1992. Kappa opioid mediation of fetal responses to milk. Behav. Neurosci. 106: 396–407.
30. MOODY, C. A., L. P. SPEAR, S. R. ROBINSON & W. P. SMOTHERMAN. 1991. Behavioral responses to D1 and D2 receptor manipulation in fetal rat pups. Int. Soc. Dev. Psychobiol. (New Orleans, La.)
31. PRECHTL, H. F. R. 1985. Ultrasound studies of human fetal behaviour. Early Hum. Dev. 12: 91–98.
32. THOMAN, E. B. 1990. Sleeping and waking state in infants: a functional perspective. Neurosci. Biobehav. Rev. 14: 93–107.
33. OYAMA, S. 1985. The Ontogeny of Information. Cambridge University Press. Cambridge, England.
34. SCHONER, G. & J. A. S. KELSO. 1988. Dynamic pattern generation in behavioral and neural systems. Science 239: 1513–1520.
35. THELEN, E. 1989. Self-organization in developmental processes: can systems approaches work? Neb. Symp. Child Dev. 24: 77–117.
36. ROBINSON, S.R. 1989. A comparative study of prenatal behavioral ontogeny in altricial and precocial murid rodents. Doctoral dissertation. Oregon State University.
37. ROBINSON, S. R. & W. P. SMOTHERMAN. Behavioral response of altricial and precocial rodent fetuses to acute umbilical cord compression. Behav. Neural Biol. (In press.)
38. ROBINSON, S. R. & W. P. SMOTHERMAN. 1991. The amniotic sac as scaffolding: prenatal ontogeny of an action pattern. Dev. Psychobiol. 24: 463–485.
39. ROBERTSON, S. S. 1988. Mechanism and function of cyclicity in spontaneous movement. In Behavior of the Fetus. W. P. Smotherman & S. R. Robinson, Eds.: 77–94. Telford Press. Caldwell, N.J.
40. ROBINSON, S. R. & W. P. SMOTHERMAN. 1987. Environmental determinants of behaviour in the rat fetus. II. The emergence of synchronous movement. Anim. Behav. 35: 1652–1662.

41. SMOTHERMAN, W. P., S. R. ROBINSON & S. S. ROBERTSON. 1988. Cyclic motor activity in the fetal rat (*Rattus norvegicus*). J. Comp. Psychol. **102**: 78–82.
42. BRUNJES, P. C. 1990. The precocial mouse, *Acomys cahirinus*. Psychobiology **18**: 339–350.
43. ROBINSON, S. R. & W. P. SMOTHERMAN. Motor competition in the prenatal ontogeny of species-typical behavior. Anim. Behav. (In press.)
44. FAGEN, R. M. & D. Y. YOUNG. 1978. Temporal patterns of behaviors: durations, intervals, latencies and sequences. *In* Quantitative Ethology. P. W. Colgan, Ed.: 79–114. John Wiley & Sons. New York, N.Y.
45. CORNER, M. A. 1977. Sleep and the beginnings of behavior in the animal kingdom — studies of ultradian motility cycles in early life. Prog. Neurobiol. **8**: 278–295.
46. ROBERTSON, S. S. 1987. Human cyclic motility: fetal-newborn continuities and newborn state differences. Dev. Psychobiol. **20**: 425–442.
47. ROBERTSON, S. S. & W. P. SMOTHERMAN. 1990. The neural control of cyclic activity in the fetal rat. Physiol. Behav. **47**: 121–126.
48. ASHBY, W. R. 1956. An Introduction to Cybernetics. Chapman & Hall, Ltd. London, England.
49. HAILMAN, J. P. 1982. Ontogeny: toward a general theoretical framework for ethology. *In* Perspectives in Ethology. Ontogeny. P. P. G. Bateson & P. H. Klopfer, Eds. **5**: 133–189. Plenum. New York, N.Y.
50. BAKEMAN, R. & J. M. GOTTMAN. 1986. Observing Interaction: an Introduction to Sequential Analysis. Cambridge University Press. Cambridge, England.
51. DeGHETT, V. J. 1978. Hierarchical cluster analysis. *In* Quantitative Ethology. P. W. Colgan, Ed.: 115–144. John Wiley & Sons. New York, N.Y.
52. WOLFF, P. H. 1966. The causes, controls and organization of behaviour in the neonate. Psychol. Issues Monogr. **5**(17).
53. PRECHTL, H. F. R. 1974. The behavioral states of the newborn infant (a review). Brain Res. **76**: 185–212.
54. PRECHTL, H. F. R. 1984. Continuity and change in early neural development. Clin. Dev. Med. No. 94: 1–15.
55. DREYFUS-BRISAC, C. 1970. Ontogenesis of sleep in human prematures after 32 weeks of conceptional age. Dev. Psychobiol. **3**: 91–121.
56. TIMOR-TRITSCH, I. E., L. J. DIERKER, R. H. HERTZ, C. DEAGAN & M. G. ROSEN. 1978. Studies of antepartum behavioral states in the human fetus at term. Am. J. Obstet. Gynecol. **132**: 524–528.
57. NIJHUIS, J. G., H. F. R. PRECHTL, C. B. MARTIN, JR. & R. S. G. M. BOTS. 1982. Are there behavioural states in the human fetus? Early Hum. Dev. **6**: 177–195.
58. CURZI-DASCALOVA, L., P. PEIRANO & F. MOREL-KAHN. 1988. Development of sleep states in normal premature and full-term newborns. Dev. Psychobiol. **21**: 431–444.
59. DAVIS, D. H. & E. B. THOMAN. 1987. Behavioral states of premature infants: implications for neural and behavioral development. Dev. Psychobiol. **20**: 25–38.
60. FIELD, T. M. 1990. Neonatal stress and coping in intensive care. Infant Ment. Health J. **11**: 57–65.
61. NATHANIELSZ, P. W., A. BAILEY, E. R. POORE, G. D. THORBURN & R. HARDING. 1980. The relationship between myometrial activity and sleep state and breathing in fetal sheep throughout the last third of gestation. Am. J. Obstet. Gynecol. **138**: 653–659.
62. BARCROFT, J. & D. H. BARRON. 1939. The development of behavior in foetal sheep. J. Comp. Neurol. **70**: 477–502.
63. NATALE, R., F. CLEWLOW & G. S. DAWES. 1981. Measurement of fetal forelimb movements in the lamb in utero. Am. J. Obstet. Gynecol. **140**: 545–551.

64. MARTEL, J., G. POORE, D. W. SADOWSKY, T. CABALUM & P. W. NATHANIELSZ. 1990. Pulsatile oxytocin (OT) administered to ewes at 120 to 135 days gestational age (dGA) increases rate of synchronization and maturation of fetal biparietal electrocorticogram (FECoG) into distinct high voltage (HV) and low voltage (LV) epochs. Soc. Gynecol. Invest. 154.

65. RICHMOND, G. & B. D. SACHS. 1980. Grooming in Norway rats: the development and adult expression of a complex motor pattern. Behavior 75: 82–96.

66. GOLANI, I. & J. C. FENTRESS. 1985. Early ontogeny of face grooming in mice. Dev. Psychobiol. 18: 529–544.

67. JOHANSON, I. B. & E. G. SHAPIRO. 1986. Intake and behavioral responsiveness to taste stimuli in infant rats from 1 to 15 days of age. Dev. Psychobiol. 19: 593–606.

68. BARLOW, G. W. 1977. Modal action patterns. In How Animals Communicate. T. A. Sebeok, Ed.: 98–134. Indiana University Press. Bloomington, Ind.

69. GRILLNER, S. 1985. Neurobiological bases of rhythmic motor acts in vertebrates. Science 228: 143–149.

70. DREWETT, R. F., C. STATHAM & J. B. WAKERLEY. 1974. A quantitative analysis of the feeding behaviour of suckling rats. Anim. Behav. 22: 907–913.

71. HALL, W. G. & J. S. ROSENBLATT. 1977. Suckling behavior and intake control in the developing rat pup. J. Comp. Physiol. Psychol. 91: 1232–1247.

72. ROBINSON, S. R. & W. P. SMOTHERMAN. 1992. Organization of the stretch response to milk in the rat fetus. Dev. Psychobiol. 25: 33–49.

73. GRILL, H. J. & R. NORGREN. 1978. The taste reactivity test. I. Mimetic responses to gustatory stimuli in neurologically normal rats. Brain Res. 143: 263–279.

74. SHAIR, H. N., S. C. BRAKE & M. A. HOFER. 1984. Suckling in the rat: evidence for patterned behavior during sleep. Behav. Neurosci. 98: 366–370.

75. BLASS, E. M. & E. FITZGERALD. 1988. Milk-induced analgesia and comforting in 10-day-old rats: opioid mediation. Pharmacol. Biochem. Behav. 29: 9–13.

76. BLASS, E. M., A. M. JACKSON & W. P. SMOTHERMAN. 1991. Milk-induced opioid-mediated antinociception in rats at the time of cesarean delivery. Behav. Neurosci. 105: 677–686.

77. SMOTHERMAN, W. P. & S. R. ROBINSON. 1990. Olfactory bulb transection alters fetal behavior after chemosensory but not tactile stimulation. Dev. Brain Res. 57: 175–180.

78. SMOTHERMAN, W. P. & S. R. ROBINSON. Opioid control of the fetal stretch response: implications for the first suckling episode. Behav. Neurosci. (In press.)

79. SMOTHERMAN, W. P. & S. R. ROBINSON. Prenatal experience with milk: fetal behavior and the kappa opioid system. Neurosci. Biobehav. Rev. (In press.)

80. SMOTHERMAN, W. P. & S. R. ROBINSON. 1992. Fetal heart rate response to milk predicts expression of the stretch response. Physiol. Behav. 51: 833–837.

81. SHAIR, H. N., S. C. BRAKE, M. A. HOFER & M. M. MYERS. 1986. Blood pressure responses to milk ejection in the young rat. Physiol. Behav. 37: 171–176.

82. THELEN, E., J. A. S. KELSO & A. FOGEL. 1987. Self-organizing systems and infant motor development. Dev. Rev. 7: 39–65.

83. FIFER, W. P. & C. MOON. 1988. Auditory experience in the fetus. In Behavior of the Fetus. W. P. Smotherman & S. R. Robinson, Eds.: 175–190. Telford Press. Caldwell, N.J.

84. SMOTHERMAN, W. P. & S. R. ROBINSON. 1988. The uterus as environment: the ecology of fetal experience. In Handbook of Behavioral Neurobiology. Developmental Psychobiology and Behavioral Ecology. E. M. Blass, Ed. 9: 149–196. Plenum. New York, N.Y.

Behavioral and Cardiovascular Traits

Broken Links and New Associations

MICHAEL M. MYERS

Department of Psychiatry
Columbia College of Physicians and Surgeons
and
New York State Psychiatric Institute
722 West 168th Street
New York, New York 10032

INTRODUCTION

The focus of this chapter is to review results from studies that were designed to address the general issue of how to view the nature of associations between physiologic and behavioral traits. I will concentrate on experiments that have addressed the specific issue of relationships between behavior and cardiovascular function, with a special emphasis on the development of hypertension. Although the review will be selective and egocentric, I believe the principles and questions that emerge from the discussion of these studies will stimulate interest in the important problem of how to probe and describe phenomena that are inherently products of interactions between biological and psychological processes.

The topics I will discuss are divided into two broad areas. First, I will describe several genetic co-segregation studies that highlight the importance of questioning and testing presuppositions about how traits might be linked. Myron Hofer has, in an all too rare unveiling of the true process of scientific investigations, expressed the embarrassment that was prompted by a review of his early ideas and assumptions about the effects of mother/infant interactions.[1] I too will divulge errors of simplistic thinking, but I hope to convince the reader that this is a flaw only to the extent that these ideas remain untested. The studies in the second area focus on a different view of how behavioral traits of organisms come to be associated with certain characteristics of adult cardiovascular function. These studies demonstrate that although associations between behavioral and cardiovascular traits may not be of the type I had originally envisioned, there are other types of relationships that deserve further examination.

Two homozygous strains of rats have been used in nearly all of the studies I will review. One of these, spontaneously hypertensive rats (SHR), was derived by selectively mating animals with high systolic blood pressures.[2] SHR have now been inbred for well over 50 generations.[3] The second strain, Wistar Kyoto (WKY) rats, is a normotensive strain which was the progenitor strain for SHR. Although inbreeding within this strain started at a later date than the SHR, WKY have also been inbred for a sufficient number of generations to be considered genetically homozygous.[3]

TESTS FOR GENETIC LINKAGE

Behavioral Activity and Cardiovascular Function

The first area in which I studied the nature of relationships between cardiovascular function and behavior was with regard to potential associations between blood pressure and motoric activity. The origins of this work, which was conducted in Dr. Edith Hendley's laboratory at the University of Vermont, stemmed from the notion held by many researchers using SHR and WKY that differences between these strains were not limited to peripheral cardiovascular mechanisms, but also included differences in central nervous system neurotransmitter function. Our simple idea was that this hypothesis would be supported if there were strain differences in behavior. We used the open field test for determining if there were measurable differences between SHR and WKY rats with regard to their patterns of behavior. In this test, animals are placed into a large open box whose floor is demarcated into smaller squares with white lines. The data of interest are the number of square entries. A square is counted when all four paws of the animal are within a square. In addition, as animals normally tend to stay close to the walls of the field, the number of "center-square" entries are also counted. In our initial tests we found that there were indeed marked strain differences in behavior, with SHR exhibiting both a greater total number of square entries and a greater number of center-square entries.[4] In a later study, we replicated these observations and expanded the findings to include longer tests.[5] In this study we also showed that SHR activity was somewhat reduced by the administration of amphetamine. During this period of time, other investigators had documented independently the increased activity of SHR as well as a number of other behavioral differences.[6] These studies clearly suggested that, in addition to there being important differences in blood pressure between these strains, there were also fundamental differences in central nervous system function.

An intuitive question to emerge from these studies was to ask if there was a linkage between the blood pressure and behavioral traits that distinguished SHR from WKY. Asking this question was made more intriguing by the nature of these potentially linked traits. McCarty, Chiueh, and Kopin had showed that when SHR were stressed, they exhibited exaggerated sympathetic responses.[7] Witnessing the behavior of SHR, especially in direct comparison to the hypoactive WKY, led me to think that the "hyperactivity" of the SHR was a behavioral manifestation of the autonomic imbalances that were considered by many to be at the root of hypertension in these animals. This idea also seemed to fit generally with the contention that there are important associations between cardiovascular disease and behavioral traits in humans.[8] One obvious way to explain these associations was to propose that there was a common genetic basis for the co-occurrence of increased behavioral activity and hypertension.

Fortunately, there is a relatively simple way to test, at least in a preliminary way, for evidence of genetic linkage. This technique is called co-segregation analysis.[9] In essence, the paradigm involves taking males and females from two inbred strains and conducting breedings that will "reshuffle" the genes from the two strains. In our studies we have used segregating, F_2, populations derived from crossing SHR males with WKY females to produce F_1 offspring and then randomly mating F_1 males and females to produce F_2. If the genes responsible for two different traits are the same or closely linked, we would expect that in the F_2 population these traits would be highly correlated. That is, if some animals inherit predominantly SHR genes, then they should be both hypertensive and very active in the open field and, conversely, F_2 with genes mostly from their WKY grandparents would exhibit low behavioral activity and low blood pressure. The results from such an experiment were surprisingly clear, but not what I had expected.[10] As shown in FIGURE 1, there was no hint of a positive correlation between activity and blood pressure in F_2. Indeed, Hendley and her colleagues have since used a program of selective breeding to produce strains of rats derived from SHR and WKY that have high adult blood pressure and either high or low behavioral activity, as well as animals with low blood pressure with either high or low activity.[11] I will return to a discussion of these important animals in a subsequent section.

Salt Appetite and Blood Pressure

Some years following the study that had indicated that behavioral activity and hypertension could be dissociated, Dr. Brandon Yongue joined our department and he was interested in studying relationships between blood pressure regulation and mineral balance. In particular, he wanted to investigate the issue of whether there were common mechanisms for the determination of strain differences in blood pressure and salt appetite. Again, the SHR and WKY strains seemed appropriate models to approach this question. As was the case for strain differences in behavioral activity, there had been a number of studies showing that SHR had considerably greater need-free appetite for salt,[12,13] and that this enhanced appetite for salt was evident very early in life.[14] As SHR had also been shown to be salt sensitive, that is, have greater increases in blood pressure in response to high amounts of dietary salt,[15] their enhanced appetite would appear to be quite maladaptive. Perhaps it

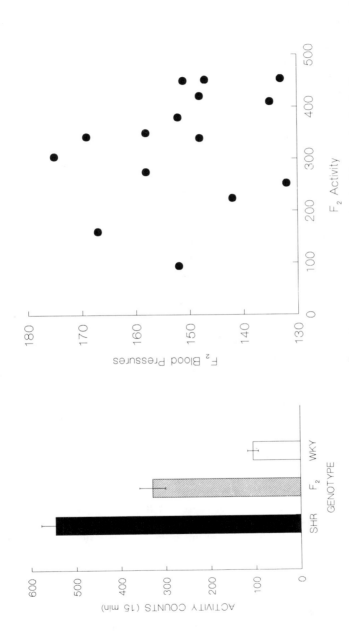

FIGURE 1. The panel on the left shows mean [± standard error (SE)] activity counts from an automated activity test chamber for three groups of male rats: SHR, F_2, and WKY. On the right is a scatter plot of adult blood pressure versus activity in 15 F_2. Note the lack of significant correlation between activity and blood pressure ($r = -0.28$). Graphs are adaptations of data reported in Hendley, Atwater, Myers, and Whitehorn, 1983.[10]

could be no other way. Maybe the same genes that account for SHR having high blood pressure also influence mechanisms that regulate salt appetite.

As in the previous studies, the means of testing the possible genetic linkage between a behavioral trait, salt appetite, and high blood pressure was to conduct co-segregation analyses. The two studies we performed provided results that were very easy to interpret. There was absolutely no evidence that the traits of high blood pressure and high salt appetite, measured in a number of different ways, are genetically linked (see FIGURE 2).[16,17] Once again, results from a co-segregation study using F_2 rats had forced us to reconsider the nature of relationships between behavioral traits and cardiovascular function. It is important to note that the absence of correlation between salt appetite and blood pressure does not mean there are no issues to be addressed in this area. It is clear that high dietary salt can be detrimental to individuals who are salt sensitive and continued investigation of mechanisms that regulate salt sensitivity and salt appetite is critical. Indeed, the F_2 model, in which salt appetite and blood pressure appear genetically unrelated, affords a valuable model for studying genetically independent but functionally overlapping central nervous system (CNS) controls of these traits.

Cardiovascular Reactivity and Hypertension

The preceding sections summarized two attempts to determine if there was evidence for genetic linkage between adult hypertension and two behavioral traits. Unfortunately, in each case there was a failure to confirm any such linkage. However, the choice of traits investigated was intuitive and the evidence suggesting these behavioral traits should be linked to hypertension was circumstantial. On the other hand, another trait, cardiovascular reactivity, had not only been long associated with hypertension but there were also compelling theories to explain why there should be a linkage between levels of blood pressure and reactivity.[18] However, recent data collected using the strains of animals derived from SHR and WKY by Edith Hendley[11] suggest that this association also needs to be scrutinized very carefully. In one of these studies, the plasma catecholamine responses of the four strains were measured.[19] Recall that these strains represent four combinations of traits: high blood pressure–high activity; low blood pressure–high activity; high blood pressure–low activity; low blood pressure–low activity. The important observation made by these investigators was that, contrary to what might be expected, exaggerated catecholamine responses to stress appeared to be more strongly associated with the characteristic of high activity rather than high blood pressure (see FIGURE 3, panel A). In another study, detailed measurements of blood pressure, heart rate, and vascular resistance in response to air-jet stress again indicated that reactivity to stress is not genetically linked to hypertension in the SHR model; rather, most measures of increased cardiovascular reactivity were found to be more closely linked to heightened be-

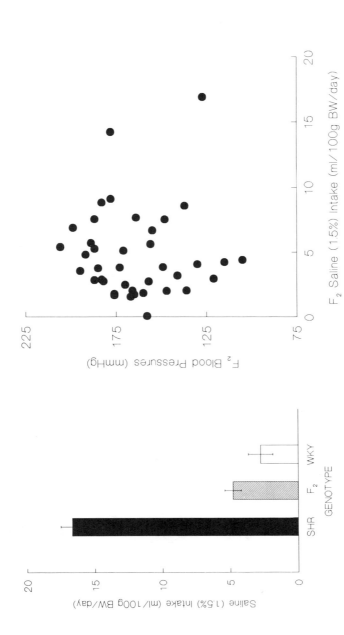

FIGURE 2. The panel on the left shows mean (± SE) saline intake measured over three consecutive days for three groups of male rats: SHR, F$_2$, and WKY. On the right is a scatter plot of adult blood pressure versus saline intake in 39 F$_2$. Note the lack of significant correlation between saline intake and blood pressure ($r = -0.05$). Graphs are adaptations of data reported in Yongue and Myers, 1988.[16]

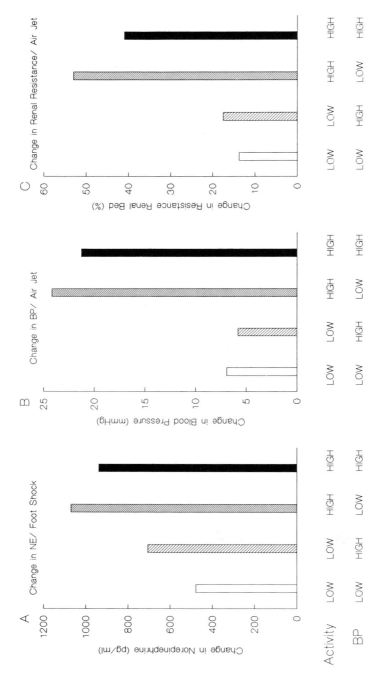

FIGURE 3. In **panel A** are bar graphs of mean changes in plasma norepinephrine concentrations (NE) in response to foot shock. The four groups of animals were derived from SHR and WKY breeding stock and represent four phenotypes: low activity-low blood pressure; low activity-high blood pressure; high activity-low blood pressure; high activity-high blood pressure. Data were adapted from Hendley, Cierpial, and McCarty, 1988.[19] Note that the two groups with the greatest NE responses are those with high activity, not high blood pressure. **Panels B** and **C** are similar presentations except the measures taken are changes in blood pressure and renal resistance in response to the first minute of air-jet stress. These plots are adaptations of data reported in Knardahl and Hendley, 1990.[20]

havioral activity.[20] Representative results from this study have been re-plotted and are shown in panels B and C of FIGURE 3.

TRAIT RELATIONSHIPS: ANOTHER APPROACH

In the previous sections, I discussed how co-segregation and selective breeding studies were used to disassociate certain behavioral and cardiovascular traits. These experiments showed that the co-occurrence of distinct physiologic and behavioral phenotypes in inbred strains cannot be taken as evidence for genetic linkage between these traits. However, these genetic analyses do not provide information about other types of relationships between traits. In this section I will review several experiments that investigated relationships between behavioral and cardiovascular traits from a different perspective. In these studies the emphasis was on the interplay between genetic and behavioral mechanisms acting on developmental processes. In particular, I will address the issue of how variations in naturally occurring maternal activities might influence blood pressures of offspring much later in life.

Relationships between Adult Blood Pressure and Mother/Infant Behavioral Interactions

Our investigations of possible early life correlates of adult blood pressure began by characterizing the preweaning environments to which rat pups are exposed. At this time, there were a few studies that suggested that the early environment might influence the expression of adult blood pressure. In one of these, Tang and Gandelman reported that daily handling of pups during the preweaning period resulted in decreased adult blood pressure of SHR.[21] Using a different strategy, McMurtry, Wright, and Wexler had reported that Sprague-Dawley pups that were cross fostered to SHR dams had increased systolic blood pressures from 35 to 90 days of age, and that blood pressures of SHR were different when they were reared by either Sprague-Dawley or WKY foster mothers than when reared by SHR mothers.[22] Following these investigations, a number of researchers provided convincing data that, in contrast to McMurtry, Wright, and Wexler findings, SHR adult blood pressures were lower if these animals were reared by normotensive mothers.[23-26] From these studies we drew the general conclusion that characteristics of the preweaning environment can play an important role in shaping adult blood pressure. However, it was not apparent exactly what factors were mediating these effects of cross fostering.

A study of maternal behavior by Cierpial, Shasby, and McCarty provided important clues as to what mothers might be doing to influence the adult blood pressure of their offspring.[27] These investigators reported that there were significant differences in key behavioral interactions between SHR mothers and their young as compared to WKY. Specifically, SHR mothers spent more time in contact with their offspring, groomed them more, and were seen nursing more often. We too conducted a study in which daily observations of naturally occurring activities in the maternal nest environment of SHR and WKY litters were made.[28] Using principal component analyses, we found that maternal behavior of SHR and WKY dams was qualitatively similar; however, there were a number of highly significant quantitative differences between these strains. The most pronounced of these differences were that SHR mothers were seen in certain nursing postures more often, they licked and groomed their pups more often than did WKY dams, and SHR mothers were seen in contact with their young more often. These results were strikingly similar to those reported by Cierpial, Shasby, and McCarty[27] and provided additional impetus to investigate mother/infant behavioral interactions as environmental mediators of blood pressure development.

Another important finding in our study of SHR and WKY maternal behavior was that, within strains, the behavior of individual mothers differed significantly from each other on nearly all variables measured. Our interpretation of this finding was that pups from different litters, as well as those from different strains, must be exposed to differences in early life experiences that are embedded in maternal/young interactions. These individual differences in maternal care patterns suggested a strategy we used in the second part of our study. Our goal was to attempt to identify what specific behavioral interactions would most likely influence adult blood pressure of the offspring.

The approach we used to extend the observations of strain differences in maternal behavior involved determining if there were significant correlations between the mother/infant interaction variables and adult blood pressures of the offspring. We found that within each strain, a combination of three variables — arched nursing, pup licking, and mother-in-contact-with-pups — was positively correlated with adult blood pressures of the offspring measured at four months of age.[28] From these correlations we concluded that a significant portion of the variation among individuals in adult pressure was attributable to variation in naturally occurring experiences of early life. Furthermore, because SHR dams engage in more of those activities that are positively correlated with adult blood pressure of the offspring, it seems likely, as was indicated by the cross-fostering studies mentioned previously, that they make an environmental contribution to the severity of hypertension in their pups.

Effects of Pup Phenotype on Strain Differences in Maternal Behavior

As discussed previously, we found there were significant differences in maternal behavior between SHR and WKY dams. But, we also noted significant differences in the behavior of the pups from these two strains. SHR pups were consistently more active, both while mothers were in contact with the litters and while they were away.[28] In a follow-up fostering study, we obtained results that suggest that the strain differences in maternal behavior might actually be stimulated by differences in the characteristics of the pups. In this experiment, we produced populations of pups of uniform genetic background (i.e., F_1 offspring from SHR male $\times$ WKY female breedings), fostered these pups to SHR and WKY lactating females, and then repeated our observation procedures. We found that all of the strain differences in maternal behavior observed in the first study were eliminated when SHR and WKY dams were caring for pups of the same genetic background.[29] Moreover, unlike studies by other workers in which SHR and WKY pups were cross fostered, in this experiment, where there were no strain differences in maternal behavior, there was also no effect of the strain of the mother on adult blood pressures of the F_1 offspring.

Together, these results suggest that effects of cross fostering on adult blood pressure, as well as effects of naturally occurring, within-strain differences in maternal behavior, may be dependent upon the behavioral phenotype of pups influencing maternal care patterns. This conclusion is supported by a study conducted by Cierpial, Murphy, and McCarty[30] in which it was found that strain differences (SHR vs. WKY) in maternal behavior (e.g., nursing) were reversed when mothers reared pups of the opposite strain. Although results from these two studies are not in complete agreement, the conclusion that the characteristics of the pups being reared is critically involved in determining maternal behavior phenotype is solidly supported in each study.

Blood Pressure Responses of Infant Rats to Feeding

Although our studies that indicated that adult blood pressure was correlated with certain maternal behaviors involved a composite of three types of mother/infant interactions, we have been particularly interested in one of these variables, the arched nursing posture. We have recently summarized results obtained from several genetically diverse groups of animals with regard to the correlation between adult blood pressure and this single maternal behavior variable. In these retrospective analyses involving data from 42 litters, we found that there was a highly significant positive correlation ($r = 0.50$, $p < 0.001$) between the number of times mothers were seen in the arched nursing posture and adult blood pressure of their offspring.[31] This observation is made most interesting because we know that rat mothers release milk intermittently and that during periods of milk ejection they assume the arched nursing posture.[32] These findings stimulated our interest in investigating relationships between feeding and cardiovascular function.

A few years ago we made an observation concerning blood pressure and feeding that we believe is relevant to the findings just described. In this work, we found that freely behaving rat pups exhibit a dramatic surge in blood pres-

sure each time they receive milk from their mothers.[33] The magnitude of
blood pressure increases in two-week-old pups ranged from 10 to 50% depending on the conditions of the experiment. These are larger changes in
blood pressure than those associated with virtually all other naturally occurring pup activities. We also found that active behavioral interaction between
mother and pups is not necessary for eliciting blood pressure increases
during feeding since these responses could be elicited from pups receiving
milk from anesthetized dams. Following our report of blood pressure increases to feeding in outbred Wistar rats, we conducted additional studies
which have demonstrated that these blood pressure responses to feeding are
larger in SHR pups than in WKY[34] and have shown that the responses depend on intact sympathetic nervous system activity.[35] These immediate
changes in blood pressure are apparently a component of the "preadaptive"
responses to nutrient intake which include rapid increases in insulin, glucose, plasma norepinephrine, and heat production.[36,37]

There is a very interesting point to be made about blood pressure responses to feeding in infancy. These responses have been observed in the

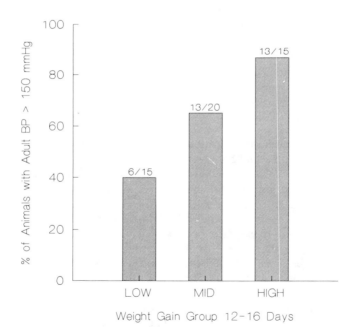

FIGURE 4. These bar graphs show the percentage of male F_2 rats with adult blood pressure greater
than 150 mmHg as a function of rates of body weight gain from 12 to 16 days of age. The range of
weight gain for each group was LOW = 1.1–1.5; MID = 1.6–2.3; and HIGH = 2.3–2.8 g/day. These
percentages were extracted from the data of a study population that was reported in Myers, Shair,
and Hofer, 1992.[31]

young of many species including lambs,[38] calves and kids,[39] and piglets (F. M. Scalzo, personal communication). Importantly, results from a case report[40] and our own recent work[41] demonstrate that pronounced blood pressure responses to feeding also occur in human infants. Our results showed that while heart rate appears to respond to sucking, blood pressure increases are more specifically linked to delivery of nutrient. In some infants these responses can be quite dramatic, with increases in systolic blood pressure reaching 30 mmHg above resting levels. Thus, we now know that repetitive activation of blood pressure responses occurs not only in a variety of research animals, but also in human infants.

Taken together, the studies presented thus far offer a fascinating sequence of findings. We have learned that offspring of dams that were seen more often in the nursing posture most closely associated with milk delivery had increased blood pressures as adults. This was true regardless of whether the offspring were SHR, WKY, or F_1 pups. We also have learned that each time mothers assume the arched nursing posture and deliver milk, blood pressures of the nursing pups rise dramatically, and that these sympathetic-mediated increases in blood pressure are much larger in SHR pups than in WKY. Our work also demonstrates that these strain differences are not dependent upon unique qualities of SHR mothers' milk or behavior. From these results we suggest there are fundamental linkages between feeding in infancy and the course of blood pressure development. The remaining sections summarize some recent work that supports this contention.

Correlations between Weight Gain in Infancy and Adult Blood Pressure of F_2 Rats

As discussed in previous sections, we have conducted a number of studies using F_2 rats in which the goal was to find correlates of adult hypertension. Although most of the measurements we made turned out not to be reliable markers, other results from these studies indicate that the rate of weight gain in infancy is a surprisingly good predictor of adult blood pressure. In two separate experiments, we found that there was a strong positive correlation between adult blood pressure of male F_2 rats and the rate at which they gained weight in infancy.[31] What made this finding even more interesting was the fact that this relationship between early life weight gain and adult blood pressure was restricted to rates of weight gain from around 10 to 16 days of life. Weight gain prior to and after this period was not correlated with adult blood pressure. One way of presenting this relationship is shown in FIGURE 4. This figure summarizes data from 50 male F_2 rats which had body weight measurements made at 12 and 16 days of age and blood pressures taken at 20 weeks of age. The animals were divided into three groups based on their rates of weight gain. The figure shows that while animals with relatively slow rates of weight gain had an incidence of adult blood pressure over 150 mmHg of 40%, 87% of animals in the high-weight-gain group had pressures greater than 150 ($p < 0.025$).

We had not entirely anticipated this result, but our previous studies suggested the outcome of this experiment. High levels of nursing behavior in SHR and WKY dams were associated with higher adult blood pressures of the offspring. Results from our weight-gain experiments appeared to be consistent with this observation. F_2 pups that gained weight rapidly were more likely to have high blood pressures as adults. This finding raises an interesting question. Is the relationship between early weight gain and adult blood pressure attributable to the co-segregation of genetically determined traits, or is this an environmental effect? That is, are there genes that influence rates of growth early in life and do these same genes, or ones closely linked, also determine levels of adult blood pressure? Or, do behavioral interactions between mothers and their young lead to different feeding patterns which in turn modify development of the cardiovascular system? The data collected thus far do not allow an unequivocal dissociation of these two possibilities but, as we have discussed elsewhere, further analysis of these two experiments, in which the data were partitioned into within and between litter effects, more strongly supports the environmental mediation alternative.[31] Additional studies using homozygous strains will be required to resolve this issue, but we felt our results were sufficiently indicative of an environmental effect to warrant a preliminary test of this hypothesis.

Effects of Litter Size on Adult Blood Pressure

The previous studies indicated that naturally occurring differences in body weight gain during a specific period of early development are positively correlated with levels of adult blood pressure. The strong dependence of this relationship on differences between litters suggested that the effect was due to environmental factors influencing infant weight gain which, in turn, are linked to alterations in cardiovascular system development. If this tentative conclusion is correct, we reasoned that manipulations of the early environment that modify weight gain should also alter adult blood pressure. To test this hypothesis we have performed an experiment in which weight gain of F_2 pups from 10 to 16 days of age was manipulated by altering litter size. Briefly, litters were culled to 4 males, 4 females on day 2 and left undisturbed until day 10. At that time, 2 males and 2 females from half of the litters were fostered to F_1 dams with 8 pups, thus forming litters of either 4 or 12 pups. At day 16, the fostered pups were returned to their natural mother, thereby reconstituting litters of 8. All animals were weaned on Day 21. Weight gain of these pups from 10 to 16 days was as predicted. Pups reared in the small litters gained nearly twice the weight of the 12/litter F_2 over the period of time in which litter size was altered. After being returned to their natural mothers, the F_2 that had been in litters of 12 exhibited considerable "catch-up growth" from 16–21 days but were still lighter than their 4/litter counter-parts at 21 days. The main purpose of this experiment was to determine if the litter-size manipulation would alter adult blood pressure. Male F_2 that had gained weight rapidly, due to being in small litters from 10–16 days, had significantly higher adult blood pressures than males in the slower growth, 12 pups/litter group (171 mmHg vs. 156 mmHg; $p < 0.025$). However, blood pressures of females from these two litter-size groups were not different.[31]

It is important to note that these effects of litter-size manipulation are con-sistent with observations made over 25 years ago. Widdowson and colleagues reported that rats reared in small litters (rapidly grown) had larger hearts and double the incidence of kidney lesions at the time of death when compared with animals from large litters.[42,43] However, this effect was specific to males. In light of our data, it is interesting to speculate that their rapidly grown males may have had more kidney disease and larger hearts due to a greater incidence of hypertension.

CONCLUSIONS

In this brief review I have summarized studies that represent two different strategies for investigating interactions between behavioral and cardiovas-cular traits. In the first section, the emphasis was on the potential genetic linkage of hypertension to activity, salt appetite, and responsiveness to envi-ronmental challenge. In each case, co-segregation analyses and selective breeding experiments lead to a rejection of the hypothesis of genetic linkage. It is worth noting again that these failures do not address other ways in which these traits might be functionally associated. Intuitively, it seems likely that if a genetic predisposition to consume large amounts of salt is overlaid on a genetic predisposition to be salt sensitive, this would lead to higher blood pressures if there were increased free-choice access to dietary salt. However, it is important to point out that to my knowledge, the validity of this assump-tion has never been tested. Hopefully, the results from the studies of the first section in this chapter convince the reader that intuitive hypotheses like this must be thoroughly investigated.

The studies summarized in the second part of this review investigated a different type of association between behavioral traits and cardiovascular function. The results of this work clearly demonstrate that adult blood pres-sure is a phenotype that is a product of important interactions between ge-netic characteristics and influences of the early environment. There is no doubt that genetic factors can influence adult blood pressure, maternal be-havior, and pup activity. But, significant differences between litters within homozygous strains with regard to mother/infant behavioral interactions and adult blood pressure tell us there must be important environmental modifiers of each of these variables. Results from cross-fostering studies, in combina-tion with our correlational studies, suggest that specific types of mother/

infant interactions shape offspring blood pressure. Moreover, the results from our study in which F_1 pups were reared by SHR and WKY foster dams indicate that certain, as yet unknown, characteristics of pups are likely to influence the very kinds of mother/infant interactions that can influence the course of blood pressure development. Our studies also offer strong support for the contention that feeding patterns during critical periods of early life play an important role in shaping cardiovascular system development and act, along with genetic characteristics, as a co-determinant of levels of adult blood pressure.

One of the fascinating questions raised by these studies is why the effects of weight gain are isolated to a narrow period of development. Slotkin and colleagues find an increased rate of sympathetic nervous system activity during this period and have suggested that these surges are instrumental for shaping development of target organs.[44,45] Recent results obtained by McCarty and colleagues, in which the effects of cross fostering on SHR adult blood pressure were shown to be confined to the first two weeks of life, clearly support the notion that it is during this period when environmental events can have a great impact on blood pressure development.[26] It is also interesting that recent studies reported by Kirby and Johnson showed that there is a dramatic increase in the responsiveness of plasma renin secretion to β_1 adrenergic stimulation in rat pups from 10 to 15 days of age.[46] This suggests a strategy of using selective pharmacologic blockers administered during specific periods of development as an approach to the identification of mechanisms that underlie early experience effects.

There is much work to be done with regard to characterizing the nature of relationships between physiologic and behavioral traits. It is particularly important for us to better understand how genetic and environmental factors act in concert to determine adult traits. This is not an easy task. Indeed, the goal of simply defining more specifically what is meant by gene/environment interaction often seems unattainable. However, I believe that the studies presented demonstrate some useful strategies for addressing these issues. There is no doubt that solving the puzzle of how complex systems are interrelated is a massive challenge. But, studies of relationships between the mother/infant environment and adult cardiovascular function are one area in which we can expect progress toward this goal.

REFERENCES

1. HOFER, M. A. 1982. Seeing is believing: a personal perspective on research strategy in developmental psychobiology. Dev. Psychobiol. **15:** 399–408.
2. OKAMOTO, K. & K. AOKI. 1963. Development of a strain of spontaneously hypertensive rats. Jpn. Circ. **27:** 282–293.
3. RAPP, J. P. 1983. Genetics of experimental and human hypertension. *In* Hypertension: Physiopathology and Treatment. J. Genenst, O. Kuchel, P. Hamet & M. Cantin, Eds.: 582–598. McGraw-Hill. New York, N.Y.

4. MYERS, M. M., D. McCROREY, C. A. BULMAN & E. D. HENDLEY. 1977. Open-field behavior and brain norepinephrine uptake in spontaneously hypertensive rats and Wistar/Kyoto normotensive controls. Fed. Proc. **36:** 1047.
5. MYERS, M. M., R. E. MUSTY & E. D. HENDLEY. 1982. Attenuation of hyperactivity in the spontaneously hypertensive rat by amphetamine. Behav. Neural Biol. **34:** 42–54.
6. TUCKER, D. C. & A. K. JOHNSON. 1981. Behavioral correlates of spontaneous hypertension. Neurosci. Biobehav. Rev. **5:** 463–471.
7. McCARTY, R., C. C. CHIUEH & I. J. KOPIN. 1978. Spontaneously hypertensive rats: adrenergic hyperresponsivity to anticipation of electric shock. Behav. Biol. **23:** 180–188.
8. WEINER, H. 1979. Psychobiology of Essential Hypertension. Elsevier. New York, N.Y.
9. RAPP, J. P. 1983. A paradigm for identification of primary genetic causes of hypertension in rats. Hypertension 5(Suppl. I): I198–I203.
10. HENDLEY, E. D., D. G. ATWATER, M. M. MYERS & D. WHITEHORN. 1983. Dissociation of genetic hyperactivity and hypertension in SHR. Hypertension **5:** 211–217.
11. HENDLEY, E. D. & W. G. OHLSSON. 1991. Two new inbred rat strains derived from SHR: WKHA, hyperactive, and WKHT, hypertensive, rats. Am. J. Physiol. **261:** H583–H589.
12. DiNICOLANTONIO, R., F. A. O. MENDELSOHN & J. S. HUTCHINSON. 1983. Sodium chloride preference of genetically hypertensive rats. Am. J. Physiol. **245:** R38–R44,
13. FREGLY, J. J. 1975. NaCl intake and preference threshold of spontaneously hypertensive rats. Proc. Soc. Exp. Biol. Med. **149:** 915–920.
14. MOE, K. 1985. Neonatal spontaneously hypertensive rats show an exaggerated NaCl preference. Neurosci. Abstr. **11:** 554.
15. LOUIS, W. J. & S. SPECTOR. 1975. The effect of salt intake and adrenal steroids on blood pressure in a genetic strain of hypertensive rats. Clin. Exp. Pharmacol. Physiol. Suppl. 2: 131–163.
16. YONGUE, B. G. & M. M. MYERS. 1988. Cosegregation analysis of salt appetite and blood pressure in genetically hypertensive and normotensive rats. Clin. Exp. Hypertens. Theory Pract. **A10:** 323–343.
17. YONGUE, B. G. & M. M. MYERS. 1989. Further evidence for genetic independence of blood pressure and salt appetite in spontaneously hypertensive and Wistar-Kyoto rats. Clin. Exp. Hypertens. Theory Pract. **A11:** 25–33.
18. FOLKOW, B. 1978. Cardiovascular structural adaptation: its role in the initiation and maintenance of primary hypertension. Clin. Sci. Mol. Med. **55:** 3–27.
19. HENDLEY, E. D., M. A. CIERPIAL & R. McCARTY. 1988. Sympathetic-adrenal medullary response to stress in hyperactive and hypertensive rats. Physiol. Behav. **44:** 47–51.
20. KNARDAHL, S. & E. D. HENDLEY. 1990. Association between cardiovascular reactivity to stress and hypertension or behavior. Am. J. Physiol. **259:** H248–H257.
21. TANG, M., R. GANDELMAN & J. L. RALK. 1982. Amelioration of genetic (SHR) hypertension: a consequence of early handling. Physiol. Behav. **28:** 1089–1091.
22. McMURTRY, J. P., G. L. WRIGHT & B. C. WEXLER. 1981. Spontaneous hypertension in cross-suckled rats. Science **211:** 1173–1175.
23. AZAR, S. & W. HRUSHESKY. 1985. Environmental factor(s) during suckling exert effects upon blood pressure in genetic hypertension. Clin. Res. **33:** 882A.
24. CIERPIAL, M. A. & R. McCARTY. 1987. Hypertension in SHR rats: contribution of maternal environment. Am. J. Physiol. **253:** H980–H984.

25. DiNicolantonio, R., S. J. Marshall, J. A. Nicolaci & A. E. Doyle. 1986. Blood pressure and saline preference of cross-suckled genetically hypertensive and normotensive rats: role of milk electrolytes. J. Hypertens. 4(Suppl. 3): S253–S254.
26. McCarty, R., M. A. Cierpial, C. A. Murphy, J. H. Lee & C. Fields-Okotcha. 1992. Maternal involvement in the development of cardiovascular phenotype. Experientia 48: 315–322.
27. Cierpial, M. A., D. E. Shasby & R. McCarty. 1987. Patterns of maternal behavior in the spontaneously hypertensive rat. Physiol. Behav. 39: 633–637.
28. Myers, M. M., S. A. Brunelli, J. M. Squire, R. D. Shindeldecker & M. A. Hofer. 1989. Maternal behavior of SHR rats and its relationship to offspring blood pressures. Dev. Psychobiol. 22: 29–53.
29. Myers, M. M., S. A. Brunelli, H. N. Shair, J. M. Squire & M. A. Hofer. 1989. Relationships between maternal behavior of SHR and WKY dams and adult blood pressures of cross-fostered F_1 pups. Dev. Psychobiol. 22: 55–67.
30. Cierpial, M. A., C. A. Murphy & R. McCarty. 1990. Maternal behavior of spontaneously hypertensive and Wistar-Kyoto normotensive rats: effects of reciprocal cross-fostering of litters. Behav. Neural Biol. 54: 90–96.
31. Myers, M. M., H. N. Shair & M. A. Hofer. 1992. Feeding in infancy: short and long term effects on cardiovascular function. Experientia 48: 322–333.
32. Lincoln, D. W., A. Hill & J. B. Wakerly. 1973. The milk-ejection reflex of the rat. An intermittent function not abolished by surgical levels of anesthesia. J. Endocrinol. 57: 459–476.
33. Shair, H. N., S. C. Brake, M. A. Hofer & M. M. Myers. 1986. Blood pressure responses to milk ejection in the young rat. Physiol. Behav. 37: 171–176.
34. Myers, M. M. & F. M. Scalzo. 1988. Blood pressure and heart rate responses of SHR and WKY rat pups during feeding. Physiol. Behav. 44: 75–83.
35. Scalzo, F. M. & M. M. Myers. 1991. Pharmacologic blockade of blood pressure and heart rate increases following milk ingestion in 15-day-old SHR and WKY rat pups. Physiol. Behav. 50: 525–531.
36. LeBlanc, J., M. Cabanac & P. Samson. 1984. Reduced postprandial heat production with gavage as compared with meal feeding in human subjects. Am. J. Physiol. 246: E95–E101.
37. Nicolaidis, S. 1969. Early systemic responses to oro-gastric stimulation in the regulation of food and water balance. Ann. N.Y. Acad. Sci. 157: 1176–1203.
38. Harding, R., P. Johnson, M. E. McClelland, C. N. Mcleod, P. L. Whyte & A. R. Wilkinson. 1978. Respiratory and cardiovascular responses to feeding in lambs. J. Physiol. Lond. 275: 40P–41P.
39. Bloom, S. R., A. V. Edwards, R. N. Hardy, K. Malinowska & M. Silver. 1975. Cardiovascular and endocrine responses to feeding in the young calf. J. Physiol. 253: 135–155.
40. Gupta, J. M. & J. W. Scopes. 1965. Observations on blood pressure in newborn infants. Arch. Dis. Child. 40: 637–644.
41. Cohen, M., M. M. Myers & D. Brown. 1992. Blood pressure responses of newborn infants to feeding. Dev. Psychobiol. 25: 291–298.
42. Widdowson, E. M. & G. C. Kennedy. 1962. Rate of growth, mature weight and life span. Proc. R. Soc. Lond. 156B: 96–108.
43. Widdowson, E. M. & R. R. S. McCance. 1960. Some effects of accelerating growth. I. General somatic development. Proc. R. Soc. Lond. 152B: 188–206.
44. Slotkin, T. A., B. Levant, L. Orband-Miller, K. L. Queen & S. Stasheff. 1988. Do sympathetic neurons coordinate cellular development in the heart and

kidney? Effect of neonatal central and peripheral catecholaminergic lesions on cardiac and renal nucleic acids and proteins. J. Pharm. Exp. Ther. **244**: 166–172.

45. SLOTKIN, T. A., W. L. WHITMORE, L. ORBAND-MILLER, K. L. QUEEN & K. HAIM. 1987. Beta adrenergic control of macromolecule synthesis in neonatal heart, kidney and lung: relationship to sympathetic neuronal development. J. Pharm. Exp. Ther. **243**: 101–109.

46. KIRBY, R. F. & A. K. JOHNSON. 1992. Regulation of sodium and body fluid homeostasis during development: implications for the pathogenesis of hypertension. Experientia **48**: 345–351.

Developmental Analysis in Behavioral Systems
The Case of Bird Song

CHERYL A. LOGAN

Department of Psychology
The University of North Carolina at Greensboro
Greensboro, North Carolina 27412-5001

Empirically informed debate about the convergence of nature and nurture in the development of behavior has contributed greatly to our understanding of behavioral origins. Nowhere are the issues and concerns more clearly drawn than in the contemporary literature on the development of bird song.[1-3] By now, most participants in the debate agree on the fundamentals at issue: *both* organismic (genes, embryology) and environmental (acoustical, social, ecological) influences are involved in song development, and each influence contributes to a causal network within the context of the limitations placed on it by other elements in that network. It is misleading to segregate out the "parts" that result from one influence versus those that result from another and attempt to uncover the "pure" manifestation of each. Such an approach assumes an additive relation among causal influences in which each operates in isolation just as it would in concert with others. Many students of behavioral development now argue that this assumption is inaccurate. No such pure isolation of separate influences is possible. Rather, development proceeds in patterns of interconnectedness, and song results from relationships among varying sets of influences. No one influence need universally pervade the process of development; and often their history of interconnectedness is as or more important than the nature of any single influence.

Despite widespread agreement on general perspectives hard won by 20 years of difficult and dedicated research, there is little consensus on where our efforts to understand song development should go next. On the one hand, Timothy Johnston criticizes the common attempt to distinguish between innate elements of song that are presumed to be under genetic control from those produced by experiential influences. He argues that this tradition commits the study of bird song to "an outmoded view of behavioral development that seeks to attribute elements of behavior separately to one of two sources: genetic information and environmental information [p. 617]."[1] On the other hand, while Peter Marler acknowledges that "all behaviour develops out of genomic-environment interactions"[2] (p. 43), he also states that "scientific crippling *inhibitions* about acknowledging genetic contributions to behav-

102

ioural development"[2] (p. 43, italics mine) jeopardize a complete understanding of the evolution of bird song. How can general agreement on conceptual fundamentals coexist with disagreement on how to proceed in specific empirical programs? I intend to explore here the position that many of our standards for empirical assessment prohibit consensus on specifics despite general conceptual agreement. Understanding how this could be the case turns on two problems of central concern in any empirical program in developmental psychobiology. Both are well illustrated, though neither has been resolved in the study of bird song. They are (1) the problem of defining the phenomenon under study in developmental research, and (2) methodological problems introduced by the integrated and contingent nature of behavioral development. A discussion of the impact of these problems on our understanding of the development of bird song provides a useful example of how similar problems affect our approach to other behavioral systems. What follows is not a comprehensive review of avian song development; rather, I have selected only those empirical works that highlight what I take to be the central issues of concern.

THE PHENOMENON OF BIRD SONG

What is bird song and how would one determine what features are central to an analysis of the phenomenon? The pioneering scientific work in the development of bird song focused primarily on the development of acoustical structure in the signal produced by a singing male. While acoustical structure is an important aspect of bird song, it is by no means the entire picture. The function of bird song is in communication, and at least two other ingredients are required for communication. In addition to a signal (the song's acoustical structure), communication requires a message (which may or may not be correlated with song structure), and a receiver, an individual whose activities are affected by the presence of the signal.[4] Recent empirical work suggests that singing must be approached as a pattern of interrelationships among several interacting influences including at least these three.[5,8] If we consider the development of song structure in isolation, we draw different conclusions about the processes of song development than if we examine it in the context of other features central to the phenomenon of bird song.

Peter Marler's pioneering work on the development of song in white-crowned sparrows (*Zonotrichia leucophrys*)[6] suggested that the attainment of species-typical adult song structure depended on three aspects of early experience: (1) young birds must be exposed to some variety of white-crowned sparrow song; (2) they must hear song during an early period of from 10–50 days of age before the young bird itself begins to sing; and (3) the young bird must have the opportunity to hear itself practice singing beginning at about 5 months of age. With the acoustical feedback provided by hearing itself practice, its unstructured vocal output gradually takes on the developed characteristics of adult song by about 8–10 months of age. The model of song development that resulted from this early work was used to reflect general features of song development potentially applicable to many avian species and perhaps to human language development.[7] More recent work suggests that this picture must be substantially revised. In what follows, I shall discuss three kinds of factors requiring a reconceptualization of bird song.

The Social Context of Development

Considerable work now indicates that social factors can affect the development of singing both during motor development, when acoustical production is first formed, and during adulthood, when structure and function may be altered by the social context in which adult communication occurs. Bird song is a social as well as an acoustical phenomenon. The work of Petrinovich and Baptista has shown that several aspects of signal development in white-crowned sparrows depend upon the kind of social stimulation available during development.[8] Marler's work suggested that birds presented tape-recorded songs could learn variants of white-crowned sparrow song, but not the songs of other species, and that normal development depended on acoustical exposure occurring during a sensitive period for song development at 10–50 days of age. Baptista and Petrinovich found that when the model song was presented by a live social tutor (a singing bird), rather than by a tape recorder, young white-crowns could learn the songs of other sparrow and finch species. Also, with social tutoring the period of flexible sensitivity to the model extended beyond 50 days to as long as 100 days of age. After exposure to conspecific song presented by a live tutor during the 41-day sensitive period, beginning at 51 days of age birds heard a second live white-crowned tutor singing a different song dialect. When recorded as adults, seven of 10 birds sang only the song of the second tutor heard after the sensitive period.[9] Therefore, the limited period of flexibility seen with taped song presentation was doubled if birds received acoustical input socially, and preferences for conspecific song established acoustically could be erased or overridden by social stimulation.

DeWolfe, Baptista, and Petrinovich have extended the importance of social stimulation during song development to incorporate the complex social environment sustaining song development in the wild.[10] Once again, the results suggest that the pattern of development described for changes in acoustical structure in isolation need not generalize to situations in which several aspects of the phenomenon co-occur. These authors recognized that Nuttall's subspecies of the white-crowned sparrow does not migrate; rather males reside in the coastal northwest throughout the year, and song and territory defense occur year round. For this reason, while still juveniles, birds hatched in spring and summer must use "adult" song to defend territories in early September. DeWolfe *et al.* reasoned that the roughly 120-day period between song exposure and the production of adult song reported for laboratory-reared Nuttall males must be accelerated in free-living territorial juveniles. Censuses of the Nuttall population residing year round in San Francisco's Golden Gate Park indicated that 80% of the juveniles were singing immature song (termed subsong) in the month of July; over 50% sang immature, but modified song in August. While DeWolfe *et al.* do not give the exact ages of the juveniles, the *oldest* would have hatched in April, 70–80 days before the onset of subsong in July. The youngest may have hatched as few as 50–60 days before subsong began at roughly half of the age presumed required for white-crowned sparrow song development. In the field, a very different pattern of timing can occur. DeWolfe *et al.*'s work also shows that the early developing autumn songs of juveniles were effective in establishing territory, the primary function of adult song in white-crowned sparrows. Nine juveniles were singing "adult" song in September and October, and seven of the nine held territories and bred the following spring near the areas where they sang in autumn. In autumn, many juveniles were heard countersinging with adults, answering the mature singing of older neighbors with near exact renditions of the adult song of the neighbor. Most strikingly, DeWolfe *et al.* report several instances in which juvenile birds singing immature song changed *immediately* to produce adult song when challenged by a singing adult.[10]

In some species, the developing individual itself may play a role in guiding social input.[5] For example, Clayton has shown that when given a choice between two social tutors, young male zebra finches selectively copy the songs of the adult that behaves most aggressively toward them.[11] If the young males are able to evoke aggression, they might guide their own tutoring. These observations indicate (1) that the timing of song development in a classically "restricted" species can vary dramatically with the social and communicative conditions of development; and (2) that "motivational" influences, such as a challenge provided by an established territorial resident or a social tutor, may play a role in the timing and character of song's structural development. It is important to point out that Marler's initial conclusions were not in error. They have been replicated several times *in that context*. Rather, they were limited to the context in which song structure was examined, and that context incorporated only a few of the many interconnected features of the phenomenon of bird song. The error is in the attempt to generalize results obtained under a restricted set of influences to more complex situations, i.e., the wild, where other aspects of the phenomenon are manifest. In nature, when the pattern of interconnectedness changes, the regularities of song development may change too.

The Relation between Signal and Message: the Development of Meaning

In many bird species, structurally distinct acoustical signals are used in different communicative contexts, and receivers react in a functionally appropriate manner to one signal versus another. For example, several acoustical differences distinguish the "spontaneous" songs of the willow warbler (*Phylloscopus trochilus*) from those produced during territorial fights. Playback studies show that these structural and contextual differences are accompanied by differences in how territorial residents respond to intruders' songs played in their territories. Residents attack the less threatening "spontaneous" song, but they withdraw from the more threatening aggressive song,[12] as if distinct acoustical structures signal different meanings.

Most early studies of song development finessed the difficult problem of the development of the message sent, and therefore of meaning, by assuming that the nature of the message was consistently reflected in the acoustical structure of the signal. In some species this may be the case. In others, it appears not to be the case, and these instances further illustrate the importance of recognizing that the phenomenon of bird song represents a dynamic complex of interrelated elements. How does a potentially arbitrary acoustical structure acquire the meaning of a specific message? Donald Kroodsma has examined the problem of contextually appropriate signal use in the blue-winged warbler (*Cercopiithecus aethiops*).[13] In this species, acoustically distinct type I and type II songs are used in functionally distinct ways. After males return to their territories in early spring, they produce a mixture of both song types. But by late in the breeding season, most type I songs occur in the daytime under intense light levels and most type II songs are produced at dawn under low light levels. Moreover, different song types signal different meanings: type I songs are used in territory pronouncement, while type II songs occur in interactions with mates. Kroodsma presented blue-winged warbler nestlings with recorded type I and type II songs under normal and reversed conditions. Some birds heard type I song only in the afternoon at more intense light levels and type II song only at dawn under dim light (simulating the natural type I/type II context); others heard type I songs under dim light at dawn and type II songs under bright light at dusk (simulating reversed conditions). A third group was given no contextual information. Four to five months later, when the tutored birds began to sing, those exposed to conditions that reversed the normal pattern reversed the type of song produced.[13] Birds that heard type II songs at daytime and under high light levels were more likely to produce them under those conditions, despite the fact that this reversed normal production conditions. Birds that received no contextual information failed to use either song type consistently in context. Similar results have been obtained for Grace's warbler, *Dendroica graciae*,[14] and the yellow warbler, *Dendroica petechia*.[15]

Syllables, defined as a specific pattern of acoustical frequency modulation that may recur during singing, are the usual currency in song-development studies and the usual basis for defining song types. Cynthia Staicer's work on Grace's warbler suggests that song types (or syllables) must be distinguished from singing behaviors and that the two can develop independently.[14] Grace's warblers produced several distinct syllables, but they also display two distinct patterns of song production which Staicer termed singing behaviors. Though they involved many of the same syllables, the amount of syllable repetition and the diversity of patterning differed: one song behavior involved more repetition of a few song types; the other employed more song types with greater variation in the patterned sequencing of those types. Further, singing behaviors, but not song types, consistently occurred in different song contexts. More elaborate patterns were used after pairing and later in the season, and more stereotyped patterns dominated early in the season and in unpaired males. In paired birds, the singer used the more repetitive pattern when the female was nearby, but the more elaborate pattern when undisturbed or countersinging with competing males. Finally, singing behavior varied independently of the acoustical structure of the signals used. That is, there was no association between song type and the singing behavior: song types used predominantly by one male in the more complex song behavior pattern might be used by a different male in the less complex pattern. The relationship between the pattern of frequency modulation in syllables, the context in which song was used, and the meaning of a given syllable structure appeared to depend upon patterns established in individuals during song development.

These studies show that the development of a signal's acoustical structure is only one part of the song-development process. Studies assuming that the development of syllabic structure is the key to song development may overstate the role that signal structure plays in communication. Birds that sing distinct songs carrying different messages must also learn the appropriate situations in which to use those songs. Further, the relationship between syllable structure and song function may be an arbitrary one based not on absolute features of syllable structure, but upon the way singing behaviors and context are joined in development. Developmental differences in the pattern of interconnectedness may account for numerous individual differences in the structure and function of song seen in many species.[16]

Song Production and Song Recognition: Signaler-Receiver Interactions

Research suggests that birds store more information about song than simply that reflected in their own song production. For example, in some species females who normally do not sing nonetheless make fine discriminations in the songs produced by males. These studies point to a third critical aspect of the phenomenon of bird song: the reaction of the receiver to the signal. In dunnocks (*Prunella modularis*), a European sparrow, some females have two mates residing on their territories; others mate monogamously with only one male. In trios, only if the female mates with the second male (the beta male) will he provide parental care for her young, and beta male attempts to entice her to mate with his song. Wiley *et al.* have demonstrated that female dunnocks mating in trios discriminate the songs of their mates from those produced by their nearest neighbor.[17] Some females heard their primary mates' songs, and others heard only their beta males' songs. When their response to each was compared with that to their neighbors' songs, they approached their beta mates' songs but not their primary mates' song.[17] Females clearly discriminated differences in the songs of individual males, even when mating with both. Wiley *et al.* suggest that the female may respond more strongly to her beta male versus her primary male's song in an effort to secure extra paternal care from the former.

The female dunnocks suggest that a male's behavior may be altered by a female's reaction to his song. But, what the nature of this reaction is, or how it affects singing itself, is not known. Meredith West and Andrew King's work on signal-receiver interactions in the brown-headed cowbird offers a more precise account of the effect of the receiver's reaction on song development. This research illustrates an important, but rarely emphasized, point in the study of bird song development. The receiver is not a passive recipient that simply responds to song as a finished product. Rather, the reaction of a potential receiver can alter song development both in species whose songs become fixed early in life and probably in those whose songs continue to develop throughout life.[18]

Eastern brown-headed cowbird song (*Molothrus ater*) simultaneously contains elements that are received by males with whom the singer competes for position in a dominance hierarchy and by females from whom the male may be soliciting copulation.[19,20] West and King have shown that cowbird song develops differently if young males are reared with females. Though females do not sing, the presence of a female cowbird alters male song development even if birds receive female social input in acoustical isolation. The effect is not a general social one; rather, it depends upon specific responding provided by the female. The juvenile male's immature subsong is functionally effective in evoking copulatory solicitation from females.[18] Females distinguish among four variants of immature cowbird song, preferring some over others, though each is more effective than the songs of other species. The males of different cowbird subspecies sing structurally distinct songs, and females usually prefer the song of their own subspecies. However, when males of one subspecies were housed with females of another, the males developed songs containing elements most preferred by females, irrespective of the males' subspecies. Therefore, juvenile male song develops in different ways depending upon the kinds of vocal structures preferred by specific females.[21] Females do not normally produce copulatory responses in late winter and early spring, when young males' songs are developing. However, at this time females respond to some young males' songs with a subtle wing-stroke response. West and King have shown that the songs most effective in evoking a wing stroke during development were also those most effective in soliciting copulation in their mature forms.[18] These findings strongly suggest that mature female cowbirds shape the singing of juvenile males during the process of song development itself. West and King speculate, however, that juvenile singers receive social stimulation from adult males and from females in mixed-sex flocks during development. If this is the case, feedback from the female must be integrated with social input from competing males. Different kinds of social input may shape the development of song in different ways, producing a dynamic complex of competing social influences whose balance may dictate differences in the effectiveness of adult song.[21]

Perhaps most strikingly, the effect of specific shaping by the female is not restricted simply to the character of the song produced. Rather, the processes of song production are themselves changed by the nature of the social input. At least three distinct processes of song development are thought to be involved in bird song: (1) vocal copying, in which the young bird mimics the sounds provided by a tutor; (2) improvisation, in which the young bird produces song variants that are distinct from, yet similar to, the songs provided by a tutor, and (3) invention, in which though exposed to a tutor's song, the young bird produces novel songs which bear little acoustical similarity to the song of the tutor, but which would not have occurred without some acoustical stimulation. King and West raised 30–50 day old male cowbirds within hearing of tutor songs for three months. Each male was also given an adult female companion. Analysis of the male's songs produced at 150 and 300 days of age showed that at 150 days of age most songs were unlike those sung by the tutor; only 9% of the males' songs were copies of tutors songs, 4% were improvised, 7% were original invented songs, and the rest could not be classified. These songs were compared to those generated by male cowbirds that heard the *same* stimulus songs but who were housed with canaries rather than with female cowbirds. At 150 days of age these males sang an average of 71% copied songs, 4% were improvised, none were invented, and the rest could not be classified. By 300 days of age the differences were more extreme: in the final recording session, 97% of the songs of males housed with canaries were copied; in contrast, 54% of the songs of males housed with female cowbirds were invented, 26% were improvised, and only 20% were copied. The developed songs clearly differed, despite identical acoustical stimulation. Moreover, differences appear to have resulted from the effect of social shaping on the stimulation of distinct processes of development.[22] West and King suggest that in cowbirds the processes of song development are not absolute, but depend on the song's signal value as indexed by prospective receivers.

Comparable social shaping may occur throughout the lives of birds like the northern mockingbird (*Mimus polyglottos*), whose songs may change throughout life.[23] In mockingbirds both males and females sing in the fall, but only males sing during the breeding season. Males' repertoires are quite distinct in the spring compared to the fall, and very few song types overlap.[24] Though research must be done to demonstrate this, it is possible that the female's fall song shapes the male's fall song to render it distinct from that produced (and often heard by the same female) the prior spring. If so, she may help generate the song she prefers to hear for the following spring when his song is central to their breeding effort.[25]

The potential for developmental interaction between song production and song recognition may also occur when males respond in adaptive ways to differences in songs they themselves are not able to produce. Territorial great tits (*Parus major*) recognize and discriminate among songs that they do not produce.[26] McGregor and Avery presented great tits that had resided in the same territory for at least two years with the songs of an old territorial neighbor and those of a newly arrived neighbor. Males responded to both old and new neighbors' songs in boundary-appropriate fashion. That is, they responded strongly to the neighbor's song if it was played on the inappropriate boundary, and much less to the same song if it was played on the appropriate boundary where they are accustomed to hearing the neighbor sing. However, comparison of the old versus new neighbor condition indicated that the boundary discrimination was much stronger when the birds were tested with the songs of their old neighbors. McGregor and Avery explored this difference by looking at the specific acoustical structures of the stimulus songs used. The ability of residents to distinguish the new neighbor's song played on the correct versus incorrect boundary depended on whether the old and new neighbors of a given subject both sang the song versions used in testing. The magnitude of the discrimination of new neighbors *decreased* as the number of song versions shared by the old and new neighbors *increased*. Similarities in song structure, however, had no effect on the resident's discrimination of boundary-appropriate versus boundary-inappropriate playback of the old neighbors' songs. McGregor and Avery conclude that the songs an individual has learned to recognize in the past may affect his future recognition of similar songs. Similar influences may affect future song production in other large-repertoire species, yet little work has examined influence of earlier developmental relations on the continued flexibility of song in adulthood.[27]

Research on bird song has shown us that explanations of song cannot be based on consideration of only one or a few influences operating at a given point in time; rather they require charting a pattern of interconnected elements whose interrelations change across time. Empirical illustration of the importance of any one influence in an isolated preparation can speak to the *potential* importance of that influence, but not to the actual role that influence may have played in producing a given developed outcome.

IMPLICATIONS OF BIRD SONG FOR DEVELOPMENTAL SCIENCE

Developmental science is not a branch of behavioral science. Rather, it is a mode of historical explanation necessary for a complete understanding of any psychological phenomenon.[28] Unfortunately, in much of the behavioral sciences, development has been equated with one subdiscipline that focuses on the young. This misrepresents the central role of developmental analysis in all psychological explanation. The literature on bird song illustrates that developmental analysis is essential to understanding the origins of adult function and the processes guiding it. Development is not just what comes before; it is the historical basis for the explanation of adult function and the processes underlying it.

Recognition of the importance of development in explanation has several direct implications for how we conduct psychological research and for the kinds of inferences drawn from that research.[8,30] These implications require a serious revision of what scientific psychology should look like. For this reason, though there is a general acceptance of many of the features of an interactionist approach to behavioral development,[1,2,8,9,29,30] their specific implications are rarely put into practice. I suggest that a conservative model of science prevents us from pursuing what many believe to be the most reasonable approach to understanding complex behavioral phenomena. If we accept the interactionist approach to development and the importance of development in explanation, several standards of science taken for granted by psychologists must be questioned. I shall present some of the most important, and with each discuss why they are at variance with a more dynamic approach to development.

Prediction and Generality

No single aspect of development is predetermined, and at any point in time novel products of development may emerge as a result of system interactions occurring earlier.[29] The impact of any single influence occurring now can only be understood in the context of the cumulative history of prior development, and what may appear to be minor differences in the set of interacting influences can produce dramatic differences in both the outcome and the processes of development. As a result, any single outcome cannot be predicted *a priori*. Rather each must be traced retrospectively from knowledge of the final product. For this reason, developmental explanation begins and ends retrospectively, with the causally unprejudiced outcome of development providing the ultimate criterion against which hypothesized developmental influences must be judged. Retrospective analysis is at variance with our traditional scientific standard that explanatory statements must rely on prior, not posterior, knowledge. However, in the development of flexible systems, this cannot be the case. If any number of outcomes are possible, if each results from a different pattern of influence, and if different patterns of influence produce different outcomes, rules accounting for observed regularities can only be stated after the fact, after the set of interacting influences and their historical causes have been traced.

This position presumes an end point to development. But, all points of departure in development are more or less arbitrary. This is equally true of the "end." However, simple empirical descriptions of psychological stability will serve. For example, natural history descriptions of bird song in some species suggest that songs used in some contexts stabilize relatively early in life, with little or no additional change thereafter. In other species, songs continue to change throughout life. The criterion reference points for retrospective developmental analysis should vary accordingly, and influences that produce change should be evaluated against the extent to which they enable the system to converge on a normative level of stability. But this level may change from species to species, and from situation to situation within a species. The example of nonmigratory, juvenile white-crowned sparrows defending territories in their first fall will illustrate. These birds face different social circumstances than those migrating in their first fall, and different social contingencies guide different processes of song development. The outcome of the nonmigratory juveniles' unusual historical circumstances cannot be predicted by rules representing a different (though more typical) migratory circumstance. Only after the impact of autumn social interactions has been described can we explain their impact on the timing and character of song development.

Two clarifications are in order. First, this does not mean that the nature of each causal influence itself is not deterministic. Each is, but the final outcome results from the conjoint occurrence of many interacting influences. The specific set of elements occurring at any point in time and their pattern of interaction can rarely be known beforehand. Secondly, this does not preclude the use of empirical predictions restricted to specific experimental situations. In most cases, specific experimental paradigms will *not* include input by all features of the complex network of influences guiding development. This need not abrogate the value of experimental analysis in isolated situations. Analyses of the effect of a variable on an isolated preparation can be made *so long as the predicted outcome is not assumed to reflect the ultimate role played by that influence when operating in the context of other features of the complex.* In the example of the white-crowned sparrow progression from subsong to adult song, the 120-day age of subsong onset reliably holds in isolated laboratory preparations. But, because developmental processes change when the organism must behave in the context of adult territorial challenge, the results do not generalize from one context to the other. The problem arises when results obtained from isolated preparations are presented *as generalized explanations* and uncritically exported to other contexts in which the impact of the influence in question may be negligible.

The problem of generality raises another issue at variance with our traditional model of science. Traditional views assume that if our experiments isolate the critical element (see below), because that element is so critical, its effects will transcend changes in context, such as the addition of social influence. That is, generality is assumed a priori, rather than evaluated empirically. The interactionist view presumes that the generality of explanations produced by a given developmental trajectory will be limited as the conditions of development vary.[8] That is, in contrast to our traditional model, generality is something to be concluded empirically after the fact of historical analysis, and not something to be assumed before that analysis occurs.

Partly to deal with the problem of generality, Petrinovich has outlined the use of "representative designs" in the experimental analysis of bird song.[8] Representative designs are those in which the variables manipulated under controlled circumstances are arranged to represent a subset of the complex operating in the natural situation. This proscription depends on a near complete description of the phenomenon at a relatively stable point in development, one conducted under the conditions of primary interest. It also depends upon deciding which of an enormous number of features might define relations more central than others. We should not underestimate the difficulty of these steps, but Petrinovich argues that the effort is repaid in the greater generality of the explanations that result.

Essential Irreducible Elements

Except in unusual cases of longitudinal research, prior interactions that provide the baseline for developmental change are often unknown in psychology. Psychologists usually "plug into" development at a relatively advanced point in time, and with little knowledge of the baseline provided by prior conditions of development.[1] Faced with these unknowns, we often assume that there are one or a few fundamental elements or processes, somehow more basic (and usually smaller!) than the rest. These are assumed to either operate in isolation at earlier points in development or to wield exclusive influence earlier, when things were simpler. Such assumptions of molecular and construct reductionism haunt our judgments about what prior influences have dominated development.[1,8,31] The study of bird song has shown that even the most obvious "central" element, acoustical input, may or may not be central depending on its interconnectedness with other factors defining the context of development.[5] At each point in development, processes and outcomes reflect the integrated influence of several interacting aspects. In bird song the social influence is not added on after the acoustical influence has established itself. Rather, during development, the acoustical and the social work together (with hormonal, ecological, and genetic factors) to effect change.

Despite several well-articulated accounts of why reductionistic methodologies are inadequate to the task of behavioral analysis,[8,31] reductionistic metaphors abound. Most surprisingly, they appear in the writings of those committed to a dynamic interactionist perspective on behavioral development. For example, Lerner argues that organism-context relations are the basic processes of development. The literature certainly shows that they may be central, but why *need* they be so? The qualities of the elements involved in those relationships must also be involved, and in some contexts, but not others, quality may outweigh the influence of the relationship itself. Similarly, Gottlieb retains the language of hierarchies in behavioral development: genes and molecules are "lower" in the hierarchy, while extraorganismic and social influences are "higher" in the hierarchy.[29] Though he intends it merely as a linguistic convenience reflecting how a question is framed rather than how nature is organized, the hierarchical metaphor allows others to mistakenly infer that genetic and molecular accounts are *causally* more basic than others.

Both molar and molecular research now indicates that the widespread presumption that smaller is more basic must be revised. In cowbird song development, experiential influences on singing cannot be reduced to a pattern of acoustic receptor or auditory nervous system influences produced by a particular pattern of acoustical input. The same acoustical stimulus results in a different developed song produced by a different developmental process if it is accompanied by female social guidance. Reducing song development to acoustical receptor activation oversimplifies complex developmental interactions on which it depends. Similarly, the literature shows that song development and production depend upon neuroendocrine influences.[32] But neuroendocrine effects themselves may depend upon social factors.[33] Neither is more fundamental to the outcome than the other. They work together.

Marler argues that despite the complex system interactions on which the development of bird song depends, genes provide the "substrates" for the development of song.[2] The "substrates" metaphor is also reductionistic, suggesting that genes establish an absolute baseline prior to the impact of, for example, social or endocrine influences. Genes are represented as an influence that is unaffected earlier in development by endocrine or social factors. But, this need not be the case. Earlier social influences could have combined with earlier genetic influences to produce a very different baseline for further development than that occurring in the absence of a social influence. If this is the case, subsequent development may be different from that occurring in the absence of early social influence, and the action of the "substrate" will have depended upon the context of development.

The only universally more basic feature of developmental analysis is timing—that which has come before. Prior interactions will involve numerous interconnected influences, no one of which need be "more basic" than the others. Moreover, the earlier influence of any one feature need not be retained throughout subsequent development and may be entirely overshadowed later. If this is the case, in what sense can any one factor define an unchanging substrate for others? The appropriate point of departure for developmental analysis is not the state of any one influence at a prior point in time, but the interrelationship among all. Reductionism assumes that one feature of the complex defining the prior history of development is *necessarily* more important than others. And in the extreme, reductionistic explanations assume that earlier interrelations are either unidimensional or simpler than those apparent later, when the empirical analysis is done. This need not be, and in most psychological systems will not be, the case. Development may proceed from categorically distinct patterns of prior interaction that are equally or more complex than those being measured, and the impact of a given influence later in time simply does not speak to the impact of that influence earlier in time. The nature of the pattern of influences operating earlier is a separate empirical question.

Our experimental preparations are usually designed to isolate the most basic influence. However, that no single influence need be most basic throughout does not mean that experimental isolation is inappropriate. It does mean that the results of experimental analysis of isolated systems must be used differently than is usually the case in experimental psychology. As Petrinovich suggests, the description of the fully developed system in context must precede experimental analysis. The explanatory validity of isolated experimental preparations depends critically on this step. Results obtained from isolated experimental preparations must be assessed in terms of two additional kinds of information: (1) simple description of the phenomenon of interest in the context of all of the influences affecting it; and (2) reconstruction of historical patterns of interrelationships that explain why the isolated influence operates as it does.

SUMMARY

Development is contextual, and change occurring at any one point in time may depend as much on accumulated historical contingencies as on the absolute character of influences manifest at that point in time. I have used research on the development of bird song to illustrate the value of a dynamic interactionist approach to behavioral development. The points raised are not new. However, I have tried to show that they oblige us to view development as explanation; this in turn requires reevaluation of the adequacy of received paradigms of scientific analysis. Developmental science forces us to revise our paradigms of inquiry to deal with the complex, contingent, and continuous nature of psychological phenomena.

ACKNOWLEDGMENTS

I am grateful to Gilbert Gottlieb for valuable comments provided on an earlier draft of the manuscript.

REFERENCES

1. JOHNSTON, T. D. 1988. Development and explanation in the ontogeny of birdsong: nature/nurture redux. Behav. Brain Sci. **11:** 631–675.

2. MARLER, P. 1991. Differences in behavioral development in closely related species. *In* The Development and Integration of Behaviour. P. Bateson, Ed.: 41–70. Cambridge University Press. Cambridge, England.

3. KROODSMA, D. E. & B. E. BYERS. 1991. The function(s) of bird song. Am. Zool. **31**: 318–328.

4. GUILFORD, T. & M. S. DAWKINS. 1991. Receiver psychology and the evolution of animal signals. Anim. Behav. **42**: 1–14.

5. TEN CATE, C. 1989. Behavioural development: toward understanding processes. *In* Perspectives in Ethology. P. Bateson & P. Klopfer, Eds. **8**: 243–269. Plenum. New York, N.Y.

6. MARLER, P. 1970. A comparative approach to vocal learning: song development in white-crowned sparrows. J. Comp. Physiol. Psychol. **71**: 1–25.

7. MARLER, P. 1970. Birdsong and speech development: could there be parallels? Am. Sci. **58**: 669–673.

8. PETRINOVICH, L. 1990. Avian song development: methodological and conceptual issues. *In* Contemporary Issues in Comparative Psychology. D. A. Dewsbury, Ed.: 340–359. Sinauer. Sunderland, Mass.

9. PETRINOVICH, L. & L. F. BAPTISTA. 1987. Song development in the white-crowned sparrow: modification of learned song. Anim. Behav. **35**: 961–974.

10. DEWOLFE, B. B., L. F. BAPTISTA & L. PETRINOVICH. 1989. Song development and territory establishment in Nuttall's white-crowned sparrows. The Condor **91**: 397–407.

11. CLAYTON, N. S. 1987. Song tutor choice in zebra finches. Anim. Behav. **35**: 714–721.

12. JARVI, T., T. RADESATER & S. JAKOBSSON. 1980. The song of the willow warbler *Phylloscopus trochilus* with special reference to singing behaviour in agonistic situations. Ornis Scand. **11**: 236–242.

13. KROODSMA, D. E. 1988. Song types and their use: developmental flexibility of the male blue-winged warbler. Ethology **79**: 235–247.

14. STAICER, C. A. 1989. Characteristics, use, and significance of two singing behaviors in Grace's warbler (*Dendroica graciae*). Auk **106**: 49–63.

15. SPECTOR, D. A., L. K. MCKIM & D. E. KROODSMA. 1989. Yellow warblers are able to learn songs and situations in which to use them. Anim. Behav. **38**: 723–725.

16. KING, A. P. & M. J. WEST. 1990. Variation in species-typical behavior: a contemporary issue for comparative psychology. *In* Contemporary Issues in Comparative Psychology. D. A. Dewsbury, Ed.: 321–339. Sinauer. Sunderland, Mass.

17. WILEY, R. H., B. J. HATCHWELL & N. B. DAVIES. 1991. Recognition of individual males' songs by female dunnocks: a mechanism increasing the number of copulatory patterns and reproductive success. Ethology **88**: 145–153.

18. WEST, M. J. & A. P. KING. 1988. Female visual displays affect the development of male song in the cowbird. Nature **334**: 244–246.

19. DUFTY, A. M. 1986. Singing and the establishment and maintenance of dominance hierarchies in captive brown-headed cowbirds. Behav. Ecol. Sociobiol. **19**: 49–55.

20. WEST, M. J. & A. P. KING. 1988. Vocalizations of juvenile cowbirds (*Molothrus ater*) evoke copulatory responses from females. Dev. Psychobiol. **21**: 543–552.

21. KING, A. P. & M. J. WEST. 1988. Searching for the functional origins of song in eastern brown-headed cowbirds, *Molothrus ater ater*. Anim. Behav. **36**: 1575–1588.

22. KING, A. P. & M. J. WEST. 1989. Presence of female cowbirds (*Molothrus ater*) affects vocal imitation and improvisation in males. J. Comp. Psychol. **103**: 39–44.

23. DERRICKSON, K. C. 1987. Yearly and situational changes in the estimate of repertoire size in northern mockingbirds (*Mimus polyglottos*). Auk **104**: 198–207.

24. BURNETT, L. 1978. Mockingbird song: an investigation within and across seasons. Master's Thesis. University of North Carolina at Greensboro. Greensboro, N.C.

25. LOGAN, C. A., L. E. HYATT & L. GREGORCYK. 1990. Song playback initiates nest building during clutch overlap in mockingbirds (*Mimus polyglottos*). Anim. Behav. **39**: 943–953.

26. SHY, E., P. K. McGREGOR & J. R. KREBS. 1986. Discrimination of song types by male great tits. Behav. Proc. **13**: 1–12.

27. McGREGOR, P. K. & M. I. AVERY. 1986. The unsung songs of great tits (*Parus major*); learning neighbours' songs for discrimination. Behav. Ecol. Sociobiol. **18**: 311–316.

28. LOGAN, C. A. 1985. Development as explanation: beyond the unicorn mind. *In* Applied Developmental Psychology. F. Morrison, C. Lord & D. Keating, Eds. **2**: 1–32. Academic Press. New York, N.Y.

29. GOTTLIEB, G. 1991. Experiential canalization of behavioral development: theory. Dev. Psychol. **27**: 4–13.

30. LERNER, R. M.. 1991. Changing organism-context relations as the basic process of development: a developmental contextual perspective. Dev. Psychol. **27**: 27–32.

31. FENTRESS, J. C. 1991. Analytical ethology and synthetic neuroscience. *In* The Development and Integration of Behaviour. P. Bateson, Ed.: 77–120. Cambridge University Press. Cambridge, England.

32. MARLER, P., S. PETERS & J. WINGFIELD. 1987. Correlations between song acquisition, song production and plasma levels of testosterone and estradiol in sparrows. J. Neurobiol. **18**: 531–548.

33. RUNFELDT, S. & J. WINGFIELD. 1985. Experimentally prolonged sexual activity in female sparrows delays termination of reproductive activity in their untreated mates. Anim. Behav. **33**: 403–410.

Fetal Audition

M. C. BUSNEL,[a] C. GRANIER-DEFERRE,[b]
AND J. P. LECANUET[b]

[a]Genetique, Neurogenetique et Comportement
UFR Biomédical
University of Paris V
URA CNRS 1294
45, rue des St. Pères
75006 Paris, France

[b]Laboratory of the Psychobiology of Development
EPHE–CNRS (URA 315)
41, rue Gay Lussac
75005 Paris, France

In the beginning of the century, there was a marked discrepancy between what physicians and scientists believed about the sensory capacities of fetuses and the observations of many pregnant women who felt their fetuses moving and kicking in response to strong noises. It was only in the 20s that scientists started to take interest in the existence of fetal audition.[1,2] Since that time, with the appearance of ultrasonographic techniques (cardiotocography and real-time scanning systems) allowing fine description of fetal reactions to acoustic stimulation, a growing number of studies have brought about a more complete picture of prenatal auditory competencies.

Although we will only describe the acoustic domain, it must be kept in mind that the near-term fetus, in spite of its apparently sensory deprived/protected condition, receives a noticeable amount of stimulation through several sensory modalities.[3,4] For methodological reasons each sensory system is studied separately and, as mentioned above, because auditory responsiveness seemed obvious from maternal experience, it was hearing that triggered the earliest prenatal experiments, while vision attracted most of the early postnatal studies. But, one may legitimately hypothesize that the intersensory/interactions that have been described in the newborn baby and infant[5-7] may also be found in the prenatal period. However, very little is known about the nature of intersensory relationships during this period of development. Nothing is known for instance of a potential dominance of one sensory channel over the others in the fetus, as Lewkowicz emphasizes it in the infant.[8]

We will here summarize the history of advances in the fetal hearing field. The developmental course of the anatomy of the human auditory apparatus[9] will not be described, but demonstrations of its functioning and characteristics of the external sounds that can activate it *in utero* will be reviewed. Studies investigating human prenatal auditory learning will be briefly recalled, and to conclude, we will propose some current hypotheses on the consequences of prenatal audition on fetal and newborn behavior.

THE NATURE OF INTRAUTERINE SOUNDS

Data on the acoustical characteristics of internal noises and of external sounds transmitted *in utero* obtained in the human female from different intraabdominal recording sites—inside the vagina or the cervix,[10-13] inside the uterus after amniotomy before labor[14] and during labor[15-17]—will not be detailed. Only general conclusions from the studies using the most precise and refined acoustic equipment and analyzer are summarized below:

1. The mean level of the internal background noise far from the placenta is 28 dB SPL (sound pressure level) and has its highest energy at very low frequencies, under 40 Hz,[17] where the human auditory system has its highest thresholds. Therefore, the background noise appears to be unlikely to mask a wide range of external noises. For example, the fundamental of a male voice (at 100 Hz) spoken at 60 dB SPL near the mother is only very partially masked by the intrauterine noise. According to Querleu *et al.*,[18] it is the placental noise and not the maternal heart-beat sound that is the noisiest component of the internal background noise.[18] Indeed, when recordings are not performed during labor, maternal cardiovascular sounds are not an important component of the background noise.[11,13] The latter has been confirmed in sheep studies.[19-22] Vince *et al.*, with very long duration recordings (up to 3 weeks) before and during labor, found that cardiovascular sounds were particularly enhanced during labor.[19]

2. Most external sounds at or above 60 dB SPL, emitted near the mother, are well transmitted *in utero*. Pressure loss is negligible in the low frequencies: 0 to 2 dB SPL at and below 250 Hz. It increases as a function of frequency to about 20 dB SPL at 1000 Hz and does not exceed 40 dB SPL for higher frequencies in the human audible range.[18]

Data from pregnant goats[23] and sheep;[19,21,22,24,25] obtained with chronically implanted hydrophones near the fetal head and in other intrauterine sites, show that these attenuation values are lower than those measured in women. They are negligible, 0 to 5 dB SPL, at frequencies up to 500 Hz; pressure loss then increases by 6 dB/octave up to 4 kHz.[21] Above these frequencies, recordings show that the intensities inside the uterus rise again, so that the classical view claiming that the higher the frequency of external sounds, the higher their attenuation might not be correct along the whole frequency continuum.[21,22] This intensity rise may be due to resonance phenomena.

Some human[17] and sheep data[19,21,22,24,25] show that sound pressure levels are not uniform inside the amniotic cavity. Both maternal background noise and intrauterine restitution of external noises have different intensities depending on the site of the recording; they vary according to distance from the sound source. Discrepancies between measured values published by different teams in the same species, and those between species, may be partially explained if one considers the differences in hydrophone or microphone locations; these differences may also contribute to the understanding of the relatively high inter- and intraindividual differences reported within the same species.[19,21,22]

Because of obvious anatomical differences, direct generalization of the data from sheep to human might be problematic. However, the results obtained on both species are very similar, and the animal model has allowed recording directly from inside the amniotic sac, without any fluid loss and not during the periparturitional period when the internal background noise intensity is increased by generalized cardiovascular activation.

Considering that the developing auditory apparatus is more susceptible to acoustic trauma than the adult one,[26,27] it is necessary to take into account the pressure levels transmitted to the uterus. This is especially important in clinical studies (for reviews, see References 28–30) using, in daily practice, very high intensity vibroacoustic stimulation (VAS) applied on the maternal abdomen (thus, almost without any pressure loss) to diagnose fetal distress.

DEMONSTRATION OF FETAL AUDITION IN ANIMALS AND HUMANS

The earliest studies in this field[1,31–33] used ill-defined stimuli (e.g., automobile horn, door bell, and buzzer directly applied on the maternal abdomen) that did not allow differentiating between activation of the auditory system and activation of skin receptors that could be receptive to low-frequency vibrations. Only a few experiments have avoided this drawback by assessing fetal responses to specific auditory stimulation (filtered in their low frequencies).

Auditory Evoked Potentials

Fetal brain stem and cortical auditory evoked potentials have been extensively studied *in utero* in the chronically implanted guinea pig[34] and sheep (see review in Reference 35). These potentials show the same characteristics and the same developmental course as those recorded *ex utero*. In the human, they have been recorded with electrodes placed on the fetus' scalp during labor.[36–38]

Short, middle, and late latency evoked auditory responses have been extensively studied in the premature baby. All three may be recorded, but are not consistently detected at 24–25 weeks gestational age (GA). Detectability progressively increases with age, and the detectability of major components is stable by 30–32 weeks.[39-47] At 25 weeks, brain stem responses are consistent and reproducible, but with very high thresholds. Thresholds gradually decrease with development and, by 35 weeks GA, are no more than 10–20 dB hearing level different from the adults' threshold. The five principal components showing neural activation from the cochlear nerve to the inferior colliculus are then regularly obtained but are still immature with regard to peak and interpeak latencies, and amplitudes.

Local Cerebral (14-C) 2-Deoxyglucose Uptake

This method, which allows investigation of functional fetal brain activity *in utero* through cerebral glucose utilization (energy metabolism) (for review, see Reference 48), has been used in two animal models, the fetal guinea pig[49,50] and the fetal sheep.[51,52] It has been shown that acoustic stimulation, pure tones in guinea pigs and VAS in sheep, induce a marked increase in (14-C) 2-deoxyglucose (2-DG) uptake in auditory structures, in the brain stem in the guinea pig and in all auditory structures, including the auditory cortex, in the fetal sheep. In the latter, bilateral cochlear removal results in a widespread diminution in glucose uptake.[51] In the guinea pig, frequency-specific auditory labeling has been obtained to loud, external free-field pure tones up to 20 kHz. The location of the labeling in the cochlear nucleus and in the inferior colliculus is a function of the frequency of the tones. They reflect the increased metabolic activity of isofrequency populations of cells in response to the auditory stimulation. Therefore, the tonotopic organization of the structures can be evidenced *in utero* with external airborne acoustic stimulation.

Cardiac and Motor Responses

The most extensively used procedure is to record in conjunction with acoustic stimulation (1) fetal heart rate (FHR) modifications, either transient (accelerative, decelerative, or biphasic) or sustained, such as a behavioral state change, and (2) reflex movements, which can be considered as homologous to startle components observed in the newborn (blink reflex accompanied with head movements and flexion/extensions of the limbs), or both.

If studies using nonspecific (VAS) auditory stimulation are included, more than 40 experiments have been published in the last 20 years. It has been found that stimuli above 105 dB SPL elicit these responses as early as 24 weeks GA in some fetuses; they are consistently evoked in all subjects at 28 weeks GA.[33,53] In near-term fetuses (35–41 weeks GA), as in newborns, these responses are modulated by characteristics of both the stimulus (intensity, frequency, spectrum, duration, interstimulus interval) and the fetuses (state of alertness).

Different states of alertness can be observed in the near-term fetus.[54] In our experiments, reported below, the effect of the auditory stimulation was examined in two states: (1) low-variability fetal heart rate (FHR) state (corresponding to quiet sleep) and (2) high-variability FHR state (corresponding to active sleep). We will see that interactions exist between state of alertness and nature of the stimulus in the elicitability and characteristics of the responses.

Responsiveness to High-Intensity Auditory Stimuli

Our group stimulated near-term fetuses (36–40 weeks), through a loudspeaker placed 20 cm above the maternal abdomen, with 5-second broadband noise (filtered below 800 Hz, to eliminate proprioceptive activation) and octave-band noises centered around specific frequencies.[55-58] In order to eliminate maternally mediated responses, mothers listened to continuous loud music through earphones. FHR was picked up by a Doppler tococardiograph recorded and computed for data treatment. Fetal movements (leg extension/flexion) were videotaped from a real-time ultrasound scanning system.

Loud stimuli, above 105 dB SPL *ex utero*, induce a high proportion of short-latency FHR accelerations generally accompanied by reflex motor responses. Less intense stimuli (100 dB) still trigger a significant proportion of cardiac responses but with a reduced motor response rate.

When motor reactions are induced, mean amplitude of FHR accelerations is higher (22 beats/minute; ranging from 6 to 48 beats/minute) than when there are no concomitant fetal movements (12.5 beats/minute),[56,57] thus reflecting a somatocardiac effect.

When either intensity or frequency of the stimulus is enhanced,[57-59] motor and cardiac accelerative response rates, and acceleration amplitudes, increase in both quiet and active sleep. A 5-dB SPL difference is sufficient to modify fetal responsiveness. Low frequencies, such as a 500-Hz centered noise, induce very few motor responses.

Responses are also modulated by fetal behavioral states: in active sleep, both cardiac and motor responsiveness are greater, cardiac accelerations have higher amplitudes and are more often accompanied with a motor response than during quiet sleep,[57,58,60] where cardiac acceleration amplitudes rise with intensity and/or frequency.[57,58] Schmidt *et al.* also found a greater reactiveness in quiet (3F) and active (4F) wakefulness compared to sleep states.[60] When stimuli are above 110 dB SPL, or VAS, response ratios are no longer modulated by state; when given in quiet sleep they induce an immediate change to active sleep (state 2F) or wakefulness with movement (state 4F).[29,30,59]

Responsiveness to Lower-Intensity Auditory Stimuli

A variety of stimuli between 85 and 100 dB SPL *ex utero*, either continuous or rhythmic (medium-frequency octave-band noises, music and speech sequences), induce mostly transient cardiac decelerations in both states, which are never accompanied by limb movements; cardiac response rates, however, are higher in quiet sleep than in active sleep.[58,61,62] The amplitude of the deceleration is largely dependent on stimulus characteristics and on FHR prestimulation variability. The deceleration response, however, is generally smaller than the acceleration response (range: –3 to –18 beats/minute). In newborns, decelerations are generally induced in a quiet alert state, but they were also observed during quiet sleep to moderate intensity speech stimuli.[63,64]

Near-term fetuses react, with a small-amplitude FHR deceleration (4 beats/minute on average), to a sentence repeatedly uttered by a recorded male or female voice at 90–95 dB SPL *ex utero*. Few FHR accelerations are elicited by this type of stimulation.[65]

Results have also shown that a change in some acoustical characteristics of a regularly repeated brief auditory stimulus evokes the same type of transient cardiac deceleration. Thus, with a habituation-dishabituation type procedure derived from the Clarkson and Berg study (demonstrating that newborns can discriminate between the vowels *a* and *i*),[66] we showed that near-term fetuses can perform acoustical discriminations. They discriminated between (1) two voices, one male and one female uttering at the same hearing level the same short sentence with the same prosodic contour[67] and (2) BABI and BIBA or the reverse order BIBA versus BABI.[61] This discrimination may have been performed on the basis of an intensity difference perception between the *ba* and the *bi*. Since intensities of the two syllables were equalized physically by the sound pressure level meter, we cannot be certain that they do appear at the same intensity to the fetal ear.

These results are not surprising since (1) various studies have provided evidence of the prenatal learning of the human voice (see below), and (2) intraabdominal recordings in both humans[13,17] and sheep[20–22] clearly demonstrated that *in utero* human voices are audible and somewhat intelligible for adult listeners. Speech prosody (rhythm, intonation, melodic contours) and some phonetic characteristics are well preserved *in utero*. Mother's voice is more intense than other speakers' voices, emitted at the same intensity (60 dB SPL) in the mothers' vicinity. Mother's voice emerges from background noises by 24 dB, while other voices, male and female, emerge from 8 to 12 dB SPL. Intrauterine restitution of male and female voice spectra are comparable.[17,18] When intrauterine recordings of external voices were recently made using a very sensitive microphone in the sheep, it was found that the speech was totally intelligible for adult listeners.[22]

Effect of the Repetition of High-Intensity Stimulus

The number of repetitions necessary for a significant response decrease, or total waning of a response, depends on the characteristics of the stimulus, on interstimulus time interval, and is variable from one fetus to another.

With auditory stimulation at or lower than 110 dB SPL *ex utero*, motor responses significantly decrease or disappear after only 2–4 stimulations.[1,55,57,68–70] As in the premature or term newborn, the fetal cardiac response is slower to habituate than the motor response. Significant reduction or disappearance of this response is obtained after 2 to 7 stimulations.[57,70,71] The amplitude of the cardiac acceleration also diminishes after a few repetitions of the stimuli.[57,72,73]

With a classical habituation/dishabituation procedure, Kisilevski and Muir have obtained a significant decrement of both cardiac accelerative and movement responses to a complex noise, at 110 dB SPL, followed by a recovery of these responses to a novel VAS.[70]

With strictly auditory stimulation, the decrement of the response also depends on fetal state. Habituation is faster during quiet sleep than during active sleep. For example, after 3 repetitions of a pink noise, proportions of cardiac acceleration show almost no change in active sleep, while they significantly decreased in quiet sleep.[57]

With VAS, a more intense stimulation, motor response rate decrement is much slower; it needs at least 6–40 stimulations to occur depending on fetal age and habituation criteria.[70,74–77] The authors do not notice any difference as a function of state. Kisilevski and Muir did not observe any statistically significant FHR accelerative response decline after eight VAS trials, but only a trend in that direction.[70]

AUDITORY PRENATAL LEARNING

Since a large variety of external sounds, including maternal and other voices, are available to the human fetus, and since the fetus exhibits auditory discriminative capacities, prenatal life appears to be a period during which the baby to be gets acquainted with some components of its future environment. One may wonder (1) if some auditory acquisitions stem from this early auditory experience, (2) what kind of learning processes can take place *in utero*, and (3) to what extent an early acoustical familiarization contributes to the adaptation of the neonate to its postnatal environment.

These questions had been asked as early as the thirties, after prenatal audition was experimentally demonstrated. For example, Ray[32] and Spelt,[78] in human fetuses, investigated the possibility of a classical conditioning between two acoustic stimuli. There was a renewed interest in the topic in the sixties, when psychologists took note of the imprinting process in birds and speculated about its possible role in the human neonate, specifically, the postnatal effects of (1) the maternal internal noise and (2) the maternal voice were considered.

Heartbeat and Other Internally Generated Sounds

Following Salk[79,80] there was a wide array of investigation of the effects of maternally generated internal noises. Initially, these studies were largely restricted to an examination of the soothing impact of maternal cardiac noises on the neonate. Probably as a result of differences in experimental design, such as the use of different types of stimuli or different observation timing (short-term or long-term), results were ambiguous,[15,81-90] some describing a soothing effect that others did not confirm. These uncertainties did not, however, prevent hasty commercialization and use of records and cassettes of these sounds by parents to calm their infants. This seems inadvisable until potential effects of such stimulation on neonates' behavioral development are better understood.

Maternal Voice

Another indirect observation was considered to favor the interpretation of the contribution of prenatal experience with the maternal voice: it was its particularly attractive effect on less than 2-week-old neonates,[91-94] precociously evidenced in less than 2-hour-old newborns tested in the delivery room.[17]

The positive valence of these two categories of prenatal stimuli was confirmed using nonnutritive sucking choice procedures: (1) DeCasper and Sigafoos confirmed the reinforcing value of the heart-beat sound,[95] and (2) a group of studies demonstrated the 2- to 4-day-old neonate's preference for the mother's voice. DeCasper and Fifer[96] and Fifer,[97] using airborne versions of these voices, first showed that infants preferred the mother's voice over other female voices. It was argued that the results could not be considered as unquestionable demonstrations of prenatal learning, since experimental conditions did not exclude the possibility of a very fast postnatal acquisition. The authors then compared the preference between airborne versions of this voice to its "intrauterine," low-pass-filtered, versions. No particular choice was then evidenced by Spence and DeCasper (while the newborns did prefer an airborne version of another woman's voice; this was considered a demonstration of a prenatal contribution to the neonates' global preference for the mother's voice).[98] Finally, Fifer and Moon, with a modified version of the "intrauterine" mother's voice (either mixed or not with maternal cardiovascular sounds), found that newborns preferred an "intrauterine" form of their mother's voice over an airborne version.[99,100]

Furthermore, DeCasper and Prescott found that 2- to 3-day-old babies did not prefer their father's voice to another male voice even after 4 to 10 hours of postnatal contact with their father;[101] this postnatal contact was thus insufficient to induce a preference to this voice. These results suggest that the nondevelopment of a preference for the father's voice is due to a smaller amount of prenatal experience to his voice compared to the mother's.

Specific External Sounds (Speech and Music Sequences, Language)

In the past 10 years, a series of studies directly demonstrated effects of prenatal familiarization to specific external sounds in premature and term newborns. When presented with different categories of sounds to which they had been repeatedly exposed during the last months of pregnancy, without any postnatal exposure other than during testing, they showed (a) a specific behavioral state modification, from state 6 (wakefulness with cry) to state 4 (quiet, attentive, alert wakefulness) as defined by Brazelton,[102] and (b) a significant preference for the previously experienced sound detected with DeCasper's nonnutritive sucking choice procedure.

Specific Musical Sequences

Satt found that 2- to 3-day-old babies preferred the recording of a prenatally delivered lullaby to an unfamiliar one, both lullabies being sung by the mother.[103] Feijoo in the delivery room[104] and Hepper on 4- to 5-day-old babies[105] observed that the infants were significantly soothed and attentive to music their mothers had listened to daily during the last three months of pregnancy. Feijoo delivered the bassoon part of Prokoviev's *Peter and the Wolf*;[104] in Hepper's observation, it was the musical theme of the mothers' favorite British TV series "Neighbors."[105]

In a study made by Busnel *et al.*[106] and Mosser[107] these observations were extended to prematurely born babies (32–37 weeks GA). Testing long-term modification of behavioral states (as attested by heart rate variability) during the exposure to different types of music, it was found that even though most music soothed a high percentage (50% to 90%) of agitated or crying babies in the five minutes following onset, the most soothing music was that which the mother had extensively listened to during pregnancy.

Specific Speech Sequences

DeCasper and Spence showed that 2- to 3-day-old newborns preferred hearing a story their mother had read out loud for 6 weeks before birth to an unknown one.[108] As no difference was found during testing if the story was read by the mother or another female voice, prenatal learning of some acoustic features of the story, probably prosodic, is suggested. Another demonstration of fetal learning of a short sentence, spoken loudly and repeatedly for a few weeks by the father during late pregnancy, was also given by Feijoo.[104] The babies were observed just after birth, and control testing showed that the soothing effect was not due to the father's voice alone but was an effect of that particular sentence read by him.

One of us (Busnel) is presently studying fetal and prematures' heart rate changes to different types of mothers' speech prosody (motherese or not).

Maternal Languages

In the following studies, the neonates had some postnatal experience with the maternal language before they were tested, either for a specific preference for this language or for their capacity to discriminate between the maternal language and another one. Using a nonnutritive sucking choice procedure, Moon *et al.* recently demonstrated that 2-day-old newborns preferred their mother's language, either Spanish or English.[109] Demonstration of a preference for mother's language at such an early age favors an interpretation of Mehler *et al.*'s data[110] in terms of a prenatal familiarization. In their study, 4-day-old babies discriminated between two languages (French/Russian or English/Italian) only if one of them was the mother's native tongue.

Long-Term Habituation to Startling Stimuli

Prenatal learning is also suggested by two studies of long-term habituation. Human and guinea pig neonates are significantly less disturbed by a startling sound if they were repeatedly exposed to it prenatally. The longer the prenatal exposure of a human neonate—living in the Osaka airport neighborhood—to airplane noises, the better he slept compared to babies whose mother's had lived in the area of the airport for shorter times during pregnancy.[111,112] In the same line, prenatally exposed neonate guinea pigs are less responsive (no significant heart rate change) to the vocalization of a Bantam hen than control animals, who had not been exposed to this sound during gestation.[113]

CONCLUSION

One can therefore conclude that prenatal exposure to maternal and external sounds not only allows the fetus to get acquainted with his future sound environment, but affects the development of preferences for sounds that will be relevant during postnatal life. It might also contribute to the development of auditory perceptive capacities.

With Fifer,[97] one is led to reconsider the earliest phases of attachment since the baby shows discrimination and preferential responsiveness for his mother over other women at birth and not at the 8–12 weeks proposed by Bowlby[114] and Ainsworth.[115] To follow Cairns' interactionist theory,[116] the very early recognition of the mother's voice probably organizes the discrimination and recognition of other maternal characteristics that will be gradually associated with already familiar ones. Among these, maternal olfactory features might have a particular status since newborns discriminate their mother's odor from that of alien mothers.[117] The human newborn might also be able to trace in the colostrum and milk, flavor compounds already present in the amniotic fluid. Animal experiments have indeed demonstrated the induction of postnatal olfactory preferences and aversions through prenatal experience (for reviews, see References 118 and 119).

Since so little is known about optimal prenatal stimulation, this corpus of data should not serve as an inducement, such as those provided in the media and in "prenatal universities," for future mothers to give to their fetus more stimulation than what they normally receive. However, it might be important to provide premature babies who are separated from their mothers and lack some of the sensory stimulation that newborns carried to term would normally receive, a variety of patterned sounds, including the parents' voices. This auditory experience would, in spite of important changes in the biological context, give them an environmental continuity as close as possible to what a near-term baby would experience.

ACKNOWLEDGMENTS

We wish to thank "Scientific Consultant," Bièvres, France, for providing scientific help for some of the research mentioned here. The authors are very grateful to A. Lehmann and B. Schaal for their helpful comments on the manuscript.

REFERENCES

1. PEIPER, A. 1925. Sinnesempfindugen des Kinder vor Seiner Geburt. Monatsschr. Kinderheilk. **29:** 236–241.
2. BUSNEL, M-C. & C. GRANIER-DEFERRE. 1983. And what of fetal audition? *In* The Behaviour of Human Infants. A. Oliveirio & M. Zappella, Eds.: 93–126. Plenum Press. New York, N.Y.

3. BRADLEY, R. M. & C. M. MISTRETTA. 1975. Fetal sensory receptors. Physiol. Rev. **55**: 352–382.

4. LECANUET, J-P., C. GRANIER-DEFERRE & M-C. BUSNEL. 1989. Sensorialité foetale: Ontogenése des systemes sensoriels, conséquences de leur fonctionnement foetal. *In* Médecine Périnatale. J. P. Relier, J. Laugier & B. L. Salle, Eds.: 201–225. Médecine-Sciences. Flammarion. Paris, France.

5. TURKEWITZ, G., T. MOREAU, H. G. BIRCH & L. DAVIS. 1971. Relationships among response in the human newborn: the non-association and non-equivalence among different indicators of responsiveness. Psychophysiology **7**: 233–247.

6. LEWKOWICZ, D. J. & G. TURKEWITZ. 1981. Intersensory interaction in newborns: modification of visual preferences following exposure to sound. Child Dev. **52**: 827–832.

7. MAURER, D. & C. MAURER. 1988. The World of the Newborn. Basic Books. New York, N.Y.

8. LEWKOWICZ, D. J. 1988. Sensory dominance in infants. I. Six-months-old infant's response to auditory visual compounds. Dev. Psychol. **24**: 155–171.

9. PUJOL, R. & A. UZIEL. 1986. Auditory development: peripheral aspects. *In* Handbook of Human Biologic Development. P. S. Timiras & E. Meisami, Eds.: 109–130. C.R.C. Press. Boca Raton, Fla.

10. JOHANSSON, B., E. WEDENBERG & B. WESTIN. 1964. Measurement of tone response by the human fetus. A preliminary report. Acta Otolaryngol. **57**: 188–192.

11. BENCH, R. J. 1968. Sound transmission to the human fetus through the maternal abdominal wall. J. Genet. Psychol. **113**: 1172–1174.

12. HENSCHALL, W. R. 1972. Intrauterine sound levels. J. Obstet. Gynecol. **112**: 577–578.

13. BUSNEL, M-C. 1979. Measures intravaginales du niveau et des distorsions acoustiques de bruits maternels. Electrodiag. Ther. **16**: 142.

14. WALKER, D. W., J. C. GRIMWADE & C. WOOD. 1971. Intrauterine noise: a component of the fetal environment. Am. J. Obstet. Gynecol. **109**: 91–95.

15. MUROOKA, H., Y. KOIE & D. SUDA. 1976. Analyse des sons intrautérins et de leurs effets tranquillisants sur le nouveau-né. J. Gynecol. Obstet. Biol. Reprod. **5**: 367–376.

16. QUERLEU, D., X. RENARD & F. VERSYP. 1981. Les perceptions auditives du foetus humain. Med. Hyg. **39**: 2101–2110.

17. QUERLEU, D., X. RENARD, F. VERSYP, L. PARIS-DELRUE & P. VERVOORT. 1988. Fetal hearing. Eur. J. Obstet. Gynecol. Reprod. Biol. **29**: 191–212.

18. QUERLEU, D., X. RENARD, C. BOUTTEVILLE & G. CREPIN. 1989. Hearing by the human fetus? Semin. Perinatol. **13**(5): 430–433.

19. VINCE, M. A., S. E. ARMITAGE, B. A. BALDWIN, Y. TONER & B. C. J. MOORE. 1982. The sound environment of the fetal sheep. Behaviour **81**: 296–315.

20. VINCE, M. A., A. E. BILLING, B. A. BALDWIN, J. N. TONER & C. WELLER. 1985. Maternal vocalisations and other sounds in the fetal lamb's sound environment. Early Hum. Dev. **11**: 179–190.

21. GERHARDT, K. J. 1989. Characteristics of the fetal sheep sound environment. Semin. Perinatol. **13**(5): 362–370.

22. LECANUET, J-P., B. GAUTHERON, C. LOCATELLI & A-Y. JACQUET. In utero sheep transmission of external sounds. In preparation.

23. BENCH, R. J., J. H. ANDERSON & M. HOARE. 1970. Measurement system for fetal audiometry. J. Acoust. Soc. Am. **47**: 1602–1606.

24. BALDWIN, J. N., J. N. TONER, M. A. VINCE & C. WELLER. 1983. Recording the

fetal lamb's sound environment using an implantable radiohydrophone. J. Physiol.
    343: 6–7.
25. GERHARDT, K. H. & R. M. ABRAMS. 1987. The sound environment of the fetal
    sheep in utero. Fed. Proc. **46:** 356–358.
26. LENOIR, M., G. R. BOCK & R. PUJOL. 1979. Supranormal susceptibility to acoustic
    trauma of the rat pup cochlea. J. Physiol. **75:** 521–524.
27. LALANDE, N. M., R. HÉTU & J. LAMBERT. 1986. Is occupational noise exposure
    during pregnancy a risk factor of damage. Am. J. Ind. Med. **10:** 427–435.
28. ROMERO, R., M. MAZOR & J. C. HOBBINS. 1988. A critical appraisal for fetal
    acoustic stimulation as an antenatal test for fetal well-being. Obstet. Gynecol.
    71: 781–786.
29. GAGNON, R. 1989. Stimulation of human fetuses with sound and vibration. Semin.
    Perinatol. **13:** 393–402.
30. VISSER, G. H. A., H. H. MULDER, H. P. WIT, E. J. H. MULDER & H. F. R.
    PRECHTL. 1989. Vibro-acoustic stimulation of the human fetus: effect on behav-
    ioural state organization. Early Hum. Dev. **286:** 296–312.
31. FORBES, H. S. & H. B. FORBES. 1927. Fetal sense reaction: hearing. J. Comp.
    Physiol. Psychol. **7:** 353–355.
32. RAY, W. S. 1932. A preliminary study of fetal conditioning. Child Dev. **3:** 173–177.
33. SONTAG, L. W. & R. F. WALLACE. 1936. Changes in the rate of the human fetal
    heart in response to vibratory stimuli. Am. J. Dis. Child. **51:** 583–589.
34. SCIBETTA, J. J. & M. G. ROSEN. 1969. Response evoked by sound in the fetal guinea-
    pig. Obstet. Gynecol. **33:** 830–836.
35. WOODS, J. R. & M. A. PLESSINGER. 1989. Fetal sensory sequencing: application
    of evoked potentials in perinatal physiology. Semin. Perinatol. **13:** 380–392.
36. BARDEN, T. P., P. PELTZMAN & J. T. GRAHAM. 1968. Human fetal electroenceph-
    alographic response to intrauterine acoustic signals. Am. J. Obstet. Gynecol.
    100: 1128–1134.
37. SCIBETTA, J. J., M. G. ROSEN, C. J. HOCHBERG & L. CHICK. 1971. Human fetal
    brain response to sound during labor. Am. J. Obstet. Gynecol. **109:** 82–85.
38. STALEY, K., V. IRAGUI & M. SPITZ. 1990. The human fetal auditory evoked brain-
    stem. Electroencephalogr. Clin. Neurophysiol. **77:** 1–3.
39. STARR, A. R., N. AMLIE, W. H. MARTIN & S. SANDERS. 1977. Development of
    auditory function in newborn infants revealed by auditory brainstem potentials.
    Pediatrics **60:** 831–839.
40. SCHULMAN-GALAMBOS, C. & R. GALAMBOS. 1979. Brainstem evoked response
    audiometry on newborn hearing screening. Arch. Otolaryngol. **105:** 86–90.
41. GOLDSTEIN, P. J., A. KRUMHOLZ, J. K. FELIX, D. SHANNON & R. F. CARR. 1979.
    Brainstem evoked responses in neonates. Am. J. Obstet. Gynecol. **135:** 622–628.
42. KRUMHOLZ, A., J. K. FELIX, P. J. GOLDSTEIN & E. MCKENZIE. 1985. Maturation
    of the brain-stem auditory evoked potential in premature infants. Electroenceph-
    alogr. Clin. Neurophysiol. **62:** 124–134.
43. SALAMY, A., T. MENDELSON & W. H. TOOLEY. 1982. Developmental profiles for
    the brainstem auditory evoked potentials. Early Hum. Dev. **6:** 331–339.
44. ROOTEVEEL, J. J., R. DE GRAAF, E. J. CONLON, D. F. STEGEMAN & Y. M. VISCO.
    1987. The maturation of the central auditory conduction in preterm infants until
    three months post term. II. The auditory brainstem response (ABR). Hear. Res.
    26: 21–35.
45. ROOTEVEEL, J. J., D. F. STEGEMAN, R. DE GRAAF, E. J. COLON & Y. M. VISCO.
    1987. The maturation of the central auditory conduction in preterm infants until
    three months post term. III. The middle latency auditory evoked response
    (MLR). Hear. Res. **27:** 245–246.

46. ROOTEVEEL, J. J., R. DE GRAAF, D. F. STEGEMAN, E. J. COLON & Y. M. VISCO. 1987. The maturation of the central auditory conduction in preterm infants until three months post term. V. The auditory cartical response (ACR). Hear. Res. 27: 95–110.

47. PASMAN, J. W., J. J. ROOTEVEEL, R. DE GRAAF, B. MAASSEN & S. L. H. NOTERMANS. 1991. Detectability of auditory evoked response components in preterm infants. Early Hum. Dev. 26: 129–141.

48. GRANIER-DEFERRE, C. & R. ABRAMS. 1989. Effects of sound on fetal cerebral glucose utilization. Semin. Perinatol. 13: 371–379.

49. SERVIÈRES, J., K. HORNER & C. GRANIER-DEFERRE. 1986. Mise en évidence de l'activité fonctionnelle du système auditif in utero du foetus de cobaye. C. R. Acad. Sci. Paris 302(série III): 37–42.

50. HORNER, K., J. SERVIÈRES & C. GRANIER-DEFERRE. 1987. Deoxyglucose demonstration of in utero hearing in the guinea-pig fetus. Hear. Res. 26: 327–333.

51. ABRAMS, R. M., A. A. HUTCHINSON, M. J. MC TIERNANN & G. E. MERWIN. 1987. Effects of cochlear ablation on local cerebral glucose utilization in fetal sheep. Am. J. Obstet. Gynecol. 157: 1438–1442.

52. ABRAMS, R. M., A. A. HUTCHINSON & K. J. GERHARDT. 1987. Local cerebral glucose utilization in fetal sheep exposed to noise. Am. J. Obstet. Gynecol. 157: 456–460.

53. BIRNHOLZ, J. C. & B. B. BENACERRAF. 1983. The development of the human fetal hearing. Science 222: 516–518.

54. NIJHUIS, J. G., H. F. R. PRECHTL, C. B. MARTIN & R. S. G. M. BOTS. 1982. Are there behavioural states in the human fetus? Early Hum. Dev. 6: 177–195.

55. GRANIER-DEFERRE, C., J-P. LECANUET, H. COHEN & M-C. BUSNEL. 1983. Preliminary evidence on fetal auditory habituation. In Noise as a Public Health Problem. G. Rossi, Ed. 1: 561–572. Edizioni Tecniche. Milan, Italy.

56. GRANIER-DEFERRE, C., J-P. LECANUET, H. COHEN & M-C. BUSNEL. 1985. Feasability of prenatal hearing test. Acta-Oto-Laryngol. Stockh. 421(Suppl.): 93–101.

57. LECANUET, J-P., C. GRANIER-DEFERRE, H. COHEN, R. LE HOUEZEC & M-C. BUSNEL. 1986. Fetal responses to acoustic stimulation depend on heart rate variability pattern, stimulus intensity and repetition. Early Hum. Dev. 13: 269–283.

58. LECANUET, J-P., C. GRANIER-DEFERRE & M-C. BUSNEL. 1988. Fetal cardiac and motor responses to octave-band noises as a function of central frequency, intensity and heart rate variability. Early Hum. Dev. 18: 81–93.

59. KISILEVSKY, B. S., D. W. MUIR & J. A. LOW. 1989. Human fetal response to sound as a function of stimulus intensity. Obstet. Gynecol. 158: 47–51.

60. SCHMIDT, W., R. BOOS, J. GNIERS, L. AUER & S. SCHULZE. 1985. Fetal behavioural states and controlled sound stimulation. Early Hum. Dev. 12: 145–153.

61. LECANUET, J-P., C. GRANIER-DEFERRE, A. J. DECASPER, R. MAUGEAIS, A-J. ANDRIEU & M-C. BUSNEL. 1987. Perception et discrimination foetale de stimuli langagiers, mise en évidence à partir de la réactivité cardiaque. Résultats préliminaires. C. R. Acad. Sci. Paris t.305(III): 161–164.

62. LECANUET, J-P., C. GRANIER-DEFERRE & M-C. BUSNEL. 1989. Differential fetal auditory reactiveness as a function of stimulus characteristics and state. Semin. Perinatol. 13: 421–429.

63. EISENBERG, R. B., A. MARMAROU & P. GIOVACHINO. 1974. Infant heart rate changes to a synthetic speech sound. J. Aud. Res. 14: 20–28.

64. STROCK, B. D. 1981. Infant reflex and excitability during quiet and active sleep. PhD Dissertation. University of Wisconsin.

65. LECANUET, J-P., C. GRANIER-DEFERRE, A-Y. JACQUET & M-C. BUSNEL. 1992. Decelerative cardiac response to acoustic stimulation in the near term foetus. Q. J.

Exp. Psychol. **44.**

66. CLARKSON, M. G. & W. K. BERG. 1983. Cardiac orienting and vowel discrimination in newborns: crucial stimulus parameters. Child Dev. **54:** 162–171.
67. GRANIER-DEFERRE, C., J. P. LECANUET, A-Y. JACQUET & M-C. BUSNEL. 1992. Prenatal discrimination of complex auditory stimulations. Presented at the 8th International Congress on Infant Studies, Miami, Fla.
68. FLEISCHER, K. 1955. Untersuchungen zur Entwickllung der Innenohrfunktion (Intra-uterine Kinderbewegungen nach Schallreizen). Z. Laryngol. Rhinol. **3:** 733–740.
69. GOUPIL, F., H. LEGRAND, G. BREARD, R. LE HOUEZEC & C. SUREAU. 1975. Sismographie et réactivité foetale. 5e Journées Nationales de Médecine Périnatale: 262–266. Le Touquet, France.
70. KISILEVSKY, B. S. & D. W. MUIR. 1991. Human fetal and subsequent newborn responses to sound and vibration. Infant Behav. Dev. **14:** 1–26.
71. GOODLIN, R. C. & E. W. LOWE. 1974. Multiphasic fetal monitoring: a preliminary evaluation. Am. J. Obstet. Gynecol. **119:** 341–357.
72. BENCH, R. J., P. J. MITTLER & C. N. SMYTH. 1967. Changes of heart rate in response to auditory stimulation in the human fetus. Bull. Br. Psychol. Soc. **20:** 14a.
73. BENCH, R. J. & D. L. MENTZ. 1978. Neonatal habituation and state change. Q. J. Exp. Psychol. **30:** 355–362.
74. LEADER, L. R., P. BAILLIE, B. MARTIN & E. VERMEULEN. 1982. The assessment and significance of habituation to a repeated stimulus by the human fetus. Early Hum. Dev. **7:** 211–283.
75. LEADER, L. R., A. D. STEVENS & E. R. LUMBERS. 1988. Measurement of fetal responses to vibroacoustic stimuli. Habituation in fetal sheep. Biol. Neonate **53:** 73–85.
76. MADISON, L. S., S. A. ADUBATO, J. K. MADISON, R. B. NELSON, R. ANDERSON, J. ERICKSON, L. M. KUSS & R. C. GOODLIN. 1986. Fetal response decrement: true habituation? J. Dev. Behav. Pediatr. **7:** 14–20.
77. KUHLMAN, K. A., K. A. BURNS, R. DEPP & R. E. SABBAGHA. 1988. Ultrasonic imaging of normal fetal response to external vibratory acoustic stimulation. Am. J. Obstet. Gynecol. **158:** 47–51.
78. SPELT, D. K. 1948. The conditioning of the human fetus in utero. J. Exp. Psychol. **38:** 338–346.
79. SALK, L. 1960. The effects of the normal heartbeat sound on the behavior of newborn infant: implications for mental health. World Ment. Health. **12:** 1–8.
80. SALK, L. 1962. Mother's heartbeat as an imprinting stimulus. Trans. N.Y. Acad. Sci. **4**(ser. 2): 753–763.
81. TAKEMOTO, Y. 1964. Sleep induction by heartbeat rhythm. Folia Psychiatr. Jpn. **7**(Suppl.): 347–351.
82. TULLOCH, J. P., B. S. BROWN, H. L. JACOBS, D. G. PRUGH & W. A. GREENE. 1964. Normal heartbeat sound and behavior of newborn infants, a replication study. Psychosom. Med. **26:** 661–670.
83. ROBERTS, B. & D. CAMPBELL. 1967. Activity in newborns and the sound of a human heart. Psychiatr. Sci. **9:** 339–340.
84. BRACKBILL, Y. 1970. Acoustic variations and arousal level in infants. Psychophysiology **6:** 517–526.
85. BRACKBILL, Y. 1973. Continuous stimulation reduces arousal level: stability of the effect over time. Child Dev. **44:** 43–48.
86. SMITH, C. R. & A. STEINSCHNEIDER. 1975. Differential effects of prenatal rhythmic stimulation on arousal states. Child Dev. **46:** 574–578.

87. PALMQVIST, H. 1975. The effect of heart beat sound stimulation on the weight development of newborn infant. Child Dev. **46**: 292–295.
88. DETTERMAN, D. K. 1978. The effect of heart beat sound on neonatal crying. Infant Behav. Dev. **1**: 36–48.
89. SCHMIDT, K., S. A. ROSE & W. H. BRIDGER. 1980. Effect of heart-beat sound on cardiac and behavioral responsiveness in sleeping preterm infants. Dev. Psycho-Biol. **16**: 175–184.
90. KATO, Y., S. TANAKA, T. TABATA & S. TAKEDA. 1985. The responses of neonates to intrauterine sound, with special reference to use for screening of hearing impairment. Wakayama Med. Rep. **28**: 9–14.
91. ANDRÉ-THOMAS, A. S. 1966. Locomotion from prenatal life. Spastic Society. Heineman. London, England.
92. WOLFF, P. H. 1969. The natural history of crying and other vocalizations in early infancy. *In* Determinants of Infant Behavior. B. M. Foss, Ed. **4**. Methuen. London, England.
93. HAMMOND, J. 1970. Hearing and response in the newborn. Dev. Med. Child Neurol. **12**: 3–5.
94. BRAZELTON, T. B. 1978. The remarkable talents of the newborn. Birth Family J. **5**: 4–10.
95. DeCASPER, A. J. & A. D. SIGAFOOS. 1983. The intra uterine heartbeat: a potent reinforcer for newborns. Infant Behav. Dev. **6**: 19–25.
96. DeCASPER, A. J. & W. P. FIFER. 1980. Of human bonding: newborns prefer their mother's voice. Science **208**: 1174–1176.
97. FIFER, W. P. 1981. Early attachment: maternal voice preference in one- and three-day-old infants. PhD Dissertation. University of North Carolina. Greensboro, N.C.
98. SPENCE, M. J. & A. J. DeCASPER. 1987. Prenatal experience with low frequency maternal voice sounds influences neonatal perception of maternal voice samples. Infant Behav. Dev. **10**: 133–142.
99. FIFER, W. P. & C. MOON. 1989. Psychobiology of newborn auditory preferences. Semin. Perinatol. **13**(5): 430–433.
100. MOON, C. & W. P. FIFER. 1990. Newborns prefer a prenatal version of mother's voice. Infant Behav. Dev. **13**: 530.
101. DeCASPER, A. J. & P. A. PRESCOTT. 1984. Human newborns' perception of male voices: preference, discrimination, and reinforcing value. Dev. Psychobiol. **17**: 481–491.
102. BRAZELTON, T. B. 1973. The Neonatal Behavioral Assessment Scale. Spastics International Public. Monograph 50. J. B. Lippincott. Philadelphia, Pa.
103. SATT, B. J. 1984. An investigation into the acoustical induction of intra-uterine learning. PhD Dissertation. California School of Professional Psychology.
104. FEIJOO, J. 1981. Le foetus, Pierre et le Loup. *In* L'Aube des Sens. Cahiers du Nouveau-né. E. Herbinet & M-C. Busnel, Eds. **5**: 192–209. Stock. Paris, France.
105. HEPPER, P. G. 1988. Fetal "soap" addiction. Lancet **1**: 1147–1148.
106. BUSNEL, M-C., J-P. RELIER & C. MOSSER. 1989. Effect of acoustic stimulation on premature infants. Abstracts of the International Neonatal Intensive Care Collegium. Nijmeguen, the Netherlands.
107. MOSSER, C. 1989. Effet physiologique des stimulations sonores chez le prématuré. PhD Dissertation. University of Paris XII. Paris, France.
108. DeCASPER, A. J. & M. J. SPENCE. 1986. Prenatal maternal speech influences newborn's perception of speech sounds. Infant Behav. Dev. **9**: 133–150.
109. MOON, C., R. PANNETON-COOPER & W. P. FIFER. 1991. Two-day-olds prefer the

maternal language. I.S.D.P. Meeting.
110. MEHLER, J., P. JUSCZYK, G. LAMBERZ, N. HALSTED, J. BERTONCINI & C. AMIEL-TISON. 1988. A precursor of language acquisition in young infants. Cognition **29**: 143–178.
111. ANDO, Y. & H. HATTORI. 1970. Effects of intense noise during fetal life upon postnatal adaptability (statistical study of the reactions of babies to aircraft noise). J. Acoust. Soc. Am. **47**: 1128–1130.
112. ANDO, Y. & H. HATTORI. 1977. Effects of noise on sleep of babies. J. Acoust. Soc. Am. **62**: 199–204.
113. VINCE, M. A. 1979. Postnatal consequences of prenatal sound stimulation in the guinea-pig. Anim. Behav. **27**: 908–918.
114. BOWLBY, T. G. R. 1969. Attachment and Loss. 1. Attachment. Hogarth. London, England.
115. AINSWORTH, M. D. S. 1979. Attachment as related to mother-infant interaction. *In* Advances in the Study of Behavior. J. S. Rosenblatt, R. A. Hinde, C. G. Beer & M-C. Busnel, Eds. **9**: 53–89. Academic Press. New York, N.Y.
116. CAIRNS, R. B. 1979. Social development: the origins and plasticity of interchanges. Freeman. San Francisco, Calif.
117. SCHAAL, B. 1988. Discontinuité natale et continuité chimio-sensorielle: modéles animaux et hypothèses pour l'homme. Ann. Biol. **27**: 1–41.
118. SMOTHERMAN, W. P. & S. R. ROBINSON. 1988. Dimensions of fetal investigation. *In* Behavior of the Fetus. W. P. Smotherman & S. R. Robinson, Eds.: 19–34. Telford Press.
119. SCHAAL, B. & P. ORGEUR. 1992. Olfaction in utero. Q. J. Exp. Psychol. **44**: 245–278.

Sexual Differentiation of the Female Spotted Hyena[a]
One of Nature's Experiments

STEPHEN E. GLICKMAN,[b] LAURENCE G. FRANK,[b]
PAUL LICHT,[c] TAMER YALCINKAYA,[d]
PENTTI K. SIITERI,[d] AND JULIAN DAVIDSON[e]

[b]Department of Psychology
[c]Department of Integrative Biology
University of California
Berkeley, California 94720

[d]Department of Obstetrics and Gynecology
University of California
San Francisco, California 94143

[e]Department of Physiology
Stanford University
Palo Alto, California 94305

INTRODUCTION

In his account of big game hunting on safari in Africa, Ernest Hemingway repeated a common myth: that spotted hyenas were hermaphrodites.[1] This was just a comparatively recent episode in a continuing history of confusion regarding the sexuality of hyenas. Aristotle had long ago denied the status of spotted hyenas as hermaphrodites.[2] However, it appears that Aristotle's conclusion was confounded by reliance on a description of the "wrong" species of hyena, the striped hyena.[3] During the many years that intervened between Aristotle and Hemingway, the compilers of a twelfth century latin bestiary wrote of the spotted hyena that "its nature is that at one moment it is masculine and at another moment feminine, and hence it is a dirty brute."[4]

The source of all this controversy is the very unusual genital anatomy of the female spotted hyena.[3,5] In this species, the clitoris has hypertrophied to the point where it is essentially the size and shape of a male penis. Female spotted hyenas also display erections that, until recently, were indistinguishable to the human observer from those of the males.[6] In addition, the vaginal labia have fused to form a "scrotum" that contains bilaterally symmetrical pads of fatty/fibrous tissue, giving the superficial appearance of small testes.

[a] The Berkeley Hyena Project is supported by a grant from the National Institute of Mental Health (MH-39917).

135

There is no external vagina. Female spotted hyenas urinate through a central urogenital canal that traverses the clitoris and ends in an opening at the tip of the glans clitordis (the urogenital meatus). During copulation, the female receives the male through the urogenital meatus. The internal reproductive anatomy of the female spotted hyena follows a typical mammalian pattern. There are four extant species within the Hyaenidae: spotted hyenas (*Crocuta crocuta*), brown hyenas (*Parahyaena brunnea*), striped hyenas (*Hyaena hyaena*), and the small, termite-eating aardwolf (*Proteles cristatus*).[7] Among the female hyaenids, only the spotted hyena displays highly "masculinized" genitals.[8]

In his classic 1939 monograph on the urogenital anatomy of spotted hyenas, Matthews linked his own observations on the relative abundance of stromal tissue in the hyena ovary with the limited available literature on androgenic facilitation of clitoral hypertrophy. He concluded that "it therefore seems possible, if not probable, that in the hyena we have an animal in which androgenic substances are developed in the ovary to an unusual extent, so the peculiar organization, so closely resembling the male externally, is produced" (p. 74).[3] Matthews further noted the "striking resemblance" between the normal female spotted hyena and the pathological state of the external genitalia observed in a human female as the result of adrenal virilism. It is not entirely clear whether Matthews was suggesting that virilization of the female genitalia in the spotted hyena was due to androgens secreted by the fetal ovary, or the maternal ovary.

The preceding account forms the point of departure for the research program described in the present report. However, a great deal has been learned about the mechanisms of mammalian sexual differentiation, and the behavior of spotted hyenas in nature, since the Matthews monograph was written. These more recent observations raise the possibility that endogenous androgens, circulating in a female mammal during various stages of life, could have broad impact on behavioral and morphological development.

Androgens and Sexual Differentiation

Contemporary understanding of sexual differentiation in mammals begins with genetic specification for differentiation of the fetal gonad.[9] In male mammals, the gonads differentiate into testes, which secrete androgens, as well as a Mullerian inhibitory substance, during critical periods of fetal and neonatal life. These androgens promote the development of the male internal reproductive apparatus, masculinize the external genitals, and modify the developing nervous system to support a variety of sexually differentiated behaviors. Such androgens may also "defeminize" the substrates of typically female endocrine and behavioral responses, while the presence of Mullerian inhibitory substance results in regression of the internal female reproductive tracts. Among female mammals, in the absence of fetal/neonatal androgens, there is regression of the male Wolffian ducts, the external genitals assume a typically feminine configuration, and the nervous system develops in a manner compatible with a female endocrine/behavioral phenotype.

In considering actions of gonadal steroids, it has become conventional to distinguish between organizing and activating effects of such hormones.[10,11] Organizing effects are associated with relatively permanent changes in morphology, behavior, and the nervous system, produced by the presence of androgens during temporally limited stages of fetal or neonatal development. Activating effects are thought of as more transient changes, requiring the presence of gonadal secretions, typically after puberty. Goy and McEwen observed that some behavioral substrates require organization, but not activation (e.g., rough social play in primates), others only require the presence of an activating hormone, without prior organization (e.g., yawning in primates), while a final category requires the presence of androgens during both organizational and activational stages (e.g., male sexual behavior).[11]

Spotted Hyenas

The publication of Kruuk's monograph in 1972 marked the beginning of a new understanding of the behavioral ecology of spotted hyenas.[12] It became clear that they are primarily hunters, not scavengers. They are also highly social carnivores, living in "clans" of mixed age and sex.[12-15] Membership in a clan permits social hunting of prey as large as eland and buffalo and assists in defense of kills against lions. Members of a clan defend their territory against trespass by spotted hyenas of other clans. Females generally reside in the same clan during their entire life, while males disperse at puberty.[13] In nature, adult female spotted hyenas are heavier and more aggressive than males. Adult females dominate all immigrant male adults in a broad range of social situations.[12-17] Hyena clans are matrilineal societies in which juveniles and subadults acquire their mothers rank. As the result, small juveniles of both sexes can displace large adult males when feeding at a carcass.[14,18-20]

The communal den, typically an old aardvark (*Orycteropus afer*) burrow, constitutes the geographic core of the hyena clan. All cubs in the clan between 1 and 6 months of age spend the day in and around this burrow. Females come to nurse in the early evening, and males often join in socializing at the communal den in the late afternoon, prior to departing for nightly hunts. Adult males, and lower-ranking females without infants, typically spend their days at individual dens removed from the main group. They join in socializing at the communal den in the late afternoon, prior to departing for nightly hunts. This daily transition between solitary and social existence was first noted by Kruuk, who described the critical prosocial role played by "meeting ceremonies" which occur after separation. Such ceremonies involve two hyenas standing parallel, with the head of one adjacent to the hind quarters of the second animal. They then engage in mutual inspection of the anogenital region, including close sniffing (and sometimes licking) of the erect penis or clitoris. Kruuk noted that the subordinate animal generally displayed the first erection and presented it for inspection by the dominant member of the pair.[12]

Recent evolutionary explanations for the emergence of large, aggressive, dominant females among the spotted hyenas involve natural selection favoring androgenized females.[14,21-23] Such animals would have increased access to food in highly competitive feeding situations.[14,22,23] According to this theoretical view, the highly masculinized external genitalia of the female spotted hyena developed as a byproduct of selection for androgen-facilitated social dominance. Of course, secondary selection could then operate to favor the development of masculine genitalia used in meeting ceremonies and for signaling social subordinance. Highly competitive feeding is not characteristic of the other three hyaenid species, and they lack the unusual androgenized traits of the female spotted hyena.

THE BERKELEY HYENA PROJECT

Rationale and Specific Aims

Experimental provision of androgens to female mammals during critical stages of development produces external genitalia very similar to those that occur naturally in the spotted hyena, including hypertrophy of the clitoris and fusion of the vaginal labia.[9] Such externally supplied androgens also enhance body weight[24,25] and promote aggressive behavior.[26-29] If our current understanding of mammalian sexual differentiation is correct, the form of the external genitalia of the female spotted hyena *requires* the presence of androgens during fetal life.

The immediate impetus for our research program was the similarity between the suite of morphological and behavioral characteristics produced by exogenous androgen administration in female mammals and those appearing naturally in female spotted hyenas. We hoped that through the use of an unusual female mammal we would challenge the adequacy of current understanding of the process of sexual differentiation. In addition, we thought it likely that the work could reveal a route (or set of routes) by which endogenous androgens may influence the development of female mammals, albeit in less dramatic fashion than in female spotted hyenas. Females are larger than males in many mammalian species[30] and are also more aggressive than males, or dominant over males, rather more commonly than is generally believed.[31] Even relatively "masculinized" female genitalia occur in other mammalian species, including the European mole (*Talpa europaea*) and several viverrid species.[32] Finding an androgenic basis for the "masculine" traits of the female spotted hyena would encourage a more general exploration of natural androgens in female mammals than has taken place to date.

Since its inception, the Berkeley hyena project has had several specific aims. First, we have been searching for naturally occurring plasma androgens in female spotted hyenas that might account for the masculinization of their external genitalia and contribute to their large body size and dominance over males. We have also been interested in the source(s) of such plasma androgens. In addition, we have been tracking the development of a set of behavioral systems in which male mammals often differ from females as the result of androgens circulating during organizational periods of development. For example, in a number of mammalian species, provision of exogenous androgens to females during fetal/neonatal life leads to higher levels of vigorous social play[29,33] and increased aggression,[26-29] as well as more frequent territorial scent-marking.[34] Would the conventionally anticipated dimorphisms fail to appear, or possibly be reversed, in hyenas as a consequence of androgenization? There was an additional puzzle: given the many defeminizing aspects of circulating androgens on reproductive endocrinology and morphology,[23] how were female hyenas retaining the capacity to mate and successfully deliver their young?

As the project progressed, several broad issues emerged. First it became apparent that there were complex interactions between potential hormonal effects on behavior and the social context in which behavioral data were obtained. Such interactions are discussed in the ensuing accounts of play and aggression in hyenas. Also, our research called attention to the general problem of characterizing some behaviors (or even some morphological traits) as "organized" by fetal or neonatal androgens. For example, whatever factors produce dominance in hyenas might also secondarily influence a wide range of other behavioral (and even morphological) characteristics. If androgens worked by *direct* "organization" of the neural substrates for more persistent, effective aggression, they could then exert an *indirect* modulating influence on, e.g., play, scent-marking, and body weight. In many cases, these processes can be disentangled by purely behavioral manipulations, e.g., will sex differences disappear if we eliminate dominance as a controlling variable? The sections on body weight, play, scent-marking, and aggression all contain material relevant to this issue.

Studying Spotted Hyenas in Captivity

Although prior field studies of androgens in hyenas had provided significant information, it was apparent that detailed study of fetal endocrinology would be required for understanding the mechanisms of sexual differentiation. This necessitated development of a breeding colony in captivity. Within such a colony, we have also been able to carry out an ongoing analysis of hormonal and behavioral development throughout life, examining the emergence of sexually dimorphic and monomorphic traits. The study of peer-reared animals permitted examination of sex-linked dimorphisms, with the overwhelming impact of maternal rank eliminated from our assessment. There was a potentially negative aspect to the study of captive animals. Gains in experimental control could have been offset by behavioral pathologies that were the result of transporting animals from Africa and rearing them in unnatural peer groups. However, our peer-reared hyenas engaged in meeting ceremonies,[35] played,[36] scent-marked,[37] and eventually mated,[23] much as they do on the African savannah. Where differences in behavior between captive and free-ranging hyenas have appeared, they have inevitably been informative. For example, as detailed below, it was precisely such discrepancies between the captive and natural situations that provided us with new insights regarding the effects of coalition formation on stability of dominance in the social group, the role of male dispersal in the emergence of female dominance, or the possible influence of dispersal on sexual dimorphism in scent-marking observed in nature.

Our captive studies began with a group of 10 infant hyenas (7 females and 3 males) collected in Kenya during December 1984 and January 1985. A second cohort (5 females and 5 males) was also collected in Kenya during November and December 1985. These animals have been housed at an indoor-outdoor facility, constructed for the present project, at the Field Station for Behavioral Research in the hills above the Berkeley campus. Four females and two males had their ovaries, or testes, removed between 4–7 months of age in order to permit assessment of activating effects of gonadal hormones on behavior and morphology. Since achieving sexual maturity (at three years of age), the majority of intact females from our initial cohorts have been breeding in captivity. Within the last year, several females who were born in our colony have themselves given birth. The size of the colony fluctuates between 30 and 45 animals. We have already donated 11 animals to zoological parks, as a means of preventing overcrowding and increasing public education about these remarkable animals.

THE SEARCH FOR ANDROGENS IN FEMALE SPOTTED HYENAS

Androgens in Adult Female Hyenas

In 1979 Paul Racey and John D. Skinner published the first report of plasma androgen levels in female spotted hyenas.[38] They concluded that the traditional sexual dimorphism in testosterone levels was absent in the spotted hyena, i.e., that adult females had testosterone levels as high as those of adult males. The subsequent study by Frank, Davidson, and Smith provided an alternative interpretation for this result.[39] Working with a clan in which Frank knew the status of all individuals[13,14] permitted division of males into "resident" and "transient" groups. Under these circumstances, it was clear that resident males had testosterone levels that were substantially higher than female members of the clan. It seemed likely that the stress attendant upon dispersal, or early attempts to join a clan, might have suppressed testosterone levels in transient animals. The recent report of van Jaarrsveld and Skinner supports this view.[40] Our data, from hyenas raised and maintained in the Berkeley colony, are also in accord with this general conclusion.[41] Although male levels are quite variable, testosterone is found in greater concentrations in male than in female spotted hyenas, as in other mammalian species.[41]

However, there is another androgen, androstenedione, which is found in unusually high levels in the plasma of female spotted hyenas relative to males.[41,42] This is a robust finding which is in general accord with reports from the South African group.[38,40,43] Androstenedione is a particularly interesting steroid because of its role as a prohormone,[44] an agent that exerts its biological actions after metabolic conversion to a second, more active, hormone. Depending upon the enzymes present in target tissues, androstenedione can be converted to an estrogen, or to testosterone. The presence of aromatase is required for metabolism of androstenedione to estrogen, while the presence of 17β-hydroxysteroid dehydrogenase promotes conversion to testosterone. The status of androstenedione as a prohormone, requiring conversion to a more active form prior to exerting any biological effect, led us to suggest that this selectivity may have been critical in permitting "masculinization" of certain behaviors without accompanying defeminization. Feder cites several studies in which exogenous administration of androstenedione during neonatal life in rats achieved masculinization of sexual behavior without defeminization.[45-47] That is, a female rat provided with androstenedione during neonatal life would show male copulatory behavior (when stimulated with testosterone) or female copulatory behavior (when stimulated with estrogen and progesterone) during adult life. If testosterone had been used as the organizing hormone during neonatal life, the female rats would have exhibited male sexual behavior when stimulated with testosterone, but would not have displayed female copulatory behavior when provided with exogenous estrogen and progesterone.

Convergent evidence clearly indicates that ovarian secretions are the source of virtually all of the testosterone and the vast majority of androstenedione found in the plasma of adult, nonpregnant, female hyenas. This is suggested by comparison of androgen levels in intact and ovariectomized adult hyenas,[41,42,48] as well as by *in vitro* studies of ovarian secretions.[49] Having the ovaries serve as the primary source of androgen in a female mammal may appear to be a somewhat unusual adaptation, as endocrinologists have traditionally looked first to the adrenal cortex as a source of androgens in female mammals. However, mammalian ovaries typically manufacture estrogen through secretion of androstenedione by thecal cells, which is converted to estrogen by granulosa cells in the presence of the aromatase enzyme.[50] Thus, androstenedione is a common product of the mammalian ovary, potentially available as a source for conversion to active androgens in other mammalian species.

Fetal Androgens in Female Spotted Hyenas

Our review of the search for androgens that might account for the masculinization of the female fetus can be organized in terms of a set of questions.

Are There Androgens Present during Gestation That Could Accomplish This Masculinization?

Lindeque and Skinner provided the first data on circulating androgens in fetal hyenas,[51] and we have since obtained additional information.[52] As regards the latter stages of gestation, we agree with Lindeque and Skinner. There are substantial (and approximately equal) plasma levels of androstenedione and testosterone in male and female fetuses. Lindeque and Skinner also reported very high levels of plasma testosterone in two early gestation (31-day) fetuses, one of which was designated as "male" and the second as "female" on the basis of the size of the phallus. However, as noted below, assignment of sex was uncertain and these data are more easily interpreted if both subjects were actually male.

What Is/Are the Sources of These Androgens?

The fetal adrenal would probably be the first source to be explored in accounting for the masculinization of the female spotted hyena. In human infants, female pseudohermaphroditism is characterized by normal development of the internal urogenital system and masculinization of the external genitalia. Grumbach and Conte observe that "congenital adrenal hyperplasia accounts for most cases of female pseudohermaphroditism and approximately half of all patients with ambiguous genitalia."[53] However, as noted above, our data suggest that the ovaries are a much more potent source of androgens than the adrenals throughout the postnatal life of female spotted hyenas. Although a fetal adrenal contribution cannot be ruled out at this time, there are two views of the hormonal events underlying the "masculinization" of these female hyenas that focus on ovarian sources. Lindeque and Skinner suggested that secretion of testosterone by the fetal ovary is the critical event, while we have presented an alternative explanation, emphasizing a maternal/placental source.[52]

Our case is built upon the following observations.

1. Plasma levels of androstenedione, which are normally quite high in the adult female hyena, are further elevated during pregnancy. In addition, plasma testosterone increases 10-fold during the course of gestation.[52] The presence of these high levels of testosterone in pregnant females, equal to

the maximum levels found in male hyenas, first raised the possibility that there might be a maternal influence on the developing fetus.

2. *In vivo* studies of plasma steroids in the spotted hyena during late gestation revealed that levels of testosterone in the uterine artery (which provides blood to the placental bed) and peripheral circulation were substantially lower than levels in the uterine vein (which receives direct input from the placental bed). When the placenta was removed, during the course of cesarean section, there was a rapid fall in testosterone levels (along with estrogen and progesterone) from the uterine vein drainage (and eventually all other sites).[52] These results indicated that the placenta was the primary source of high testosterone levels previously observed in the maternal circulation and gave support to the possibility that androstenedione, converted to testosterone by the placenta, was transferred to the fetus via the umbilical vein.

3. *In vitro* analyses, carried out in the laboratory of Dr. Pentti Siiteri, indicated that there is powerful conversion of androstenedione to testosterone (and to a lesser extent, estrogen) by the placenta of the spotted hyena.[54] This suggested that the placenta might be metabolizing androstenedione, secreted by the ovary of the pregnant female, and converting it to testosterone which then appears in the maternal circulation and is transferred to the fetus. Such a result is contrary to the role of the placenta in protecting the human fetus from maternal androgens. In the human female, the placenta normally acts as a barrier, converting maternal androgens to estrogens which are bound to large proteins and do not pass to the fetus.[55] Lindeque and Skinner draw on this natural protective role of the placenta in arguing against maternal viralization of the female fetus.[51] However, in direct comparative studies, Yalcinkaya *et al.* found that there was 20- to 40-fold less aromatase activity in the hyena placenta than the human placenta.[54] On the other hand, relatively substantial levels of 17β-hydroxysteroid dehydrogenase activity in hyena placenta resulted in abundant conversion of androstenedione to testosterone.

In March, 1991, a case report appeared describing powerful virilization of the external genitalia of a human female infant.[56] The source of the problem was an aromatase deficiency in the placenta. This resulted in a hormonal profile in the mother during pregnancy that bore a striking similarity to that of the normal, pregnant spotted hyena.

4. In samples obtained from the umbilical vein (carrying blood from the placenta to the fetus) during four pregnancies, we found levels of testosterone and androstenedione that ranged from 2–5 ng/ml. In several cases, we were also able to obtain samples from the umbilical artery (carrying blood from the fetus to the placenta). The concentrations of testosterone and androstenedione were generally similar in the umbilical vein, umbilical artery and the general circulation of the fetus. These results were compatible with maternal transfer of androgen to the fetus via the placenta.[52]

Lindeque and Skinner's conclusion that plasma testosterone in the female fetus results from secretion by the fetal ovary is based on data from one male and one female fetus during a late stage of gestation similar to that studied in our subjects. They found much higher levels of testosterone in the maternal circulation and in the umbilical artery (carrying blood from the fetus to the placenta) than the umbilical vein (carrying blood from the placenta to the fetus), supporting a fetal ovarian source of testosterone.[51] In more extensive measurements, involving several pregnancies and obtained at approximately the same time during gestation, we have never observed the pattern described by Lindeque and Skinner. In all of our cases, levels of testosterone in the umbilical vein have been an order of magnitude higher than those reported by Lindeque and Skinner, and in the three cases where we were able to obtain data from both umbilical vessels, there was little difference between arteries and veins. We have no easy explanation of the difference in levels of testosterone in the umbilical veins sampled by the Berkeley and South African groups. However, our samples were obtained under the usual laboratory conditions, while Lindeque and Skinner were working under relatively difficult circumstances in the field with hyenas that had been killed as part of a culling operation.

5. Following delivery, levels of testosterone fall rapidly in neonatal females, but not in neonatal males, suggesting that the male gonads are secreting testosterone, but the female ovaries are not.

Additional data are needed regarding placental conversion of steroid and transfer to the fetus at earlier stages of development, particularly during the time associated with differentiation of the external genitalia. Such data need to be collected in association with appropriate cytogenetic determination of sex. Lindeque and Skinner's early measurements were obtained from fetuses estimated to be 31 days of gestational age. However, they noted that, "at this stage, . . . the reproductive tract was still in the indifferent stage and the two fetuses were sexed on the basis of size dimorphism in the phallus, where the larger phallus was thought to be a male character, as was evident for older fetuses and as suggested for adults."[51] This classification may well have been correct, although it raised the problem of why the Wolffian ducts degenerated in the female fetus given equal levels of circulating androgen.

Alternately, if both fetuses studied by Lindeque and Skinner were male, it is possible that the early stages of sexual differentiation proceed in the ordinary manner, i.e., the basic masculinization of the internal reproductive system (development of the Wolffian ducts and degeneration of the Mullerian ducts) and initial development of the penis occur under the influence of testicular androgens. Then, at a somewhat later time in gestation, androgens arrive at both male and female fetuses via the placental circulation. This scenario is in accord with the adrenogenital syndrome in human females, where the external genitalia are extensively masculinized, while the internal reproductive apparatus remains essentially normal. The human pattern is attributed to the timing of androgen secretion, much as we have suggested for the female spotted hyena.[57]

SEXUAL DIMORPHISM IN BODY SIZE AND GENITAL DEVELOPMENT

Body Size in Male and Female Spotted Hyenas

In nature, female spotted hyenas are approximately 10% heavier than males and have significantly greater girth. They may also differ in body length, but these differences are smaller and more variable. It seemed possible that the greater weight of female hyenas in nature was a simple reflection of their greater access to food, as the result of behavioral dominance.[22] However, our studies of weight gain in captive hyenas indicate that, even under conditions where males have equal access to food, females become heavier than males as they approach puberty. Animals that had been gonadectomized during the juvenile period attained intermediate weights, ovariectomized females weighing slightly less than intact animals and gonadectomized males weighing slightly more than intact subjects; however, the latter differences were not statistically significant.[41,58]

The preceding comparison between field and captive data illustrates a first step in distinguishing between *direct* and *indirect* effects of hormonal influence. The fact that sex differences in weight emerged under conditions where dominance was removed as a factor in food intake leaves open the possibility that females are heavier due to androgens acting directly on some substrate underlying the regulation of body weight. Additional studies involving, e.g., the administration of antiandrogens during critical stages of development, and replacement studies with gonadectomized subjects would be the next experiments required to build the chain of evidence.

External Genitalia of the Female Spotted Hyena: Mating and Birth

One of the most puzzling questions presented by the female hyena is how she manages to mate and give birth through the clitoris. It is now clear that during the course of development, the opening at the tip of the clitoris (i.e., the urogenital meatus) enlarges[5,41] and increases in elasticity,[41] permitting the male to achieve entry. Similar enlargement is not found in females ovariectomized prior to puberty, nor does the urogenital meatus of ovariectomized females exhibit increased elasticity.[41] Although these changes, facilitated by the presence of ovarian secretions, permit copulatory behavior to occur, the opening is not large enough to permit passage of a 1.1- to 1.5-kg fetus during parturition. Having observed the birth process,[59] we now understand that the clitoris has to tear during delivery of the fetus. This typically leaves a prominent pink scar on the rear aspect of the clitoris which can easily be identified in field situations (e.g., Reference 15, p. 173). Subsequent deliveries are much easier. However, there are an apparently unusual number of stillbirths associated with initial delivery of infants by female spotted hyenas.[23,59] We have suggested that the difficulties observed in delivery account, at least in part, for the rarity of this form of female genital morphology.[23,59]

SEXUAL DIMORPHISM AND BEHAVIORAL DEVELOPMENT

Our behavioral studies have focused on patterns that are frequently sexually dimorphic in mammalian species, with emphasis on behaviors that are promoted in males by the secretion of androgens as organizing or activating hormones. If androgens have acted in female spotted hyenas, we might expect that such sexual dimorphisms would be absent, or perhaps even reversed, in our subjects.

Play

A number of investigators have reported naturally occurring sex differences in vigorous social play in rhesus monkeys[29] and laboratory rats,[33] with males engaging in such play more frequently than females. This dimorphism is dependent upon organizational effects of androgen. That is, provision of exogenous androgens to female rats, or monkeys, during organizational periods of fetal/neonatal life, increases the levels of social play. Our observations suggest that this sex difference in social play is absent in spotted hyenas, and may even reverse under appropriate contextual circumstances.[36] A group of five female hyenas from our second cohort engaged in much more vigorous social play (chasing, wrestling) than a group of five males from that cohort, when they were tested in all-female, or all-male, groups. However, when tested in mixed-sex groups, there were no differences in social play; the females apparently stimulated the males to increase levels of social play, while the presence of males depressed the levels of social play in females. Even in the mixed-sex groups, there was a sex difference in play, with female hyenas engaging in more individual locomotor play than males (running, jumping, climbing). There were no comparable sex differences in object play.

There is precedent for finding complex contextual effects on levels of social and locomotor play. Goldfoot and Neff observed that female rhesus monkeys increased their levels of social play when housed with single males.[60]

However, the latter effect disappeared following introduction of a second male, as the two males now played with one another and "ignored" the females. In regard to sex differences in object play, Barrett and Bateson found that male kittens engaged in more object play than females when they were reared in all-male, or all-female, groups.[61] However, rearing kittens in mixed-sex groups stimulated the play of the female kittens, eliminating sex differences in object play. There were no sex differences in social play in kittens, irrespective of the social context. At the present time, the quantitative literature on social play is seriously skewed towards species in which "traditional," more-play-in-males is the rule. We have no idea of the extent of species variation in sex differences in play, or of the role played by naturally occurring androgens on the development of play in female mammals. We return to this theme at the conclusion of the present paper.

Finally, it should be noted that Panksepp and his colleagues have challenged the idea of sexual differentiation of play by androgens in rats.[62] They suggest that the sex differences in play are actually the result of sex differences in dominance, i.e., that male rat pups play more than females because they dominate females and play is not maintained in the presence of excessive imbalance in dominance relationships. Whether or not Panksepp *et al.* are correct in dismissing the sexual differentiation of play, they have raised a distinction that is a major theme of the present paper: that it is important to distinguish between *direct* and *indirect* effects of androgens on the emergence of any behavior, including play. If there is reason to suspect direct androgenic effects on dominance, then the possibility of indirect effects on play would have to be explored. Once again, behavioral data can be used to assist in resolving the question. In studies of play involving our original groups of 10 animals, frequency of vigorous social play was not significantly correlated with dominance in either cohort.[63] This argues against an indirect influence of dominance on play. However, as in the case of body weight cited above, additional studies would be needed before claiming a direct organizing influence of androgens on social play. Once again, the logical starting point of such studies involves elimination of androgenic influence on the developing fetus/neonate during the presumptive organizational period.

Scent-Marking

There are a number of species in which territorial scent-marking is more frequent in males than females and in which frequency of scent-marking is related to dominance status.[64] Among a more limited set of species, androgens have been found to stimulate such marking, generally as the result of organizing and activating effects.[34] Spotted hyenas mark territories by depositing paste from anal scent glands on vegetation, particularly at borders between clans. The hyena typically straddles the plant or other object and, with tail raised, drags the bulging gland over the target in a semisquatting position.[12,15] Mills and Gorman have reported a detailed examination of pasting by spotted hyenas in the natural habitat.[65] The only sex difference they observed was linked to more frequent marking by males entering new territories. However, since these males were highly subordinate to resident females, they concluded that the typically positive correlation between marking and dominance was reversed in hyenas. Observations in our captive colony were in basic accord with Mills and Gorman, except for the effects of dominance status. In both cohorts, we found a significant correlation between frequency of spontaneous scent-marking and dominance status, as in all other carnivores studied to date.[37] Obviously there are fundamental differences between our conditions of observation and those in the field. Two are of particular importance. First, in captivity there was no dispersal, so males and females were always marking familiar areas. Second, under captive conditions, female dominance is not as all-powerful as it is in nature (see below).[58] In the natural setting, female hyenas rarely disperse, so one cannot compare male and female rates of marking in new territories. It would be of interest to determine whether males and females in our colony, allowed to move to a new area, would continue to exhibit the sex differences observed in nature. If they did, that would suggest that this aspect of scent-marking was sexually dimorphic. However, if the sex difference observed in nature disappeared in captivity, when both sexes were exposed to the stimulating effects of a novel environment, that would indicate that the sex difference in nature was an indirect consequence of male dispersal and might not be an example of a sexual dimorphism resulting from direct effects of steroids on the substrates of scent-marking.

Aggression and Dominance

Our studies of aggression and dominance were undertaken in an effort to determine whether sexual dimorphism in female aggressiveness/dominance emerged prior to puberty, as such differences emerge in the normal course of male androgenization in dogs[27] or rhesus monkeys.[29] We were also interested in whether the complete dominance of females over immigrant males would appear in our captive colonies, or whether there was some "cultural tradition" through which female dominance was maintained in nature. In order to understand the emergence of sexually dimorphic dominance and aggression in spotted hyenas, one must examine the stages of life during which aggression and dominance appear in nature. In particular, we have focused on four life stages that pose different problems for the developing hyena.

The Neonatal Period

In the course of examining sex ratios for litters in the field, Frank had noted that, given the number of mixed-sex litters, there were fewer all-male or all-female litters, and more singleton litters, than one would have expected by chance. He had begun to suspect that there was some mechanism through which litters of same-sex twins were reduced to singletons. Subsequently, while collecting infants in the field, Frank and Glickman observed a marked disparity in size between members of same-sex litters collected at natal dens, and noted correlated wounds on the back of the smaller twin. We also observed that one twin would frequently attack its sibling when we were attempting to feed the infants in our tents. This raised the possibility that there was serious intralitter aggression. However, we were not prepared for the intensity or the latency of aggression observed in captivity in association with delivery of twins. In every set of twins (or triplets) observed to date, there has been intense fighting, beginning shortly after delivery of the second infant, in litters born at term.[66] The fights are marked by vigorous "bite-shake" attacks directed at the upper back of the target animal. Spotted hyenas have a relatively long period of gestation (compared to striped or brown hyenas). Their cubs are accordingly very precocial, with good motor control, eyes open, and teeth fully erupted. The 6- to 7-mm long canines inflict substantial puncture wounds, and in nature, we noted serious infections accompanying these injuries. Although both twins usually survive in captivity, we suspect that is because the cubs have constant access to their mother. In nature, females give birth at the mouth of aardvark dens and when the cubs are very small, they typically are sequestered in these underground burrows when not nursing. This protects them from predation, but it also means that the mother cannot intervene in much of the neonatal fighting and, if one cub can keep its twin from emerging to nurse, that would ultimately prove fatal.

Combined data from field and captive situations suggest that female hyenas are losing as much as 25% of their reproductive potential due to neonatal aggression. Although such siblicide has been well established in predatory birds, this is the first report of regularly occurring siblicide in a mammalian species. In birds, siblicide is linked to resource availability. Although resource availability may play a role in hyenas, ultimate explanations will also have to deal with the peculiar sex linkage of the behavior, i.e., why mixed-sex twins survive in nature and same-sex twins do not. Frank has noted an unusual number of singleton sons born to the dominant females in his clan.[14] It will be of interest to determine whether the mother is contributing to this process through biased nursing, or otherwise favoring the outcome of neonatal aggression.

From our perspective, there are two particularly important aspects of this process. First, limited data from our colony and much more extensive observations from the natural situation indicate that female members of mixed-sex litters are likely to dominate their brothers. This is not an absolute effect. Among 14 mixed-sex litters, observed at communal dens in nature by Kay Holekamp and Laura Smale, females dominated males in 11, while males dominated their sisters in 3 cases.[23] Evidently, the bias towards female dominance emerges early in the life of the spotted hyena. Second, the high levels of androgen observed in both sexes during the latter stages of fetal life suggest that the intense neonatal aggression observed in this species may be dependent upon fetal androgens. The latter proposition remains to be tested.

The Juvenile Period

Recent studies by Kay Holekamp and Laura Smale indicate that the acquisition of maternal rank in nature occurs well after infants have been brought to the communal den, between 8 and 12 months of age.[18,19] At this time, juveniles begin accompanying their mothers on hunts. If they are to obtain the full benefits of acquiring their mother's rank, feeding ahead of adult males and lower ranking females, this is the time to do it. We have observed similar acquisition of maternal rank in studies of captive hyenas who are not engaged in social hunting.[67] Our studies indicate that, under captive conditions, acquisition of maternal rank can occur at an earlier age. However, at the present time, there is no evidence that this process involves sexually dimorphic components.

The Subadult Period

After they have acquired their mother's rank, there is a prolonged period prior to sexual maturity when individual hyenas continue to work out their relationships with other members of the clan. Holekamp and Smale report that during this time, subadult females are unusually persistent in aggressive interactions with adult females, engaging in such interactions more frequently than males. We have observed an analogous elevation in female-female aggression, compared with male-male aggression, during the subadult period. However, we did not observe any very general tendency for females to dominate males in our colony during this time.[58] Dominance was assessed during subadult life through (1) interactions during competitive feeding by an entire cohort and (2) by critical incident sampling of spontaneous social interactions. Although there was a significant correlation between measures of dominance in the two situations, there was no indication of sex-linked dominance.[68]

Sexual Maturity

Our two cohorts had to be split into four groups (5 hyenas per group) as they entered a pubertal period at approximately two years of age. At that time, the consequences of aggression reached an intolerable level due, in part, to the tendency of hyenas to form coalitions and initiate group attacks on low-ranking animals.[69] Hyenas participating in such coalitions, tend to follow some simple rules: (1) join the winning side, as long as you are dominant to the animal under attack, and (2) attempt to redirect a coalition attack towards an animal subordinate to you if you are threatened or attacked by a dominant animal. The net effect of such coalition formation is to maintain the status quo. The powerful social inertia that one finds in societies of long-lived, complex animals would tend to counteract any experimentally imposed hormonal manipulations.

During the period between splitting the groups and the birth of infants to females within these groups, the first clear indications of female dominance emerged within our colony. Each of the four subgroups was dominated by an intact female, as measured by competitive feeding or by critical incident sampling of spontaneous social interactions.[58,70] Also, on average, intact females were much more aggressive towards males than males were toward them. In addition, we had our first indications that ovariectomy had an effect on female aggressiveness towards males. All four ovariectomized females exhibited less aggression towards the males in their groups than males exhibited towards these females.[70] It should be noted that even during this period, all intact females did not dominate all males. Dominance is a complex trait in hyenas, as in other social mammals. Although there is substantial transsituational generality of dominance in hyenas, in nature and in captivity, the routes to dominance involve more than individual dyadic aggression. In nature, dominance of adult females over males is restricted to immigrants. Males who delay dispersal through the time of sexual maturity continue to occupy a place adjacent to their mothers in the dominance hierarchy. In captivity, where there is no male dispersal, dominance is determined by the formation of coalitions. Males who are successful in enlisting the aid of dominant females may actually rise in rank above other females in their group, despite being much smaller and almost surely unable to compete with these subordinate females in one-on-one combat.[69] After the juvenile period, natural variation in weight was not a significant determinant of dominance in our social groups.[58]

Sex Behavior

We have described above a set of changes in the clitoris that prepare the female to receive the male during copulation. However, as Matthews noted,[3] there are still substantial problems presented for the male by the anterior placement of the clitoral point of entry. A description of mating in spotted hyenas, including a useful set of photographs, has been published by Schneider.[71] During mating, the female stands quite still and keeps the clitoris retracted within the abdomen. Her tail may be erect, but there is no obvious lordosis posture. Successful copulation involves the male assuming a rather upright posture, tucking his rear quarters somewhat underneath the female, and moving his erect phallus against her abdomen until insertion is achieved. This is followed by repetitive thrusting. The male then leans forward and rests his head on the back of the female. In captivity, we have seen females display clear proceptive behavior (approaching males and grooming them during intercopulatory intervals) and exert successful choice of mates, when more than one male was present. In the latter case, a female mated with a second male after the first was exhausted, but rejected the approaches of a third hyena.

In mammalian species studied to date, masculinization through the organizational effects of androgens normally results in varying degrees of defeminization in female mammals.[11] However, female hyenas are clearly perfectly feminine in their reproductive behavior, despite the presumptive evidence for the presence of circulating androgens during fetal life. It would be of considerable interest to know whether female hyenas are capable of responding to androgens by displaying masculine mating behavior. With their ability to maintain erections that are very similar to those of the male, they are perhaps the only female mammals equipped to manage a complete masculine role during copulation. Moreover, we have observed mounting by female hyenas with malelike phallic "flips" occurring at approximately 1/second. However, we have not been able to test the extent of simultaneous masculinization of female hyenas for several reasons. First, we have been reluctant to interfere with normal mating sequences since the project has been so heavily dependent upon achieving successful breeding. Second, we have not yet determined the hormonal regimen necessary for induction of receptivity in ovariectomized females. However, we are proceeding with studies of receptivity, induced via exogenous steroids, in ovariectomized hyenas.

CONCLUSIONS

Sexual Differentiation of the Female Spotted Hyena

Androgens are circulating at potentially significant levels in female spotted hyenas during fetal life (testosterone, dihydrotestosterone, and androstenedione) and during adult life (androstenedione, primarily of ovarian origin).

Convergent evidence indicates that androstenedione, secreted by the maternal ovary during pregnancy, is converted by the placenta to testosterone and passed to the fetus via the umbilical circulation. This is a unique route for androgenization of a female fetus, dependent upon low aromatase activity in the hyena placenta. However, there is precedent for such a mode of action in the form of a human case report, where low placental aromatase resulted in masculinization of a female infant.

We have presented a hypothesis regarding sexual differentiation of the female spotted hyena that relies on the timing of various androgenic influences during gestation. We suggest that plasma testosterone does not rise signifi-

cantly in the female fetus until primary differentiation of the internal reproductive tracts has been completed. Further studies are needed that clarify
the timing of androgens circulating in male and female fetuses and explore the
sources of such androgens (placenta or fetal ovary). We also need to determine whether such androgens are the effective agents accounting for the
varied aspects of masculinization in female spotted hyenas. This would involve either inhibiting the release of these androgens, or interfering with their
activity.

There are a number of behavioral traits (play, scent-marking, and aggression) that are frequently dimorphic in mammals as the result of androgens
circulating during organizational or activational stages of development. Such
behavioral dimorphisms were absent, or reversed, in hyenas in captivity. Female hyenas engaged in as much (or more) vigorous social play, scent-
marked as frequently as males, and were as (or more) aggressive than males.

Intact female hyenas came to dominate each of the four cohorts as our
animals approached sexual maturity. Ovariectomy, which resulted in a
drastic reduction in levels of androgens and estrogens, markedly reduced female aggressiveness towards males, although we do not yet know which steroids are responsible for this effect.

High levels of androgens, circulating in fetuses of both sexes during the
latter stages of gestation, may account, at least in part, for the unusually intense neonatal aggression that results in siblicide in nature.

There is a remaining puzzle. Even if the preceding effects of androgens
were influencing development of the female hyena during fetal life, that
would merely make them equal to males, not larger than males, more aggressive than males, or dominant to males. These latter observations could be
the result of (1) sexually dimorphic hormonal profiles during postnatal life,
and/or (2) the different social environment of the female hyena. In regard to
hormonal profiles, it seems possible that the combination of androgens and
estrogens found in the normal adult female spotted hyena could have effects
on body weight and the display of aggression that are very different from
those produced in the male by androgens, in the absence of estrogens. In addition, as noted above, female hyenas living in residential matrilines face
very different challenges than males dispersing into new clans. Such differences in the social context would also be expected to have powerful interac-
tive relationships with hormonal states in modulating the emergence of behavior. Finally, it is possible that there will be sexually dimorphic features
of steroid metabolism, or receptor distribution, that influence the potency of
hormonal influence.

The preceding hypotheses, regarding the presumptive androgenization of
the female spotted hyena, rely on conventional actions of steroids that are
widely accepted in the endocrine literature. If our line of speculation is correct, only the timing and magnitude of effects are unique to the spotted hyena.
However, alternative hypotheses have not been eliminated. For example, "ab-
errations" in receptors, or postreceptor processes, may lead to activation of

systems that are normally steroid dependent in the absence of direct hormonal stimulation. Some precedent for such phenomena can be found in the recent demonstration of an activating mutation of the stimulatory G protein that results in certain sex-related pathologies in humans.[72]

General Principles from an Unusual Animal

As described above, sexual differentiation of female mammals has been viewed as an essentially passive process, i.e., what happens in the absence of circulating androgens produced by the fetal/neonatal testes. To be sure, some researchers have sought to locate fetal/neonatal ovarian influences on the organization of feminine behavior that might provide a "mirror image" for testicular influences on male behavior. Although some interesting phenomena have been revealed, after a thoughtful review of the literature, Shelton Hendricks concluded that "any organizational actions of the ovary on the development of sexual behavior are likely to be much subtler than those so far established for the testes."[73] However, it is also the case that such studies have focused on the organizational effects of ovarian estrogens/ progestins on sexual behavior in a small sample of mammalian species. We wish to raise the possibility that sexual differentiation of female mammals may be influenced by naturally circulating androgens, not as dramatically as the female spotted hyena, but contributing to individual and species differences in morphology and behavior.

In accord with prior research,[61,74] our studies have emphasized the extent to which expression of sexually differentiated traits is dependent upon the environment in which they are examined. The magnitude of sex differences in play of hyenas, cats, and monkeys is clearly dependent upon the social context in which that play is evaluated. This is also the case for the emergence of female dominance in hyenas, where dispersal of individual males places them at a serious disadvantage when confronting large, aggressive females, capable of working in coalitions, on the home territories of the females. In addition, any effects of androgens on sexual dimorphism prior to dispersal are overwhelmed by the power of matrilineal associations and acquisition of maternal rank. Lovejoy and Wallen have recently presented data compatible with this view, indicating that prepubertal sex differences in aggression that are apparent in small, artificial groups are absent in larger, more natural groups.[75] However, Wallen and his collaborators have also provided evidence for the emergence of hormonal effects on sexual behavior of rhesus monkeys only when animals were observed in an appropriately complex environment. The impact of ovarian cyclicity on mating is not observed during spatially restricted dyadic pairings, but is evident in seminatural groups studied in larger enclosures.[76]

Artificial test conditions may reveal hormonal effects that are masked by natural contextual variables. But there are also cases in which hormonal effects can only be detected when critical aspects of the field situation are recreated in captivity.[77] It is only by keeping the natural situation in mind that the scientist can appreciate the power of hormonal variables in the natural setting.

Knowledge of a species lifestyle in its natural habitat is essential for interpretation of data in captivity, while data from captivity provide clues regarding the mechanisms of behavior observed in the field. Although the preceding may seem rather obvious, studies of hyenas reviewed in this paper emphasize the specific nature of the relation between field and laboratory studies. For example, without field data, the fatal consequences and hence the significance of neonatal aggression, might have been missed in captivity. Alternately, without captive observations on aggression, it would have been nearly impossible to discern the mechanism in nature, due to the subterranean denning habits of this species. Similar examples are provided above concerned with understanding the emergence of female dominance, or interpreting the significance of sex differences in scent-marking.

Our observations of sexually dimorphic phenotypic characters in hyenas emphasize the importance of attempting to distinguish between *direct* and *indirect* effects of androgens on sexual differentiation. Direct effects involve the action of androgens on tissues responsible for a particular behavior or morphological characteristic. However, it is possible that sexual dimorphisms in play are an indirect consequence of organizational effects of androgens on dominance-related substrates, or that sexual dimorphisms in aggression are due to organizing effects of androgens on body weight. Such possibilities need to be recognized. With the exception of differentiation of sexual behavior and urogenital morphology, the possibility of indirect differentiation emerges in every data set reviewed in this paper. Because of the complex, interrelated effects of androgens on body weight, play, scent-marking, aggression, dominance, and dispersal, disentangling direct from indirect effects requires careful attention. A first approach to distinguishing between direct and indirect effects of androgens can be carried out through careful examination of behavioral data, as indicated above.

ACKNOWLEDGMENTS

We are indebted to the many individuals who have contributed to data gathering and analysis for the Berkeley Hyena Project, including Michael Baker, Fred Cabral, Nancy Krusko, Irene Powch, Joanne Pedersen, Susan Jenks, Suzanne Page, Brad Steele, Katya Woodmansee, Sonja Yoerg, and Cynthia Zabel. Drs. Cedric Shackleton and Erla Smith performed important steroid assays. We are also grateful to veterinary staff of the Office of Laboratory Animal Care on the Berkeley campus (Drs. Diana Berger, Penelope Collins, Dale Dinardo, Roy Henrickson, Phil Litwak, Caroline Reed, David Sesline, and Ms. Denise Escontrias), and to the people who cared for the hyenas with unusual devotion (Bob Baiz, Joe Bezold, Katie Hertel, Charles Matthews, Kathy Moorhouse, and Monte Pickerell). Finally, we owe a particular debt to Mary Weldele who has worked with great dedication on every phase of the project.

We also thank the Office of the President and the Ministry of Tourism and Wildlife of the Government of Kenya and the Narok County Counsel for permission to collect and assistance in assembling the original cohorts of hyenas.

REFERENCES

1. HEMINGWAY, E. 1935. Green Hills of Africa. Charles Scribner's Sons. New York, N.Y.
2. ARISTOTLE. 1965. Historia Animalium. Translated by A. L. Peck. Harvard University Press. Cambridge, Mass.
3. MATTHEWS, L. H. 1939. Reproduction in the spotted hyaena Crocuta crocuta (Erxleben). Philos. Trans. R. Soc. Lond. B 230: 1–78.
4. WHITE, T. H. 1960. The Bestiary. G. P. Putnam's Sons. New York, N.Y.
5. NEAVES, W. B., J. E. GRIFFIN & J. D. WILSON. 1980. Sexual dimorphism of the phallus in spotted hyaena (Crocuta crocuta). J. Reprod. Fertil. 59: 509–513.
6. FRANK, L. G., S. E. GLICKMAN & I. POWCH. 1990. Sexual dimorphism in the spotted hyaena. J. Zool. Lond. 221: 308–313.
7. WERDELIN, L. & N. SOLOUNIAS. 1991. The hyaenidae: taxonomy, systematics and evolution. Fossils Strata 30: 1–104.
8. WELLS, M. E. 1968. A comparison of the reproductive tracts of Crocuta crocuta, Hyaena hyaena and Proteles cristatus. East Afr. Wildl. J. 6: 63–70.
9. WILSON, J. D., F. W. GEORGE & J. E. GRIFFIN. 1981. The hormonal control of sexual development. Science 211: 1278–1284.
10. PHOENIX, C. H., R. W. GOY, A. A. GERALL & W. C. YOUNG. 1959. Organizing action of prenatally administered testosterone proprionate on the tissues mediating mating behavior in the female guinea pig. Endocrinology 65: 369–382.
11. GOY, R. W. & B. S. MCEWEN. 1980. Sexual Differentiation of the Brain. MIT Press. Cambridge, Mass.
12. KRUUK, H. 1972. The Spotted Hyena. University of Chicago Press. Chicago, Ill.
13. FRANK, L. G. 1986. Social organization of the spotted hyaena (Crocuta crocuta). I. Demography. Anim. Behav. 34: 1500–1509.
14. FRANK, L. G. 1986. Social organization of the spotted hyaena Crocuta crocuta. II. Dominance and reproduction. Anim. Behav. 34: 1510–1527.
15. MILLS, M. G. L. 1990. Kalahari Hyaenas: Comparative Behavioural Ecology of Two Species. Unwin Hyman. London, England.
16. HENSCHEL, J. R. & J. D. SKINNER. 1987. Social relationships and dispersal patterns in a clan of spotted hyaenas Crocuta crocuta in the Kruger National Park. South Afr. J. Zool. 22: 18–24.
17. TILSON, R. & W. J. HAMILTON. 1984. Social dominance and feeding patterns of spotted hyaenas. Anim. Behav. 32: 715–724.
18. HOLEKAMP, K. E. & L. SMALE. 1991. Dominance acquisition during mammalian social development: the "inheritance" of maternal rank. Am. Zool. 31: 306–317.
19. SMALE, L., L. G. FRANK & K. E. HOLEKAMP. Ontogeny of dominance in free-living spotted hyaenas: juvenile rank relations with adults. (Submitted.)

20. HOLEKAMP, K. E. & L. SMALE. Ontogeny of dominance in free-living spotted hyaenas: juvenile rank relations with other immature individuals. (Submitted.)
21. GOULD, S. J. 1981. Hyena myths and realities. Nat. Hist. **90**: 16–20.
22. HAMILTON, W. J., III, R. L. TILSON & L. G. FRANK. 1986. Sexual monomorphism in spotted hyaenas. Ethology **71**: 63–73.
23. GLICKMAN, S. E., L. G. FRANK, K. E. HOLEKAMP, L. SMALE & P. LICHT. Costs and benefits of "androgenization" in the female spotted hyena: the natural selection of physiological mechanisms. *In* Perspectives in Ethology. P. P. G. Bateson, P. Klopfer & N. Thompson, Eds. Plenum Press. New York, N.Y. (In press.)
24. BELL, D. D. & I. ZUCKER. 1971. Sex differences in body weight and eating: organization and activation by gonadal hormones in the rat. Physiol. Behav. **7**: 27–34.
25. WADE, G. N. 1976. Sex hormones, regulatory behaviors and body weight. *In* Advances in the Study of Behavior. J. S. Rosenblatt, R. A. Hinde, E. Shaw & C. G. Beer, Eds. **6**: 201–279. Academic Press. New York, N.Y.
26. MONAGHAN, E. P. & S. E. GLICKMAN. 1992. Hormones and aggressive behavior. *In* Behavioral Endocrinology. J. B. Becker, S. M. Breedlove & D. Crews, Eds.: 261–286. MIT Press. Cambridge, Mass.
27. BEACH, F. A. 1970. Coital behaviour in dogs. VII. Social affinity, dominance and sexual preference in the bitch. Behaviour **36**: 132–147.
28. BEACH, F. A., M. G. BUEHLER & I. F. DUNBAR. 1982. Competitive behavior in male, female and pseudohermaphroditic dogs. J. Comp. Physiol. Psychol. **96**: 855–874.
29. GOY, R. W. & C. H. PHOENIX. 1971. The effects of testosterone proprionate administered before birth on the development of behavior in genetic female Rhesus monkeys. *In* Steroid Hormones and Brain Function. C. H. Sawyer & R. A. Gorski, Eds.: 193–200. University of Calif. Press. Berkeley, Calif.
30. RALLS, K. 1976. Mammals in which females are larger than males. Q. Rev. Biol. **51**: 245–276.
31. FLOODY, O. R. 1983. Hormones and aggression in female mammals. *In* Hormones and Aggressive Behavior. B. B. Svare, Ed.: 39–90. Plenum Press. New York, N.Y.
32. EWER, R. F. 1973. The Carnivores. Cornell University Press. Ithaca, N.Y.
33. MEANEY, M. J., J. STEWART & W. W. BEATTY. 1985. Sex differences in social play: the socialization of sex roles. Adv. Study Behav. **15**: 1–57.
34. YAHR, P. 1983. Hormonal influences on territorial marking behavior. *In* Hormones and Aggressive Behavior. B. B. Svare, Ed.: 145–176. Plenum Press. New York, N.Y.
35. KRUSKO, N. A., M. L. WELDELE & S. E. GLICKMAN. 1988. Meeting ceremonies in a colony of juvenile spotted hyenas. Paper presented at the annual meeting of the Animal Behavior Society, Missoula, Mont.
36. PEDERSEN, J. M., S. E. GLICKMAN, L. G. FRANK & F. A. BEACH. 1990. Sex differences in play behavior of immature spotted hyenas, *Crocuta crocuta*. Horm. Behav. **24**: 403–420.
37. WOODMANSEE, K. B., C. J. ZABEL, S. E. GLICKMAN, L. G. FRANK & G. KEPPEL. 1991. Scent marking (pasting) in a colony of immature spotted hyenas (*Crocuta crocuta*): a developmental study. J. Comp. Psychol. **105**: 10–14.
38. RACEY, P. A. & J. D. SKINNER. 1979. Endocrine aspects of sexual mimicry in spotted hyaenas, *Crocuta crocuta*. J. Zool. Lond. **187**: 315–326.
39. FRANK, L. G., J. M. DAVIDSON & E. R. SMITH. 1985. Androgen levels in the spotted hyaena: the influence of social factors. J. Zool. Lond. **206**: 525–531.
40. VAN JAARSVELD, A. S. & J. D. SKINNER. 1991. Plasma androgens in spotted hyaenas (*Crocuta crocuta*): influence of social and reproductive development. J. Reprod. Fertil. **93**: 195–201.

41. GLICKMAN, S. E., L. G. FRANK, S. PAVGI & P. LICHT. 1992. Hormonal correlates of 'masculinization' in female spotted hyaenas (*Crocuta crocuta*). 1. Infancy through sexual maturity. J. Reprod. Fertil. **95:** 451–462.
42. GLICKMAN, S. E., L. G. FRANK, J. M. DAVIDSON, E. R. SMITH & P. K. SIITERI. 1987. Androstenedione may organize or activate sex reversed traits in female spotted hyenas. Proc. Natl. Acad. Sci. USA **84:** 3444–3447.
43. LINDEQUE, M., J. D. SKINNER & R. P. MILLAR. 1986. Adrenal and gonadal contribution to circulating androgens in spotted hyaenas, *Crocuta crocuta*, as revealed by LHRH, hCG and ACTH stimulation. J. Reprod. Fertil. **78:** 211–217.
44. WHALEN, R. E., P. YAHR & G. G. LUTTGE. 1985. The role of metabolism in hormonal control of sexual behavior. *In* Handbook of Behavioral Neurobiology. N. Adler, D. Pfaff & R. W. Goy, Eds. **7:** 609–663. Plenum Press. New York, N.Y.
45. FEDER, H. H. 1981. Perinatal hormones and their role in the development of sexually dimorphic behaviors. *In* Neuroendocrinology of Reproduction. N. Adler, Ed.: 127–158. Plenum Press. New York, N.Y.
46. GOLDFOOT, D. A., H. H. FEDER & R. W. GOY. 1969. Development of bisexuality in the male rat treated neonatally with androstenedione. J. Comp. Physiol. Psychol. **67:** 41–45.
47. STERN, J. J. 1969. Neonatal castration, androstenedione, and the mating behavior of the male rat. J. Comp. Physiol. Psychol. **69:** 608–612.
48. FRANK, L. G., E. R. SMITH & J. M. DAVIDSON. 1985. Testicular origin of circulating androgen in the spotted hyaena *Crocuta crocuta*. J. Zool. Lond. **207:** 613–615.
49. LICHT, P., L. G. FRANK, S. PAVGI, T. M. YALCINKAYA, P. K. SIITERI & S. E. GLICKMAN. 1992. Hormonal correlates of "masculinization" in female spotted hyaenas (*Crocuta crocuta*). 2. Maternal and fetal steroids. J. Reprod. Fertil. **95:** 463–474.
50. ERICKSON, G. F., D. A. MAGOFFIN, C. A. DYER & C. HOFEDITZ. 1985. Endocr. Rev. **6:** 371–398.
51. LINDEQUE, M. & J. D. SKINNER. 1982. Fetal androgens and sexual mimicry in spotted hyaenas, *Crocuta crocuta*. J. Reprod. Fertil. **67:** 405–410.
52. LICHT, P. & S. PAVGI. Unpublished observations.
53. GRUMBACH, M. M. & F. A. CONTE. 1985. Disorders of sexual differentiation. *In* Williams Textbook of Endocrinology. J. D. Wilson & D. W. Foster, Eds.: 312–401. W. B. Saunders. Philadelphia, Pa.
54. YALCINKAYA, T. M., P. LICHT, S. E. GLICKMAN & P. K. SIITERI. 1991. Endocrine studies in the spotted hyena (SH). Society of Gynecological Investigation 38th Annual Scientific Meeting, abstract No. 172.
55. SIITERI, P. K. & M. SERON-FERRE. 1978. Secretion and metabolism of adrenal androgens to estrogens. *In* Endocrine Function of the Human Adrenal Cortex: 251–264. Academic Press. London, England.
56. SHOZU, M., K. AKASOFU, T. HARADA & Y. KUBOTA. 1991. A new cause of female pseudohermaphroditism: placental aromatase deficiency. J. Clin. Endocrinol. Metab. **72:** 560–566.
57. MONEY, J. & A. A. EHRHARDT. 1972. Man and Woman, Boy and Girl. Johns Hopkins University Press. Baltimore, Md.
58. FRANK, L. G., S. E. GLICKMAN & C. J. ZABEL. 1989. Ontogeny of female dominance in the spotted hyaena: perspectives from nature and captivity. Symp. Zool. Soc. Lond. **61:** 127–146.
59. FRANK, L. G. & S. E. GLICKMAN. Parturition in the spotted hyaena (*Crocuta crocuta*). J. Zool. (In press.)

60. GOLDFOOT, D. A. & D. A. NEFF. 1985. On measuring behavioral sex differences in social contexts. *In* Handbook of Behavioral Neurobiology. N. Adler, D. Pfaff & R. W. Goy, Eds. **7:** 767–783. Plenum Press. New York, N.Y.

61. BARRETT, P. & P. BATESON. 1978. The development of play in cats. Behaviour **66:** 106–120.

62. PANKSEPP, J., S. SIVIY & L. NORMANSELL. 1984. The psychobiology of play: theoretical and methodological perspectives. Neurosci. Biobehav. Rev. **8:** 465–492.

63. PEDERSEN, J. M., S. E. GLICKMAN & L. G. FRANK. Play in captive spotted hyenas: a developmental study. (In preparation.)

64. RALLS, K. 1971. Mammalian scent marking. Science **171:** 443–449.

65. MILLS, M. G. L. & M. L. GORMAN. 1987. The scent-marking behaviour of the spotted hyaena *Crocuta crocuta* in the southern Kalahari. J. Zool. Lond. **212:** 483–497.

66. FRANK, L. G., S. E. GLICKMAN & P. LICHT. 1991. Fatal sibling aggression, precocial development, and androgens in neonatal spotted hyenas. Science **252:** 702–704.

67. JENKS, S., F. CABRAL, M. WELDELE, L. G. FRANK & S. E. GLICKMAN. Acquisition of maternal rank in captive spotted hyenas. (In preparation.)

68. GLICKMAN, S. E., L. G. FRANK, P. LICHT, C. ZABEL, J. M. PEDERSEN & F. A. BEACH. 1988. Hormones, morphology and behavior in the spotted hyena (*Crocuta crocuta*). Paper presented at the Conference on Reproductive Behavior, Omaha, Nebraska, June.

69. ZABEL, C. J., S. E. GLICKMAN, L. G. FRANK, K. B. WOODMANSEE & G. KEPPEL. 1992. Coalition formation in a colony of prepubertal spotted hyenas. *In* Us against Them: Coalitions and Alliances in Humans and Other Animals. A. H. Harcourt & F. B. M. De Waal, Eds.: 113–135. Oxford University Press. New York, N.Y.

70. BAKER, M. G. 1990. Effects of ovariectomy on dyadic aggression and submission in a colony of peripubertal spotted hyenas (*Crocuta crocuta*). M.A. Thesis. University of California. Berkeley, Calif.

71. SCHNEIDER, K. M. 1952. Einige bilder zur paarung der Fleckenhyane, *Crocotta crocuta* Erxl. Dtsch. Zool. Garten (NF) **19:** 135–149.

72. WEINSTEIN, L. S., A. SHENKER, P. V. GEJMAN, M. J. MERINO, E. FRIEDMAN & A. M. SPIEGEL. 1991. Activating mutations of the stimulatory G protein in the McCune-Albright syndrome. N. Engl. J. Med. **325:** 1688–1695.

73. HENDRICKS, S. E. Role of estrogens and progestins in the development of female sexual behavior potential. *In* Handbook of Neurobiology. N. Adler, D. W. Pfaff & R. W. Goy, Eds. **8.** Plenum Press. New York, N.Y. (In press.)

74. BERNSTEIN, I. S., T. P. GORDON & R. M. ROSE. 1983. The interaction of hormones, behavior and social context in nonhuman primates. *In* Hormones and Aggressive Behavior. B. B. Svare, Ed.: 535–562. Plenum Press. New York, N.Y.

75. LOVEJOY, J. & K. WALLEN. 1988. Sexually dimorphic behavior in group-housed rhesus monkeys (*Macaca mulatta*) at 1 year of age. Psychobiology **16:** 348–356.

76. WALLEN, K., L. A. WINSTON, S. GAVENTA, M. DAVIS-DASILVA & D. C. COLLINS. 1984. Periovulatory changes in female sexual behavior and patterns of ovarian steroid secretion in group-living rhesus monkeys. Horm. Behav. **18:** 431–450.

77. GLICKMAN, S. E. & G. S. CALDWELL. Studying natural behaviors in artificial environments: the problem of "salient elements." *In* Naturalistic Environments in Captivity for Animal Behavior Research. E. Gibbons, Jr., E. J. Wyers, E. Waters & E. Menzel, Eds. State University of New York Press. Albany, N.Y.

The Role of Maternal Stimulation in the Development of Sexual Behavior and Its Neural Basis[a]

CELIA L. MOORE

Department of Psychology
University of Massachusetts at Boston
Boston, Massachusetts 02125

The study of sexual development and sex differences has been one of the most active research areas in developmental psychobiology during the past three decades. Much of this work has been guided by the important discovery that male mammals secrete testosterone during embryonic or neonatal life. This discovery led to an explosion of experiments based on the manipulation of testosterone and related steroids during early developmental stages — experiments that identified hormonal effects on the development of a wide range of behavioral, physiological, and anatomical characters. The success of this approach has often left the impression that hormones act alone to organize the nervous system and that the prenatally or neonatally organized nervous system, in turn, determines the particular form that adult behavior will take.[1] However, the developmental effects of any factor are exerted within a psychobiological context of multiple determinants. For any given level of a particular hormone, these additional factors can alter developmental outcome. Furthermore, these factors can influence the pathway through which an effect of the hormone is exerted.

My own interest has been directed toward investigating the contributions of afferent input from the species-typical maternal environment to both sexual development and the emergence of sex differences in behavior. In this paper, I will describe some of the interrelationships between maternal stimulation and the hormonal condition of her pups and identify some specific contributions of maternal stimulation to behavioral and neuroanatomical development. I will also attempt to articulate some differences between understanding sexual development within an individual and understanding sex differences, which are matters of individual differences. Finally, I will raise the question of whether the maternal effects on masculine sexual development that have been found can be understood in terms of functional consequences for successful reproduction.

[a] This work was supported by National Science Foundation grants BNS 85-13687 and RII 89-05498.

160

CHARACTERISTICS OF EARLY STIMULATION

A rat is born with sealed eyes and ears, into a nest with many littermates and a single parent. The nest, littermate huddle, and many actions of the dam maintain homeostatic conditions required for survival and growth of this altricial mammal. Until the infant gains the sensory and motor competence to venture forth, its sensory world is constrained by the warm and familiar context of the nest.

Relative stability is a major adaptive consequence of the cohesion of dam, litter, and nest, but it would be a mistake to conclude that the environment of an infant rat lacks stimulation. The huddle stirs in constant slow motion, with pups on the top burrowing to the center as those on the bottom revolve to the top.[2] The dam alternates long bouts of nest attendance with time off to eat, rest, and groom. Each of her reentries to the nest brings chemical, thermal, tactile, and vestibular stimulation to her young. She brushes against and sometimes steps on pups as she shifts position over them; she nuzzles, mouths, licks, and manipulates them, moving them to and fro, and selects some to lick intently. Once settled into the crouching posture in response to the active probing of her thoroughly aroused pups, the dam becomes quiescent and the pups suckle in unison.[3] Even then, however, the steady suckling is punctuated by the periodic letdown of milk. A mouthful of milk elicits swallowing and a vigorous stretch reflex from each pup, who often then releases the nipple and searches for another.[4] Thus, events within the nest and the reactions of the young pups to them provide a rich, reliable stimulus environment that can be used to shape early behavioral development.

The dam is the primary source of stimulus flux for nest-bound infants. Dams differ from one another in patterns of nest attendance and levels of maternal behavior while in the nest, but much of the stimulation each dam provides is given simultaneously to all littermates (e.g., warmth and touch from crouching over them; tastes and odors carried on her body) or is randomly distributed among them (e.g., contacts while shifting position). However, licking and the handling that is associated with it are directed to pups one at a time. In conjunction with individual differences in pup attractiveness, this maternal behavior readily produces different stimulus levels for individuals within the same litter.[5]

VARIATION IN LEVELS OF MATERNAL LICKING

Several studies support the conclusion that two distinct behavioral patterns are subsumed under the label "maternal licking." Maternal licking that is directed to the perineum of pups is controlled by sensory and motivational mechanisms that are different from those controlling body licking, which includes snout and oral contact with the general body surface.[5] Perineal or anogenital licking (AGL) occupies more maternal time, occurring at relatively constant, high levels throughout the first 2 weeks postpartum before declining to relatively low levels by the end of the third week.[6] This coincides with the period during which pups require external stimulation to urinate and defecate. Body licking is more variable, but increases slightly toward the end of the second week, perhaps because grooming of the emerging fur is included in the category.[5] There is no evidence as yet that particular individuals are singled out for a disproportionate share of body licking, but males clearly receive more perineal licking than do their female siblings throughout the period during which this maternal behavior is performed.[6]

The biased stimulation of pups as a result of maternal AGL originates with the perinatal difference in the level of testosterone available to male and female infants.[7] The bias can be reversed by providing testosterone to females on the day of birth (FIGURE 1). Idiosyncratic differences among individual males and females, perhaps accounted for by individual differences in testosterone level, can also elicit systematic differences in level of maternal AGL. For example, male rat pups gestated by dams that were stressed by having been crowded during pregnancy elicit less licking than normally gestated males,[8] and female gerbils exposed to elevated prenatal levels of testosterone as a result of having been gestated next to males elicit more maternal licking than females gestated at a greater distance from males.[9]

Chemical stimuli carried in the urine of pups are important for eliciting

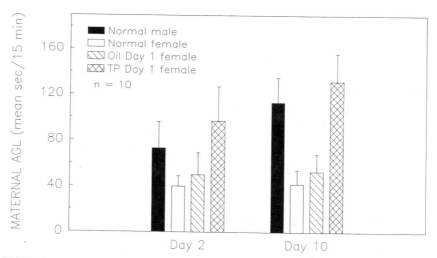

FIGURE 1. Maternal anogenital licking (AGL) during 15-minute presentations of 3 similarly treated foster pups. Treated pups were injected on the day of birth (day 1) with 0.5 mg testosterone propionate (TP) in 0.05 ml cottonseed oil. The differences between males and females and between oil- and TP-treated females were significant on both test days. (Reprinted from Reference 7 with permission. Copyright 1982 by the American Psychological Association.)

maternal licking, for guiding a dam to lick particular pups within the litter, and for directing her licking to the perineal region. Male urine is more effective than female urine for each of these functions. When dams are confronted with the opportunity to investigate two drops of urine, one from a male and the other from a female pup, presented on paper in an arena apart from the nest, they consistently direct more attention to the male urine.[10] When a piece of filter paper bearing a drop of urine from a male pup is placed inside their nests, dams respond by initiating a bout of maternal AGL; female urine is no more effective than saline.[10] When the urine is dropped on the skin of pups, dams direct licking to the treated pup, with particular attention to the region of skin bearing the scent.[11,12] Both male and female urine is effective in this context, but male urine—whether placed on males or females—leads to more licking.[11]

The preputial glands are one source of chemosignals that attract maternal licking.[12-14] These modified skin glands are found in both sexes, and they release their products through ducts that terminate near the urethral opening. Dodecyl propionate is a preputial chemosignal that has been isolated and identified as an effective elicitor of maternal AGL; it is produced by both sexes.[13] However, there is a functional difference in the preputial glands of the two sexes. Preputial gland removal eliminates the sex bias in maternal attention to pup urine, and preputial gland homegenate from male pups elicits more attention than an equal volume of homegenate from females.[14] Whether maternal discrimination is based on qualitative differences in chemosignals produced by the two sexes or on a sex difference in concentration of the same attractive chemical(s) is unknown.

There is some evidence that pups also influence the amount of licking that they receive by behavioral means. Male pups release a larger volume of urine with a longer latency after the onset of perineal stimulation.[15] Both of these factors have the effect of increasing the duration of a bout of licking. Males are also more likely than females to assume the characteristic leg extension response to perineal stimulation.[16] This response, which includes a supine, immobile posture with legs and tail extended, reliably precedes urine release and apparently assists the dam in her licking.

Recycled nutrients from pup urine are significant components of the maternal diet, and the motivation of dams to lick their pups includes an appetite for the salts and water in pup urine.[17] Differences in motivation for these dietary elements result in differences in the frequency, intensity, or duration of licking among dams. Dams may also differ in their ability to detect or in their interest in pup chemosignals. Differences among dams in propensity to lick add to the variation in maternal licking that results from differences among pups as elicitors of licking. Thus, although all developing pups must receive a minimal level of perineal stimulation in order to survive, there are reliable between- and within-litter differences in the amount of this stimulation that each pup receives during the course of early development.

MATERNAL ANOGENITAL LICKING AS
PUP STIMULATION

During anogenital licking, a dam typically uses her forepaws to turn the pup to a supine posture, with its head tucked under her. The light pressure of her body against its throat and chest has a quieting effect that inhibits the righting reflex. The dam holds the pup, usually by encircling its flanks with her warm forepaws. She then begins to lick the perineal skin with rhythmic, lapping movements. Tactile stimulation of the perineum and surrounding skin, but not other body regions, elicits the leg extension response from pups. If the pup responds, licking will continue until urine is released and consumed.[16] Odors on the ventral surface and vaginal area of the dam are readily available to a pup held for licking in the typical posture. In addition to eliciting specific postural adjustments, skeletal reflexes, and eliminative reflexes, AGL changes the arousal level of pups.[18] Thus, a bout of anogenital licking provides a characteristic cluster of vestibular, thermal, tactile, olfactory, kinesthetic, and autonomic changes for pups; these bouts are repeated several times daily throughout early development (FIGURE 2).

In addition to eliciting adaptive responses from pups that meet immediate survival needs, maternal stimulation has more general developmental conse-

FIGURE 2. A maternal rat performing anogenital licking. The close-up shows the characteristic orientation and the infant's leg-extension response.

quences for young rats. Tactile stimulation of the body surface provided by licking, handling, and contact with the dam's moving body affects growth by supporting both the release and the utilization of growth hormone and corticosterone by pups.[19] Such stimulation is also reinforcing for young infants: they will learn to approach odors that have been associated with a dam, or with stimulation that an experimenter provides with a brush so as to mimic maternal licking, handling, and contact.[20] Repeated pairings of tactile stimulation with a particular odor will lead to enduring changes in both behavioral responsiveness and the functional anatomy of the olfactory bulb.[21]

There have been no studies to compare the relative reinforcing properties of tactile stimulation applied to different body regions, and most studies using tactile stimulation as a reinforcer combine perineal with other body stimulation. In a study designed to determine whether tactile stimulation that is restricted to the perineum is a sufficient reinforcer, 18 males, 10–12 days of age, were placed, in pairs, into a warm environment permeated with the scent of wintergreen. Each pup was allowed to crawl into a holder, fashioned from rubber tubing lined with soft sponge, where they remained for 10 minutes. For 10 seconds during each minute, one member of each pair was rotated to a supine position and stroked only on the perineum with a soft brush; the other was exposed to wintergreen odor for the same amount of time, but was not stroked. An additional 9 controls were neither exposed to wintergreen nor stroked. After a 30-minute rest away from wintergreen, the pups were given 10 consecutive trials, at 4-minute intervals, in a Y-maze, with wintergreen scent in one arm but not the other. Each pup was given 40 seconds on each trial to enter fully into an arm of the maze. The groups did not differ in level of responsiveness: a choice was made on about half of the trials in each group. However, the groups made different choices. Pups in each control group chose the scented arm less than half of the time, whereas stroked pups chose the wintergreen arm over 80% of the time (FIGURE 3).

This study demonstrates that tactile stimulation that is restricted to the perineum is a sufficient reinforcer for young infants to develop an attraction to an initially aversive odor. However, many forms of stimulation, even electric shock,[22] can reinforce the formation of an attraction to novel odors in young infant rats. As Johanson and Terry have remarked,[20] it would be interesting to discover whether there is any specificity in the route of reinforcing stimulation and the behavioral or contextual nature of enduring responsiveness among adults to odors experienced during infancy.

Although the complete interaction pattern during maternal licking invokes a complex set of stimuli that engages several of the infant's modalities, the licking itself is focused on the perineum. The pattern of somatosensory input to the spinal cord from receptive fields involved in the control of lordosis has been mapped in studies of adult female rats. Inputs from pressure receptors in the skin of the perineum, posterior rump, and tail base are carried in the sensory branch of the pudendal nerve and enter the spinal cord at the dorsal roots of L5, L6, and S1.[23] Stimulation of these skin regions is

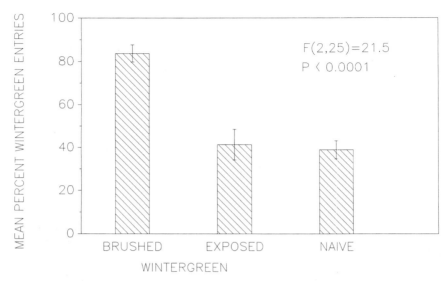

FIGURE 3. Brush stimulation of the perineum (10 seconds/minute for 10 mintues) that is paired with exposure to wintergreen leads to an attraction to that odor in 10- to 12-day-old male pups tested in a Y-maze.

a highly effective elicitor of both adult lordosis[23] and the infantile leg exten-sion response.[16] Both infantile leg extension and adult lordosis to tactile stimulation can be blocked by local anesthesia of these regions. Furthermore, it is in precisely these regions that the major share of maternal anogenital licking is concentrated. Thus, if somatosensory mechanisms are organized similarly in adults and infants, there are significant levels of maternally pro-vided input entering the spinal cord at the lumbar-sacral transition.

In adults, afferent input from the perineum and surrounding areas is car-ried to preoptic and hypothalamic brain regions where it figures importantly in many neuroendocrine and behavioral mechanisms involved in reproduc-tion.[24] Again, if input follows similar pathways in infants, the regions of the developing nervous system that will later underlie reproduction receive reli-ably high levels of afferent input from the licking behavior of the dam.

Electrophysiological studies of infant rats reveal that afferent connections to and within the hypothalamus develop primarily during the early postnatal period.[25,26] The time course overlaps with the postnatal production of gonad-al steroids and the postnatal contribution of these steroids to the developing nervous system. There is, furthermore, evidence to support the idea that the developmental effects of gonadal steroids on the hypothalamic-preoptic area require concurrent afferent input: pharmacological and surgical procedures that block afferent inputs to the hypothalamic-preoptic area interfere with the organizational effects of neonatal steroids on neuroendocrine and behavioral function.[27] Therefore, conditions in the developing nervous system are such that maternal stimulation could play an important formative role, particularly in conjunction with the primary actions of gonadal steroids.

MATERNAL STIMULATION, SEXUAL DISSIMILATION, AND SEXUAL DIFFERENTIATION

Behavioral sex differences in rats are not absolute: both males and females are capable of the full rat repertoire. Yet, the two sexes differ in a variety of behavioral patterns. Sex differences in behavior reflect differences in the threshold, rate, sensitivity, intensity, completeness, or other quantitative aspects of the components that constitute the behavior. Sex differences, like other individual differences, arise out of the developmental processes through which each of the behavioral patterns is organized within an individual. For a developmentalist, the term "differentiation" refers to the progressive elaboration of morphologically and functionally distinct systems out of uniform, undifferentiated beginnings within an individual. Thus, for sexual behavior and reproduction, these developmental processes are referred to as sexual differentiation. Of course, "differentiation" is in more general use to refer to the formation of any difference. In that sense, "sexual differentiation" is also used to refer to the formation of differences between individual males and females, whether or not these differences have anything to do with reproduction. These individual differences in behavior may arise from individual differences in sexual differentiation (strict sense), but they need not. Therefore, I suggest that it can be useful to have a more neutral term, "sexual dissimilation," to refer to the formation of individual differences between the sexes, leaving "sexual differentiation" to refer unambiguously to the development of sexual behavior and reproductive systems within an individual.

The degree of dissimilarity of the sexes varies considerably from one behavioral pattern to another: some differences are apparent in one context but not another, whereas others occur across the range of natural contexts. Play is an example of the former, and sexual behavior is an example of the latter.

The degree to which the sexes differ in some behavioral patterns can be modified by the amount of maternal stimulation provided through anogenital licking of developing infants. The normal sex bias in maternal stimulation may, therefore, contribute toward the sexual dissimilation of behavior. If greater stimulation were to make male-typical behavior more likely or more complete, then the typical within-litter variation in stimulation could account directly for some portion of the sex difference in developmental outcome. This seems to be the case for masculine sexual behavior, but not for play. This disparity suggests that not all sex differences, or the maternal contributions to them, rest on a common underlying mechanism.

Pouncing and wresting are forms of active contact play readily observed among juvenile rats. Both sexes engage in this play but, when sex differences are found, males do more of it.[28] If biased maternal stimulation mediates the sex difference in a straightforward way, males reared by dams who stimulate them less ought to play less. However, the opposite result is found. When maternal AGL was reduced by the use of perfume to mask the dam's reception of chemical stimuli,[29] by peripheral disruption of olfaction in the dam,[5] or by providing the dam with dietary salt so as to reduce her motivation to lick,[5] male offspring performed higher levels of active contact play than normally stimulated controls. Thus, sex differences in play are increased rather than diminished by reduced stimulation.

One possible explanation for these apparently paradoxical results is that general activity level is altered by maternal stimulation, with greater offspring activity associated with lesser maternal AGL. This pattern is consistent with the typical sex difference in activity level, and there is some evidence that open field activity is greater in males reared by dams that provide reduced stimulation.[5] Therefore, the observed maternal effect on play may be indirect, reflecting an interaction between an animal's activity level and some other internal or external factors that dispose males to play more than females. If this reasoning is correct, it might help to explain the inconsistent observation of sex differences in play across different studies.[28]

The contribution of maternal stimulation to sex differences in masculine sexual behavior is apparently more direct than is the contribution to differences in play. Although females can perform masculine sexual behavior, they are less likely to do so and their performance is deficient in a number of ways. Decrements in masculine sexual behavior are observed in both males and females reared by dams that provide reduced perineal stimulation.[30] The converse is also true: enhanced masculine sexual behavior results when females are provided with extra perineal stimulation during infancy.[31] Therefore, the reliable sex bias in maternal stimulation may account for some of the typical dissimilarity between the sexes in the degree to which mechanisms underlying masculine sexual behavior are developed.

The function of masculine sexual behavior is to fertilize eggs. Females, by definition, have no sperm with which to accomplish this; masculine sexual behavior can have no function for them. The argument that it would be maladaptive—risky and wasteful—for them to devote time to this pursuit is persuasive. However, the constraints of developing systems are such that it may be impossible for females to develop into functional adults without also developing at least some masculine copulatory mechanisms—and vice versa for males. A functional dilemma can be avoided by keeping in mind the distinction between the performance of behavior and the development of competence to perform it. In the usual course of events, females do not engage in masculine copulation, nor do males engage in feminine copulation. They lack the motivation to do so, in large part because they do not secrete adequate levels of the appropriate hormones. The degree to which they have the underlying capacity for the behavior may be irrelevant from a functional point of view. Indeed, much of sexual differentiation is identical for males and females within the same species, although species differ in the extent of sexual dissimilarity that emerges during the differentiation process.[32] It is for this reason that I have chosen to use "sexual dissimilation" to refer to developmental processes that produce sex differences and "sexual differentiation" to refer to the development of sexual capacity.

Although much of development among rats is shared by males and females, the testosterone secreted by males during early development both plays an important role in masculine sexual differentiation and originates a number of well-known sex differences. Testosterone and its metabolites alter developmental outcomes in many developing systems through effects that cascade from direct effects on the migration, survival, growth, and activity of cells.[33] Biased maternal stimulation as a result of differential chemosignal production by neonatal scent glands is an element in the early developmental nexus that can be traced to testosterone. It contributes both to some sex differences and to masculine sexual differentiation. In order to determine whether either or both of these effects are functionally significant, it is necessary to examine the details of the maternal effects.

MATERNAL STIMULATION AND MASCULINE REPRODUCTION

The sexually biased maternal anogenital licking stems from the differential production of chemosignals by males and females. Therefore, it has been possible to study the developmental effects of this form of maternal stimulation by interfering with the dam's ability to detect chemical stimuli from her pups. In one study, polyethylene tubing was used to line the nasal passages of dams from the day of parturition until two weeks later.[30] This procedure prevents odors from reaching the olfactory epithelium,[34] and was effective in reducing both forms of maternal licking in treated dams. The offspring were gonadectomized as adults, given identical testosterone replacement, and tested for masculine sexual behavior with hormone-primed female partners. Males reared by the treated dams had longer latencies to ejaculate and to resume sexual behavior after ejaculating; they also had longer intervals between intromissions. Regardless of rearing condition, females did not perform the motor pattern that is characteristically associated with ejaculation in males. However, the behavior of their dams did affect their performance of masculine sexual behavior: females reared by the treated dams were less likely to mount or to perform the dismount that characterizes intromission in males.

In a second, converse study, females were stroked daily with a small brush to provide them with extra perineal stimulation as neonates and then treated with testosterone as adults.[31] These females were more likely to mount a female partner and more likely to perform the intromission dismount pattern than were shoulder-stimulated sibling controls. These results, in combination with the nasal intubation study, allow one to conclude that some of the sex difference in ability for masculine sexual behavior can be accounted for by the differential stimulation males and females receive as neonates. However, regardless of level of infantile stimulation, the adult performance of the behavior requires conditions, such as adequate levels of testosterone, that are common for males and rare for females. It seems unlikely, therefore, that the sex bias in maternal anogenital licking has evolved to make the sexes different from one another. The differences that do emerge during development may simply be a byproduct of selection for other functional consequences. One possibility is selection to improve the development of copulatory mechanisms in sons so that they will be better able to compete with other males.

The nasal intubation procedure reduced maternal anogenital licking, but it also reduced body licking and produced distress in some of the treated dams.[30] Therefore, the method for altering anogenital licking has recently been refined.[5] A method that works well to reduce anogenital licking while having little if any effects on other components of maternal behavior is repeated (days 1, 2, 3, 5, 8, 11, 14 postpartum) peripheral treatment with very small quantities (0.05 ml) of 5% zinc sulfate solution while the dam is anesthetized briefly with ether. Application as a nasal spray permits small doses and apparently avoids systemic side effects that can accompany irrigation methods.[35] We did not observe illness in our dams, and the weight gain of pups, measured both at the end of treatment and at weaning, could not be distinguished from controls. We observed no effects on body licking and, if anything, the treated dams spent slightly more time in the nest, nursing their pups. However, there was a consistent reduction in anogenital licking throughout the period during which this behavior normally occurs. FIGURE 4 presents the data from a sample of treated and control dams that were videotaped for 4 hours daily in the study designed to develop this procedure.

We used the zinc sulfate procedure to rear males with reduced infantile stimulation. As adults, these males were compared with controls whose dams had simply been anesthetized on the same schedule as the dams that were anesthetized briefly during the applications of the zinc sulfate nasal spray. Unlike the intubation study, all males were left intact and received no testosterone treatment as adults. They were observed with estrous females until ejaculation had occurred on two separate occasions. Again, a number of quantitative differences in the sexual behavior of the males in the two groups was found. Perhaps the most striking difference was a reduction in copulatory efficiency for the males reared by the less stimulating dams (FIGURE 5). Copulatory efficiency refers to the proportion of mounts that include an intromission, as inferred from the characteristic form of the dismount.

We have also recently examined the effect of maternal stimulation on the copulatory behavior of males that mated to sexual exhaustion—i.e., until the male ceased copulating for the day—in each of two separate sessions. The

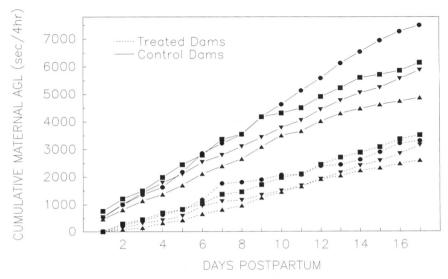

FIGURE 4. Dams with olfactory deficits perform less maternal anogenital licking (AGL) throughout the early development of their pups. Deficits were imposed by repeated treatment with zinc sulfate applied in small doses as an intranasal spray. Measurements were made from videorecordings of dams and their litters of 8 pups (half male, half female), taped in red light in time-lapse mode for 4 hours each day in the early part of the dark phase of the light cycle. Each curve represents a single dam; the 2 dams sharing a symbol were observed at the same time.

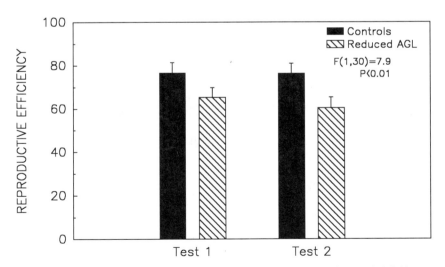

FIGURE 5. Male offspring of dams that provided them with low levels of anogenital licking as a result of zinc sulfate treatment were less likely to perform an intromission pattern upon mounting a female (reproductive efficiency) than were normally stimulated control males. The data are from 2 separate tests, each with one ejaculation.

reduced reproductive efficiency among sons of dams that provided reduced stimulation was found to persist throughout the two separate exhaustion series, each of which included multiple ejaculations over approximately 2 hours.[36]

Similar effects of maternal stimulation on masculine sexual behavior have been found by others, using perfume to mask the dam's reception of chemosignals.[29] Although the maternal effect has been relatively small in magnitude in each study, it does seem to be reliable across different methods of manipulating the dam and may play a biologically significant role in the normal development of males.

It is possible that enhanced maternal licking of males has evolved specifically for its contribution to increasing the probability of leaving second-generation offspring through sons. Clearly, males can grow and develop all of the components of masculine copulation with female-typical levels of stimulation. Although there is currently no direct evidence that the behavioral consequences of maternal stimulation would serve to enhance reproductive competition of sons, the quantitative changes in copulatory behavior that have been found after manipulation of the stimulation are suggestive of such an effect.

Rats have a polygynous mating system with male competition. Sperm competition during multiple ejaculations with the same female accounts for a great deal of the differential reproduction among males.[37] Reliable and appropriately timed intromissions and ejaculations are obvious behavioral components of this competition. Although it is unlikely that the relatively small maternal effects on masculine copulation that have been observed, such as those on ejaculatory latency and the probability of performing an intromission with each mount, would affect the male's ability to impregnate a female encountered in isolation, it is entirely possible that such effects would alter the outcome of sperm competition.

MATERNAL STIMULATION AND NEURAL DEVELOPMENT

Sperm competition is also affected by the penile reflexes that accompany copulatory behavior.[38-40] Penile reflexes are used during ejaculation to place a sperm plug so that it adheres to the female's cervix, which is a necessary condition for transcervical transport. During nonejaculatory intromissions, the reflexes dislodge the sperm plugs placed by competitors and disrupt transcervical transport. These reflexes are controlled by striated penile muscles and their motor neurons, which are located in sexually dimorphic nuclei of the lumbar spinal cord.[41]

One such nucleus is a dorsomedial nucleus in L5-L6 that innervates the bulbospongiosus muscles which encircle the bulb of the penis.[42-44] (These muscles have also been called bulbocavernosus muscles, and the nucleus has been named the spinal nucleus of the bulbocavernosus, SNB.)[42] Contraction of the bulbospongiosus muscles leads to complete erections with a flared tip to the penis and plays a role in ejaculation, formation, and placing of copulatory plugs; it is also used during removal of plugs placed by other males.[38-40] It is possible that maternal stimulation could affect the outcome of sperm competition by altering the development of this neuromuscular system.

We reared animals with dams that were treated with zinc sulfate, as described previously, or with control dams.[45] The treated dams provided reliably lower levels of maternal anogenital licking, but no detected differences in other aspects of maternal care. When the male and female offspring were adult, motor neurons in each section throughout the extent of the SNB were counted. We found that reduced perineal stimulation during infancy led to significantly fewer neurons in both males and females, but no change in neuron size. The maternal effect, which resulted in an 11% reduction in motor neuron number, was restricted to a rostral population of neurons within the SNB. There was no effect on gross lumbar spinal cord dimensions or body weight. Therefore, there was apparently no generalized effect on neural development or body growth.

It will be recalled that afferent input from perineal stimulation enters the spinal cord at the lumbar-sacral transition,[23] in the same segments in which the effect on adult motor neuron number was observed. It is possible, therefore, that the effect was mediated by a change in the level of local trophic factors, produced either by the afferents to the motor neurons or by the target muscles. Target effects on motor neuron survival are well known.[46] The sexual dimorphism in the SNB[47] stems largely from the fact that penile muscles atrophy in female neonates but are maintained in males because of masculine levels of testosterone.[48] Fewer neurons die in males than in females because of the sex difference in target.[41] However, a sex difference in afferents might also have this effect: dorsal root ablation in chick embryos leads to increased death of lumbar motor neurons, an afferent effect that is independent of the role of target muscles.[49]

It is also possible that the maternal effect on motor neuron number was mediated by some more systemic factor, such as the secretion of a hormone. The specificity of the effect argues against a hormone having generalized effects, such as growth hormone, but it is possible that differential testosterone secretion could explain the effect. If maternal stimulation of the perineum promotes testosterone secretion, then the effect could be accounted for by the well-established effect of this hormone on target muscle. Of course, this mechanism would explain the effect in developing females only if there were also a route by which maternal stimulation could increase endogenous levels of testosterone in this sex. At this point, there is no evidence with which to choose among the several plausible mediators of maternal stimulation on adult neuron number.

These results are exciting because they are the first demonstration that predictable, species-typical, afferent input from a natural source can affect the adult morphology of a sexually dimorphic nucleus in the central nervous system. They demonstrate that stimulation provided by a dam during the normal course of caring for developing young can contribute to the differentiation of neural mechanisms that underlie masculine sexual behavior. Variation among the dams that provide this stimulation can produce individual differences in neural mechanisms among males that may, in turn, affect their reproductive success. Finally, the results lead one to conclude that reliable differences in the stimulation provided to males and females contribute toward the sexual dissimilarity of nervous system morphology.

SUMMARY AND CONCLUSIONS

Both sexual differentiation, which is a matter of individual development, and sexual dissimilation, which is a matter of individual differences, result from developmental processes that are open to input from the early maternal environment. There are reliable features in both the dam and the young that ensure that males receive more perineal stimulation from maternal licking than is necessary for survival and normal growth. This stimulation contributes toward the development of masculine sexual behavior and mechanisms in the central nervous system that control copulatory reflexes. Because of differences in signals that they produce, males receive more stimulation than females. This bias in early stimulation accounts for some of the dissimilarity between the sexes in nervous system morphology and behavior. The same processes that produce sex differences can also produce individual differences among males. These differences are likely to have significant functional consequences in rats, a species in which males have a high level of intrasexual reproductive competition. Future research will be directed toward testing this functional hypothesis and toward exploring the extent of stimulative effects on the development of the sexually dimorphic brain regions that function in sexual behavior.

ACKNOWLEDGMENTS

I am grateful to the many students who worked on various aspects of this project over the years. I owe particular thanks to Karen Power, who collected many of the previously unpublished data reported herein.

REFERENCES

1. MOORE, C. L. 1985. Another psychobiological view of sexual differentiation. Dev. Rev. **5**: 18–55.
2. ALBERTS, J. R. 1978. Huddling by rat pups: group behavioral mechanisms of tem-

perature regulation and energy conservation. J. Comp. Physiol. Psychol. **92:** 231–240.

3. STERN, J. M. & S. K. JOHNSON. 1990. Ventral somatosensory determinants of nursing behavior in Norway rats. I. Effects of variations in the quality and quantity of pup stimuli. Physiol. Behav. **47:** 993–1011.

4. DREWETT, R. F. & A. M. TREW. 1978. The milk ejection of the rat, as a stimulus and a response to the litter. Anim. Behav. **22:** 907–913.

5. MOORE, C. L. & K. L. POWER. 1992. Variation in maternal care and individual differences in play, exploration, and grooming of juvenile Norway rat offspring. Dev. Psychobiol. **25:** 165–182.

6. MOORE, C. L. & G. A. MORELLI. 1979. Mother rats interact differently with male and female offspring. J. Comp. Physiol. Psychol. **93:** 677–684.

7. MOORE, C. L. 1982. Maternal behavior in rats is affected by hormonal condition of pups. J. Comp. Physiol. Psychol. **96:** 123–129.

8. POWER, K. L. & C. L. MOORE. 1986. Prenatal stress eliminates differential maternal attention to male offspring in Norway rats. Physiol. Behav. **38:** 667–671.

9. CLARK, M. M., S. BONE & B. G. GALEF, JR. 1989. Uterine positions and schedules of urination: correlates of differential maternal anogenital stimulation. Dev. Psychobiol. **22:** 389–400.

10. MOORE, C. L. 1985. Sex differences in urinary odors produced by young laboratory rats (*Rattus norvegicus*). J. Comp. Psychol. **99:** 76–80.

11. MOORE, C. L. 1981. An olfactory basis for maternal discrimination of sex of offspring in rats (*Rattus norvegicus*). Anim. Behav. **22:** 679–681.

12. BROUETTE-LAHLOU, I., E. VERNET-MAURY & J. CHANEL. 1991. Is rat-dam licking behavior regulated by pups' preputial gland secretion? Anim. Learn. Behav. **19:** 177–184.

13. BROUETTE-LAHLOU, I., R. AMOUROUX, F. CHASTRETTE, J. COSNIER, J. STOFFELSMA & E. VERNET-MAURY. 1991. Dodecyl propionate, a regulatory factor from rat pup, characterization and identification. J. Chem. Ecol. **17:** 1343–1354.

14. MOORE, C. L. & B. SAMONTE. 1986. Preputial glands of infant rats (*Rattus norvegicus*) provide chemosignals for maternal discrimination of sex. J. Comp. Psychol. **100:** 76–80.

15. CLARK, M. & B. G. GALEF. 1989. Male rat pups are more hesitant to urinate in response to anogenital stimulation than are their female sibs. Dev. Psychobiol. **22:** 81–85.

16. MOORE, C. L. & A.-M. CHADWICK-DIAS. 1986. Behavioral responses of infant rats to maternal licking: variations with age and sex. Dev. Psychobiol. **19:** 427–438.

17. ALBERTS, J. R. & D. J. GUBERNICK. 1983. Reciprocity and resource exchange: a symbiotic model of parent-offspring relations. *In* Symbiosis in Parent-Offspring Interactions. L. A. Rosenblum & H. Moltz, Eds.: 7–44. Plenum Press. New York, N.Y.

18. PEDERSON, P. E., C. L. WILLIAMS & E. M. BLASS. 1982. Activation and odor conditioning of suckling behavior in 3-day-old albino rats. J. Exp. Psychol. Anim. Behav. Proc. **8:** 329–341.

19. SCHANBERG, S. M. & T. M. FIELD. 1987. Sensory deprivation stress and supplemental stimulation in the rat pup and preterm human neonate. Child Dev. **58:** 1431–1447.

20. JOHANSON, I. B. & L. M. TERRY. 1988. Learning in infancy: a mechanism for behavioral change during development. *In* Developmental Psychobiology and Behavioral Ecology. Handbook of Behavioral Neurobiology. E. M. Blass, Ed. **9:** 245–281. Plenum Press. New York, N.Y.

21. COOPERSMITH, R. & M. LEON. 1984. Enhanced neural response to familiar olfactory cues. Science **225:** 191-197.
22. CAMP, L. L. & J. W. RUDY. 1988. Changes in the categorization of appetitive and aversive events during postnatal development of the rat. Dev. Psychobiol. **21:** 25-42.
23. PFAFF, D. W. 1980. Estrogens and Brain Function. Springer. New York, N.Y.
24. ALLEN, T. O. & N. T. ADLER. 1985. Neuroendocrine consequences of sexual behavior. In Reproduction. Handbook of Behavioral Neurobiology. N. Adler, D. Pfaff & R. W. Goy, Eds. **7:** 725-766. Plenum Press. New York, N.Y.
25. FISHER, R. S. & C. R. ALMLI. 1984. Postnatal development of sensory influences on lateral hypothalamic neurons of the rat. Dev. Brain Res. **12:** 55-75.
26. ALMLI, C. R. & R. S. FISHER. 1985. Postnatal development of sensory influences on neurons in the ventromedial hypothalamic nucleus of the rat. Dev. Brain Res. **18:** 13-26.
27. BEYER, C. & H. H. FEDER. 1987. Sex steroids and afferent input: their roles in brain sexual differentiation. Annu. Rev. Neurosci. **49:** 349-364.
28. THOR, D. H. & W. R. HOLLOWAY. 1984. Social play in juvenile rats: a decade of methodological and experimental research. Neurosci. Biobehav. Rev. **8:** 455-464.
29. BIRKE, L. & D. SADLER. 1987. Differences in maternal behavior of rats and sociosexual development of the offspring. Dev. Psychobiol. **20:** 85-99.
30. MOORE, C. L. 1984. Maternal contributions to the development of masculine sexual behavior in laboratory rats. Dev. Psychobiol. **17:** 347-356.
31. MOORE, C. L. 1985. Development of mammalian sexual behavior. In The Comparative Development of Adaptive Skills: Evolutionary Implications. E. S. Gollin, Ed.: 19-55. Erlbaum. Hillsdale, N.J.
32. MOORE, C. L. 1990. Comparative development of vertebrate sexual behavior: levels, cascades, and webs. In Contemporary Issues in Comparative Psychology. D. A. Dewsbury, Ed.: 278-299. Sinauer. Sunderland, Mass.
33. YAHR, P. 1988. Sexual differentiation of behavior. In Developmental Psychobiology and Behavioral Ecology. Handbook of Behavioral Neurobiology. E. M. Blass, Ed. **9:** 197-243. Plenum Press. New York, N.Y.
34. RUDDY, L. L. 1980. Nasal intubation: a minimally obtrusive anosmia technique applied to rats. Physiol. Behav. **24:** 881-886.
35. SLOTNICK, B. M. & L. A. GUTMAN. 1977. Evaluation of intranasal zinc sulfate treatment on olfactory discrimination in rats. J. Comp. Physiol. Psychol. **91:** 942-950.
36. MOORE, C. L. & K. L. POWER. Effects of maternal stimulation on the development of sexual behavior in male rats. (In preparation.)
37. DEWSBURY, D. A. & T. G. HARTUNG. 1980. Copulatory behaviour and differential reproduction of laboratory rats in a two-male, one-female competitive situation. Anim. Behav. **28:** 95-102.
38. HART, B. L. & P. Y. MELESE-D'HOSPITAL. 1983. Penile mechanisms and the role of striated penile muscles in penile reflexes. Physiol. Behav. **31:** 807-813.
39. SACHS, B. D. 1982. Role of the rat's striated penile muscles in penile reflexes, copulation and induction of pregnancy. J. Reprod. Fertil. **66:** 433-443.
40. WALLACH, S. J. R. & B. L. HART. 1983. The role of the striated penile muscles of the male rat in seminal plug dislodgement and deposition. Physiol. Behav. **31:** 815-821.
41. RAND, M. N. & S. M. BREEDLOVE. 1988. Progress report on a hormonally sensitive neuromuscular system. Psychobiology **16:** 398-405.
42. BREEDLOVE, S. M. & A. P. ARNOLD. 1980. Hormone accumulation in a sexually dimorphic motor nucleus of the rat spinal cord. Science **210:** 564-566.

43. McKENNA, K. E. & I. NADELHAFT. 1986. The organization of the pudendal nerve in the male and female rat. J. Comp. Neurol. **248:** 532–549.
44. SCHRØDER, H. D. 1980. Organization of the motoneurons innervating the pelvic muscles of the male rat. J. Comp. Neurol. **192:** 567–587.
45. MOORE, C. L., H. DOU & J. M. JURASKA. 1992. Maternal stimulation affects the number of motor neurons in a sexually dimorphic nucleus of the lumbar spinal cord. Brain Res. **572:** 52–56.
46. OPPENHEIM, R. W. 1981. Neuronal cell death and some related regressive phenomena during neurogenesis: a selective historical review and progress report. *In* Studies in Developmental Neurobiology: Essays in Honor of Viktor Hamburger. W. M. Cowan, Ed.: 74–133. Oxford University Press. London, England.
47. BREEDLOVE, S. M. & A. P. ARNOLD. 1983. Hormonal control of a developing neuromuscular system. II. Sensitive periods for the androgen-induced masculinization of the rat spinal nucleus of the bulbocavernosus. J. Neurosci. **3:** 424–432.
48. ČIHÁK, R., E. GUTMAN & V. HANZLIKOVÁ. 1970. Involution and hormone-induced persistence of the *M. sphincter (levator) ani* in female rats. J. Anat. **106:** 93–110.
49. OKADO, N. & R. W. OPPENHEIM. 1984. Cell death of motoneurons in the chick embryo spinal cord. IX. The loss of motoneurons following removal of afferent inputs. J. Neurosci. **4:** 1639–1652.

Opening and Closing a Hormone-Regulated Period for the Development of Courtship Song

A Cellular and Molecular Analysis of Vocal Neuroeffectors

DARCY B. KELLEY

Department of Biological Sciences
Columbia University
New York, New York 10027

DEFINING PERIODS OF HORMONE REGULATION FOR REPRODUCTIVE BEHAVIORS

The behavioral capacities of many organisms are shaped by exposure to experiential or endocrine factors during early development. For example, a brief exposure to steroid hormones around the time of birth or hatching can irreversibly modify an animal's repertoire of reproductive behaviors.[1] Sensitivity to steroids typically peaks during a limited developmental period and declines thereafter. These two characteristics, permanence of effect and stage-limited sensitivity, are generally regarded as the defining characteristics for hormone-regulated differentiation of the capacity for sex-typical behaviors.[2]

Developmentally regulated plasticity is also prominent in the ontogeny of the visual system and underlies diverse phenomena such as imprinting, binocular vision, and the alignment of auditory and visual maps. This latter example has been investigated extensively in the barn owl by Eric Knudsen and his colleagues.[3,4] Owls use spatial information derived from sound localization and visual space to pinpoint the location of prey. The neural maps for auditory and visual space are precisely aligned in the bird's optic tectum; this alignment has been shown to depend on experience and is correlated with behavioral measures of localization accuracy. The developmental period during which altered auditory or visual experience can influence the formation of aligned maps defines the *sensitive* period. The period during which it is possible to restore alignment by restoration of normal experience defines the *critical* period which thus can extend beyond the close of the *sensitive* period. These distinctions are not usually applied to hormone influences on reproductive behaviors (where *sensitive* and *critical* are often used interchangeably) but can, as we shall see, be useful in the analysis of underlying cellular and molecular mechanisms.

The timing and duration of hormone-regulated differentiation are usually investigated by providing exogenous or withholding endogenous steroids at different developmental stages and observing subsequent effects on behavior. Endocrine manipulation can provide a powerful temporal probe of steroid sensitivity. However, the provision of one or two exogenous steroids does not re-create the considerably more complex endogenous endocrine mileu of the developing animal. These experiments may lead to underestimates of behavioral plasticity by providing truncated estimates of the hormone-*sensitive* period.

If the endocrine mileu is the sole determinant of a sexually differentiated behavioral repertoire, it should be possible to completely masculinize the behavioral capacities of genetic females or feminize the capacities of males by providing or withholding hormones at appropriate developmental stages. In rats, castration at birth will diminish the display of androgen-evoked, male-typical copulatory behaviors in adulthood. Females treated with androgen shortly before or after birth display an augmented capacity for androgen-evoked male-typical behaviors.[5] The behavioral capacity of the animal, while changed, is seldom completely transformed. Thus, while such results provide support for the importance of the endocrine mileu during development, they do not provide a complete picture of the hormonal requirements of the developing system. Moreover, they do not address potential plasticity. Are the *sensitive* periods for hormone-implemented differentiation of behavior the same in the sexes? What are the limits for rescue of the masculine phenotype in males; when does the *critical* period close?

CELLULAR AND MOLECULAR BASES FOR HORMONE-REGULATED BEHAVIORAL DIFFERENTIATION

The sensory, neural, and muscular components that underlie vertebrate reproductive behaviors have been described, at least in part, in several systems.[1] The steroid sensitivity of these systems is due to the expression of intracellular proteins, steroid hormone receptors. Mutants defective in receptor expression or function fail to express appropriate behaviors and fail to exhibit sexual differentiation of underlying neuroeffectors. In other tissues, steroid receptors are known to regulate the expression of hormone target genes directly by interaction with DNA regulatory elements. The very striking overlap between the distribution of hormone-accumulating cells and effectors of hormone-regulated behaviors strongly suggests molecular mechanisms similar to those operative in other receptor-regulated systems.[6]

The regulatory effects of steroids on the capacity for reproductive behaviors are strongly correlated with their capacity to affect the development of hormone target neurons. In rats, for example, the neurons that control penile copulatory reflexes are influenced by the developmental endocrine mileu. Ex-

posure to androgenic hormones rescues these motor neurons from ontogenetic cell death in neonatal females and prevents castration-induced cell
loss in neonatal males.[7] In song birds, the number and size of neurons in telencephalic vocal nuclei are strongly influenced by exposure to estrogenic
steroids.[8] Resultant changes in song control nuclei are correlated with the capacity to display male songs in adulthood.

While correlations between behavioral capacities and neural differentiation are powerful in these rodent and avian systems, it has been difficult to
bridge the gap between the presence of a particular steroid hormone receptor
and changes in the developmental program of a cell that lead to expression
of a sex-appropriate behavioral phenotype. Part of the difficulty lies in the
complexity of the neural circuitry for reproductive behaviors.[1] For this
reason, our laboratory has focused on a portion of the neural circuitry that
is most amenable to a detailed cellular and molecular analysis, the neuromuscular synapse. The dependence of neurons on both afferent and efferent
influences presents a particular complication in hormone-sensitive systems
where all three cells in a circuit—the neuron itself, its synaptic target, and
its source of synaptic input—express high levels of steroid hormone receptor.
A focus on the neuromuscular synapse narrows the field to two players, the
muscle and the motor neuron. An additional advantage of the neuromuscular
periphery is the close and compelling relation to actual behavioral production. It is difficult to ascribe a precise behavioral function to a telencephalic
neuron. It is less difficult to pinpoint function in a motor neuron and relatively straightforward in a muscle fiber.

The goal of our work is to account for the regulation of sex-typical behaviors at the cellular and molecular levels. In particular, we wish to describe
the events that underlie hormone-sensitive and critical periods. To do so, we
have studied the sexual differentiation of courtship song in the African frog,
Xenopus laevis, and have focused our cellular and molecular studies on the
differentiation of the vocal neuromuscular synapse.

THE VOCAL SYSTEM IN *XENOPUS LAEVIS*

Male and female *X. laevis* communicate their reproductive state with
specific vocalizations. Sexually receptive males sing (mate call) to attract and
excite females.[9,10] Sexually unreceptive females tick to repel males.[11,12]
Ticking and mate calling differ in trill rate, complexity, and amplitude modulation. Mate calls consist of rapid trills with alternating fast (70 Hz) and
slow (35 Hz) phases. The fast portion of the mate call becomes progressively
louder.[9] Ticking is a slow (7 Hz), monotonous trill. Both calls are produced
by contractions of the intrinsic muscles of the vocal organ, the larynx.[13,14]
The larynx is a boxlike structure of muscle and cartilage that contains two
sound-producing discs of arytenoid cartilage that are normally tightly ap-
posed. When the laryngeal muscles contract, the discs pop apart and a click
is produced; repeated clicks comprise the trills of mate calling and ticking.

Laryngeal muscles contract to produce calls in response to activity of the laryngeal motor neurons located in cranial nerve nucleus IX–X in the caudal medulla.[15] Laryngeal muscles and motor neurons comprise a neuromuscular system dedicated exclusively to vocalization. We have outlined an anatomically connected system of brain nuclei that provides input to the calling motor neurons.[16] Based on our studies in *X. laevis* and those of Schmidt in other anurans,[17] we believe that the central nervous system (CNS) motor pathway for song includes a vocal pattern generator in the superior reticular formation (DTAM, or the pretrigeminal nucleus of the dorsal tegmental area of the medulla), interneurons within the motor nucleus and in inferior reticular formation, sensory nuclei in the thalamus (auditory, lateral line, and somatosensory), and certain nuclei of ventral diencephalon (anterior preoptic area) and telencephalon (ventral striatum).

EXPRESSION OF THE ANDROGEN RECEPTOR IN THE VOCAL SYSTEM OF *X. LAEVIS*

Androgen secretion is required for the differentiation of vocal neuroeffectors[18] and for the activation of courtship song in adulthood.[9] Androgen acts via a specific intracellular receptor protein, the androgen receptor (AR). The neurons and muscles responsible for production of vocal behaviors in *X. laevis* express very high levels of androgen receptor.[15,19] We have examined androgen receptor expression by determining androgen-binding activity autoradiographically and biochemically. Using the polymerase chain reaction, we have cloned a *Xenopus* androgen receptor using laryngeal mRNA as starting material;[20] cloned probes enable us to also monitor AR mRNA expression. Expression of androgen receptor is largely confined to brain nuclei implicated in the control of vocal behavior and functions as specific "stain" for the calling pathway. Brain nuclei that comprise the motor pathway for song (laryngeal motor neurons, inferior reticular formation, DTAM) as well as some sensory nuclei (thalamus, midbrain auditory nuclei) are heavily labeled following exposure to radioactive androgens.[21] These same brain nuclei express AR mRNA as determined using *in situ* hybridization.[22] Laryngeal muscle also expresses androgen receptor. Binding of radioactive androgen and expression of androgen receptor mRNA is higher in adult males than in females.[19,23]

A CELLULAR ANALYSIS OF THE SEXUALLY DIMORPHIC VOCAL SYSTEM

We have identified cellular properties that contribute to sex differences in vocal ability. These include sexually dimorphic CNS vocal circuitry, motor neurons, and muscles. Portions of the vocal circuitry differ in the sexes: males have a robust connection from N. IX–X interneurons to DTAM and a projection from preoptic area to DTAM which females lack.[16] N. IX–X interneurons of males have markedly longer dendrites than those of females.[24,25] Males have twice as many laryngeal motor neurons as females do.[26] There is a marked sex difference in synaptic efficacy at the laryngeal neuromuscular junction: female synapses are strong while male synapses are weak.[27] Males have twice as many laryngeal muscle fibers as females.[28] Female muscle is predominantly slow twitch, while male muscle is entirely fast twitch.[29]

Both the central nervous system and the muscular periphery contribute to sex differences in vocal behavior. The vocal pattern (mate calling or ticking) is produced within the CNS;[13,16] sex differences in connectivity described above may constrain the female's ability to produce the mate call pattern. A characteristic feature of sexually dimorphic vocal behavior, the amplitude modulation present in the mate call but not in ticking, is controlled by laryngeal motor neurons; their weak synapses contribute to the fiber recruitment responsible for the increasing loudness of the fast portion of the mate call.[13,27] We have recently shown that amplitude modulation is essential for attractive quality of the mate call.[30] The larger number of male muscle fibers and motor neurons are matched to vocal demands placed on the sexes: mate calling is loud and prolonged while ticking is quiet and brief.[11] Finally, the twitch properties of laryngeal muscle fibers determine how rapidly clicks can be produced; the all fast twitch muscle fibers of males can contract at 70 Hz while the mostly slow fibers of females cannot.[18,29]

A SEXUALLY DIFFERENTIATED PROGRAM OF DEVELOPMENT IN THE VOCAL SYSTEM

Sex differences in neurons and muscle are due to sexually differentiated programs in which the development of the male diverges from that of the female. Laryngeal motor neuron axon number becomes sexually differentiated before metamorphosis.[26] At tadpole stage 56 when the gonads first differentiate,[31] the number of axons entering laryngeal muscle is the same in males and females. Males experience a wave of axon outgrowth between stages 59 and 62; subsequently both sexes lose axons, reaching adult, sexually dimorphic values during early postmetamorphic development. At metamorphosis, muscle fiber number, twitch type, tension, and synaptic efficacy are the same in the sexes. These laryngeal characteristics masculinize progressively during the postmetamorphic period: first number, then fiber type, then tension, and finally synaptic efficacy.[18,28] Dendritic sex differences in N. IX–X interneurons also masculinize late in postmetamorphic development.[25] We have used the temporal sequence of masculinization in neuroeffectors for vocal behavior to divide male postmetamorphic development into 7 stages[18] that span the period from the end of metamorphosis (PM0: tadpole stage 66[31]) to adulthood (PM6, 1 to 2 years postmetamorphosis).

ANDROGEN REGULATION OF MASCULINIZATION

Masculinization of the laryngeal neuromuscular system requires secretion of testicular androgen. Axonal outgrowth from laryngeal motor neurons is reduced by antiandrogen and stimulated by androgen.[32] Castration arrests the postmetamorphic masculinization of muscle fiber number, twitch type, tension, and synaptic efficacy.[18,28] Treatment with exogenous androgen reinstates masculinization in castrated, developing males; implantation of a testis or of an androgen pellet masculinizes laryngeal properties in developing females. At times when androgen secretion can affect cellular events that lead to masculinization, levels of androgen receptor are elevated. In the peripheral effector organ, the larynx, binding levels and androgen receptor mRNA expression are extremely high, for both sexes, during early postmetamorphic development.[23,33] Adult, sexually dimorphic, binding levels[19] are achieved by a program of sexually differentiated decreases which can be mimicked by exogenous androgen treatment.[33]

HORMONES AND VOCAL BEHAVIOR IN *X. LAEVIS*

Secretion of testicular androgen is required for male song. During development, androgens permanently masculinize neuroeffectors for mate calling.[34] In adulthood, androgens are also necessary to "activate" the neural circuitry underlying mate calling; castrated males do not sing.[9] Despite extensive investigation, we have not yet identified a role for estrogen secretion or metabolism of androgens to estrogenic metabolites in this system. Neither laryngeal muscles nor motor neurons contain estrogen receptors.[6,19] The purely androgenic control of the song system in *X. laevis* is similar to androgenic control of other sexually dimorphic neuromuscular systems.[7] Of the androgens we have studied, the 5 α–reduced metabolite of testosterone (5 α–dihydrotestosterone) appears most effective in masculinization of behavioral neuroeffectors, regulation of the androgen receptor, and activation of the behavior in adulthood.[9,33]

SENSITIVE AND CRITICAL PERIODS FOR
MASCULINIZATION OF SONG

We have explored the sensitive period for masculinization of song by providing developing female *Xenopus laevis* with testicular transplants.[10] The sensitive period in females is extremely prolonged and lasts for a minimum of one year after metamorphosis is complete. Females were provided with testicular transplants at ages equivalent to PM1–PM6 in males and tested for vocal behavior 10 to 15 months later. All females provided with transplants between PM1 and PM5 sang, and their songs were as long as those of testis-implanted male controls. After PM3, however, the acoustical quality of songs produced by testis-implanted females diminished. In contast, the vocalizations of adult females were not masculinized by testicular transplants. We conclude that in females, the sensitive period for masculinization of vocal behavior extends through most of postmetamorphic development and closes only in adulthood.

We have addressed the critical period for masculinization of song by examining androgen effects on the physiological properties of laryngeal muscle that underlie the capacity for song.[34] These are productive of transient tension, which controls trill rate, and fiber recruitment, which controls amplitude modulation.[13] Males were gonadectomized at PM0 or PM2 and then treated with androgen at PM2 or PM6 respectively. Gonadectomy completely blocked masculinization. Tension transient production was completely masculinized by androgen treatment at either PM2 or PM6. Fiber recruitment could not be completely masculinized until the males were adult. We conclude that the critical period for androgen rescue of male courtship song remains open into adulthood. We do not know whether prior exposure to hormone (the testes were present until PM0 or PM2 in this study) is required for the maintenance of androgen sensitivity.

CELLULAR AND MOLECULAR MECHANISMS IN SENSITIVE AND CRITICAL PERIODS

The two prime candidates for opening the androgen-sensitive period for song in *Xenopus laevis* are androgen secretion itself and the onset of androgen receptor expression. Androgen receptor mRNA expression can be detected in brain and larynx as early as tadpole stage 56, before detectable androgen secretion. Laryngeal muscles and motor neurons can be prematurely masculinized by treatment with exogenous androgen from tadpole stages 48 to 62.[34] Together these results suggest that the androgen-sensitive critical period is opened by expression of androgen receptor.

What closes the sensitive period? In the larynx, sensitivity to androgen diminishes as a result of androgen-induced cell differentiation. For example, castration blocks muscle fiber addition until PM2 but has no effect thereafter. We believe that the sensitive period for androgen-evoked muscle fiber addition comes to an end when androgen-sensitive myoblasts are depleted at the end of the myogenic program. If females are treated with dihydrotestosterone at PM2, laryngeal muscle fiber numbers increase. The sensitive period for androgen-evoked myogenesis may close later in females than in males because cells do not differentiate without androgen exposure. The close of the sensitive period is determined not by developmental age but by masculinization stage. Levels of androgen receptor are high at the beginning of PM development and decrease thereafter. Thus, the amount of receptor expressed could also contribute to the duration of the androgen-sensitive period. Androgen receptor expression is high in proliferating, undifferentiated cells and low in mature cells. We suspect that down regulation of androgen receptor results from androgen-induced cell differentiation. We conclude that the sensitive period for androgen-induced masculinization of the vocal system is closed by androgen activation of a program for cell differentiation in males; down regulation of the receptor is a byproduct of this program.

The close of the sensitive period in females may be determined by a different mechanism: loss of androgen-sensitive myoblasts. Androgen-evoked muscle fiber addition diminishes with age in females. We suspect that females do not maintain enough myoblasts to permit the development of masculine fiber number after PM2. Myoblasts may require exposure to androgen before metamorphosis to survive after metamorphosis. The ability of androgen to induce fiber type switching in females also decreases with age. Four weeks of androgen treatment are sufficient during early postmetamorphic development, while 9 months of treatment are required in adult animals. If we assume that fiber switching involves myoblast fusion with existing fibers, a diminished number of myoblasts could explain this result as well.

Males maintain considerable sensitivity to androgen even after long periods of hormone withdrawal. The song-related physiological characteristics of laryngeal muscle of males castrated at PM2 (6 months PM) can be completely masculinized by a brief androgen treatment 18 months later (PM6). Thus the larynx is maintained in a capable but developmentally dormant state which can be reactivated at any time. Maintained sensitivity to androgen could be due to androgen exposure during tadpole or early postmetamorphic stages and again be mediated by myoblast survival. The continued presence of this cell type could be responsible for keeping the critical period open in males.

SUMMARY AND CONCLUSIONS

Sex differences in vertebrate behaviors are primarily controlled by the secretion of gonadal steroids. During development, gonadal secretions profoundly and permanently influence the differentiation of neurons and muscles that produce sex-specific behaviors. In adulthood, circulating steroids permit the expression of sex-specific behaviors. A central problem of this field is to understand how hormones control sexually differentiated behaviors. This problem requires that we define the sensory structures, neurons, and muscles that are involved, specifically, in producing the behavior and determine how they function. We must then uncover the cellular and molecular sex differences in neurons and muscle that are responsible for sex differences in behavior. Our research goals are to define the molecular events responsible for sexual differentiation of neurons and muscles that affect reproductive behaviors. We have developed a vertebrate experimental model in which the cellular events underlying a sexually differentiated behavior have been identified and the underlying hormone-controlled developmental events described. This system is the courtship song of the African clawed frog, *Xenopus laevis*, produced by activity of a dedicated central nervous system circuit and muscle effectors. The vocal CNS circuitry and muscles differ strikingly in adult males and females. These differences are due to a male-specific developmental program of androgen secretion from the testes. Androgen acts on target cells which contain a ligand-activated transcription factor, the androgen receptor (AR). The androgen receptor is strongly and specifically expressed in neurons of the vocal circuit and muscles in the larynx. The use of this system permits a cellular and molecular exploration of the mechanisms that underlie temporal constraints on hormone-differentiated behaviors and permits us to identify candidates for control of sensitive and critical periods.

REFERENCES

1. KELLEY, D. 1988. Sexually dimorphic behavior. Annu. Rev. Neurosci. **11:** 225–251.
2. ARNOLD, A. P. & S. M. BREEDLOVE. 1985. Organizational and activational effects of sex steroids on brain and behavior: a reanalysis. Horm. Behav. **19:** 469–498.
3. KNUDSEN, E. 1985. Experience alters the spatial tuning of auditory units in the optic tectum during a sensitive period in the barn owl. J. Neurosci. **5:** 3094–3109.
4. KNUDSEN, E. & P. KNUDSEN. 1986. The sensitive period for auditory localization in barn owls is limited by age, not experience. J. Neurosci. **6:** 1918–1924.
5. PFAFF, D. 1970. Nature of sex hormone effects on rat sex behavior: specificity of effects and individual patterns of response. J. Comp. Physiol. Psychol. **73:** 349–358.
6. MORRELL, J. I., D. KELLEY & D. PFAFF. 1975. Sex steroid binding in the brain of vertebrates: studies with light microscopic autoradiography. *In* The Ventricular System in Neuroendocrine Mechanisms. Proceedings of the Second Brain-Endocrine Interaction Symposium. K. M. Knigge, D. E. Scott & M. Kobayashi, Eds.: 230–256. Karger. Basel, Switzerland.
7. BREEDLOVE, S. M. & A. P. ARNOLD. 1983. Hormonal control of a developing neuromuscular system. I. Complete demasculinization of the spinal nucleus of the bulbocavernosus in male rats using the anti-androgen, flutamide. J. Neurosci. **3:** 417–423.
8. GURNEY, M. 1981. Hormonal control of cell form and number in the zebra finch song system. J. Neurosci. **1:** 658–673.
9. WETZEL, D. & D. KELLEY. 1983. Androgen and gonadotropin control of the mate calls of male South African clawed frogs, *Xenopus laevis*. Horm. Behav. **17:** 388–404.
10. WATSON, J. & D. KELLEY. Testicular masculinization of vocal behavior in juvenile female *Xenopus laevis* reveals sensitive periods for song duration, rate and frequency spectra. J. Comp. Physiol. A. (In press.)

11. HANNIGAN, P. & D. KELLEY. 1986. Androgen-induced alterations in vocalizations of female *Xenopus laevis:* modifiabilty and constraints. J. Comp. Physiol. A **158:** 17–528.
12. WEINTRAUB, A., D. KELLEY & R. BOCKMAN. 1985. Prostaglandin induces sexual receptivity in female *Xenopus laevis.* Horm. Behav. **19:** 386–399.
13. TOBIAS, M. & D. KELLEY. 1987. Vocalizations of a sexually dimorphic isolated larynx: peripheral constraints on behavioral expression. J. Neurosci. **7:** 3191–3197.
14. YAGER, D. A unique sound production system in the pipid anuran *Xenopus borealis.* Zool. J. Linn. Soc. **104:** 351–375.
15. KELLEY, D. B. 1980. Auditory and vocal nuclei of frog brain concentrate sex hormones. Science **207:** 553–555.
16. WETZEL, D., U. HAERTER & D. KELLEY. 1985. A proposed efferent pathway for mate calling in South African clawed frogs, *Xenopus laevis:* tracing afferents to laryngeal motor neurons with HRP-WGA. J. Comp. Physiol. A **157:** 749–761.
17. SCHMIDT, R. S. 1976. Neural correlates of frog calling. Isolated brainstem. J. Comp. Physiol. A **108:** 99–113.
18. TOBIAS, M. L., M. MARIN & D. B. KELLEY. 1991. Development of functional sex differences in the larnyx of *Xenopus laevis.* Dev. Biol. **147:** 251–259.
19. SEGIL, N., L. SILVERMAN & D. B. KELLEY. 1987. Androgen binding levels in a sexually dimorphic muscle of *Xenopus laevis.* Gen. Comp. Endocrinol. **66:** 95–101.
20. HE, W., L. FISCHER, S. SUN, D. BILHARTZ, X. ZHU, C. YOUNG, D. KELLEY & D. TINDALL. 1990. Molecular cloning of androgen receptors from divergent species with a polymerase chain reaction technique: complete cDNA sequence of the mouse androgen receptor and isolation of androgen receptor cDNA probes from dog, guinea pig and clawed frog. Biochem. Biophys. Res. Comm. **171:** 697–704.
21. KELLEY, D. 1981. Locations of androgen-concentrating cells in the brain of *Xenopus laevis:* autoradiography with ³H-dihydrotestosterone. J. Comp. Neurol. **199:** 221–231.
22. COHEN, M., L. FISCHER & D. KELLEY. 1991. Onset of androgen receptor mRNA expression in the CNS of *Xenopus laevis:* localization using *in situ* hybridization. Soc. Neurosci. Abstr. **17:** 1317.
23. FISCHER, L. & D. KELLEY. 1991. Androgen receptor expression and sexual differentiation of effectors for courtship song in *Xenopus laevis.* Semin. Neurosci. **3:** 469–480.
24. KELLEY, D., S. FENSTEMAKER, P. HANNIGAN & S. SHIH. 1988. The sexually dimorphic laryngeal motor neurons of *Xenopus laevis:* a quantitative Golgi study. J. Neurobiol. **19:** 413–429.
25. WATSON, J. & D. B. KELLEY. 1989. Development of sex differences in dendritic length in *Xenopus laevis* laryngeal motorneurons. Soc. Neurosci. Abstr. **15:** 579.
26. KELLEY, D. B. & J. DENNISON. 1990. The vocal motor neurons of *Xenopus laevis:* development of sex differences in axon number. J. Neurobiol. **21:** 869–882.
27. TOBIAS, M. & D. KELLEY. 1988. Electrophysiology and dye coupling are sexually dimorphic characteristics of individual laryngeal muscle fibers in *Xenopus laevis.* J. Neurosci. **8:** 2422–2429.
28. MARIN, M., M. TOBIAS & D. KELLEY. 1990. Hormone-sensitive stages in the sexual differentiation of laryngeal muscle fiber number in *Xenopus laevis.* Development **110:** 703–771.
29. SASSOON, D., G. GRAY & D. KELLEY. 1987. Androgen regulation of muscle fiber type in the sexually dimorphic larynx of *Xenopus laevis.* J. Neurosci. **7:** 3198–3206.
30. TOBIAS, M., R. BIVENS, S. NOWICKE & D. KELLEY. 1991. Amplitude modulation

is an attractive feature of *X. laevis* song. Soc. Neurosci. Abstr. **17:** 1403.

31. NIEUWKOOP, P. & J. FABER. 1956. Normal table of *Xenopus laevis* (Daudin). North-Holland. Amsterdam, the Netherlands.

32. ROBERTSON, J., J. WATSON & D. KELLEY. 1991. Laryngeal nerve axon number in pre-metamorphic *Xenopus laevis* is androgen dependent. Soc. Neurosci. Abstr. **17:** 1320.

33. KELLEY, D., D. SASSOON, N. SEGIL & M. SCUDDER. 1989. Development and hormone regulation of androgen receptor levels in the sexually dimorphic larynx of *Xenopus laevis*. Dev. Biol. **131:** 111–118.

34. TOBIAS, M. L., M. MARIN & D. B. KELLEY. 1991. Temporal constraints on androgen directed laryngeal masculinization in *Xenopus laevis*. Dev. Biol. **147:** 260–270.

Index of Contributors